access

GUIDE TO THE WEB

VOLUME 2

ACCESS
GUIDE TO THE WEB
VOLUME 2

EDITOR
Stephanie Chang

REVIEW EDITORS
Kaesmene Harrison, Karin Kaneps, Stephanie Rottenberg, Lauren Wiley

DESIGNERS
Gates Sisters Studio, Pat Coppola

COPY EDITOR
Laura Doyle

RESEARCHER
Margaret Doyle

REVIEWERS
Melanie Axelrod, Dennis Barker, Jeremy Caplan, Stephanie Chang, Chris Chen, Rita Cook, Laura Doyle, Danielle Durkin, Bob Feeman, Blake Ferris, Sari Goodfriend, Amy Greenleaf, Kaesmene Harrison, Kelly Hearn, Patrick Joseph, Grant Kaneps, Karin Kaneps, Luise Light, Irene Lutts, John Madden, Reuben Maness, Carmen Nobel, Jacob Park, Mara Raden, Kathryn Reed, Stephanie Rottenberg, Joyce Slaton, Karen Solomon, Tom Stanton, Joanne Trestrail, Joy Valante, Chris Verleger

COVER DESIGN
Mark Gabrenya

COVER ILLUSTRATION
Pat Coppola

access

GUIDE TO THE WEB

VOLUME 2

Stephanie Chang
EDITOR

Kaesmene Harrison, Karin Kaneps, Stephanie Rottenberg and Lauren Wiley
REVIEW EDITORS

Access Media Inc.
35 HIGHLAND CIRCLE
NEEDHAM, MA 02494
www.accessmagazine.com

Dear Reader,

As editors of Access, America's Guide to the Internet, we enjoy pointing you to the best sites on the Web each week in our magazine and on our site, accessmagazine.com.

This book, the second volume in a series, is a collection of 971 sites that have been reviewed in our magazine. Each site was carefully selected for review, based on its content, design and composition. We have updated the reviews for this book.

You can find direct links to all of the sites listed here at our Web site.

We hope you enjoy Volume 2. If you have any comments about the book or would like to suggest topics for future volumes, please e-mail me at schang@accessmagazine.com.

Happy surfing.

Stephanie Chang
Editor,
Access

contents

arts & culture

Architecture

(originally reviewed September 1999)

CASTLES ON THE WEB
www.castlesontheweb.com

There aren't any castles in the air—yet—but there are castles on hills, castles with moats, castles in the countryside, castles in the city—in fact, castles all over Europe. Did you know Belgium alone boasts 3,000 castles? From this site you can take a virtual tour of many of these impressive structures. Find links to castle-related stuff, including heraldry, myths and legends. There is a glossary of castle terminology, Castles for Kids and links to sites that sell armor and other medieval paraphernalia. ⓐⓐⓐⓐ

THE GREAT BUILDINGS COLLECTION
www.greatbuildings.com

If you know the name of an important building, its location or the architect's name, you can search this 750-item database for descriptions, photos, drawings and, for some, 3-D model views. Most of the featured buildings are covered thoroughly, and there are suggested avenues for further research, including well-chosen books. The site has nice, simple graphics and is easy to use. Let's hope its database of buildings keeps growing. ⓐⓐⓐⓐ

Wing's Castle in Millbrook, N.Y., is among the famous castles at www.castlesontheweb.com.

WORLD'S TALLEST BUILDINGS
www.worldstallest.com

Skyscrapers from around the world that reach—or aspire to reach—a height of 1,000 feet or more are cataloged at this fun site. It opens with a fantasy view of the Chicago skyline, where 12 of the world's tallest and tallest wannabes enjoy imaginary proximity. Read the latest news about behemoths under construction or on the drawing board, then navigate the site with its neat elevator buttons for photos, articles and views from Webcams. This site could help settle some arguments. ⓐⓐⓐⓐ

THE WRIGHT WEB GUIDE
www.cypgrp.com/flw

For Frank Lloyd Wright buffs, this site is a good jumping-off point to other sites that offer information and lore about the great architect and his prodigious output. On the site itself, buildings (and corresponding photos) are indexed by year from 1886 through 1959. You'll also find useful tourist information on Wright buildings that are open to the public. Overall, a good portal for the Wright stuff. ⓐⓐⓐ

ARCHITECTS USA
www.architectsusa.com

This is an easy-to-use directory of 30,000 architectural firms around the country. Click on a state, then a city, then a firm for contact information and a link to its Web site, if available. Only firms with a commercial relationship with the host site have hotlinks on the site. There's also a listing of accredited architecture schools and state licensing boards. ⓐⓐ

Banned Books

(originally reviewed September 1999)

ALA: BANNED BOOKS WEEK
ala8.ala.org/bbooks

As one of the sponsors of Banned Books Week—which is recognized each year during the last week in September—the American Library Association has a lot to say about the subject. Few other sites support the right to read with such alacrity and fervor, supporting its argument with First Amendment court cases and quotes from noted thinkers and authors. The ALA also explains the history and purpose of Banned Books Week. Lists of the most frequently banned books and authors—Judy Blume, Maya Angelou and John Steinbeck, to name a few—are offered, as is an online form for reporting challenges to books. ⓐⓐⓐⓐ

BONFIRE OF LIBERTIES
www.humanities-interactive.org/bonfireindex.html

This is an innovative way to learn about book banning and censorship. Step into the halls of this museum without walls to take in a visual history of the subject, complete with short captions explaining the material. Click on individual items in the collection, or watch a slide show of all works—political cartoons, original book jackets from banned texts, newspaper clippings and controversial works of art. ⓐⓐⓐⓐ

ACLU: BANNED BOOKS WEEK
www.aclu.org/issues/freespeech/bbwind.html

The American Civil Liberties Union's Banned Books section packs a wallop on the topic of censorship, even if the information here is from 1998. Highlights include a list of the most frequently banned or challenged books of 1997, a quiz that matches censors' comments to titles and tools for fighting censorship. You can even order banned books online. A special student section encourages students to mobilize against censorship. The ACLU pushes its agenda hard here, but the site is a good stop for anyone concerned about this subject. ⓐⓐⓐ

CENSORED: BANNED BOOK AND CENSORSHIP RESOURCES
www.georgesuttle.com/censorship/index.shtml

This simple and straightforward site is packed with resources. Links take you to sites that focus on the censorship of books and other media, the First Amendment and the Constitution, and national and international organizations that crusade for free speech. It tops off the links with a list of print resources. ⓐⓐⓐ

THE ON-LINE BOOKS PAGE PRESENTS: BANNED BOOKS ON-LINE
digital.library.upenn.edu/books/banned-books.html

Banned Books On-line has a sparse presentation but a wealth of resources. The site's creators have taken a selection of challenged books, arguably classics, and added brief summaries of the challenges against them. Each summary contains a link to the full text of the book. The Bible, Chaucer's "Canterbury Tales," Daniel Defoe's "Moll Flanders," and Walt Whitman's "Leaves of Grass" are among the titles. Note: A few of the links are broken. ⓐⓐ

CENSORSHIP AND THE ADVENTURES OF HUCKLEBERRY FINN
www.sdcoe.k12.ca.us/score/huckcen/huckcentg.html

This teacher's curriculum guide takes a look at current and past opinions on one of the most-challenged books of all time. While the resources here are good for classrooms, offering class exercises and Web resources, the site is also useful to bookworms as a case study. Banned first by the Concord (Massachusetts) Public Library in 1885 as "trash of the veriest sort," this classic has been criticized over the years—first for being too ardently anti-racist and then for perpetuating racism. Follow the reading and resource suggestions and decide for yourself. ⓐⓐ

Book Clubs

(originally reviewed October 1999)

ADBOOKS
www.geocities.com/soho/village/3503

This phenomenal book club caters to those interested in young adult literature—no matter the reader's age. The scheduled books are high quality, whether they are older classics such as L'Engle's "A Wrinkle in Time" or hot new arrivals like the Harry Potter series and Chris Lynch's "Shadow Boxer." Discussion is conducted by e-mail. Suggested reading and links to authors' sites are included. ⓐⓐⓐⓐ

OPRAH'S BOOK CLUB
www.oprah.com/obc/obc_landing.html

This section of Oprah Winfrey's nicely designed site features her current book selection, plus message boards, previous selections, reading questions, an author bio and a list of his or her favorite titles. Some messages ramble, but other discussions are interesting and fairly complex. ⓐⓐⓐⓐ

PARENT'S PLAYLAND BOOK CLUB
www.geocities.com/ppbookclub

Kind of like "The Mommies" online, this friendly, nurturing site consists of a message board and scheduled chat sessions focused on modern novels. Absolutely brimming with features—such as a reading schedule, book reviews and suggestions—the club also hosts socially interactive activities. For example, there are book swaps in which you send a partner books and discuss them via e-mail. ⓐⓐⓐ

SENIORNET
www.seniornet.org

Get to the SeniorNet book club by clicking on Book Discussions under Featured Discussions. The club covers quite a few genres—including history, fiction and mystery—with six or seven choices each month. The groups are organized by book, but the drop-in style of the club allows members to participate in any discussion about any title. ⓐⓐⓐ

YAHOO! CLUBS: BOOKWORMS
clubs.yahoo.com/clubs/bookworms

For those new to book clubs, this is a good place to start. Bookworms is one of the Yahoo! Clubs, which are quick and easy to use—just sign up to post messages and questions. Members vote on books for the month and then lead the discussions. ⓐⓐⓐ

THUMPER'S CORNER: THE COFFEE WILL MAKE YOU BLACK READING GROUP
www.aalbc.com/discussion
You might find the frames setup of this site confusing, but patience will lead you to an excellent reading and discussion group for African-American literature. Click on Book Club Info for an introduction to the group or Enter Chat Room to see if anyone is around. A serious literature club, this group tends to post messages to the bulletin board and use the chat room primarily for scheduled events. ⓐⓐ

Book Reviews

(originally reviewed November 1999)

BOOKLIST
www.ala.org/booklist
This is the online version of the American Library Association's Booklist magazine. The sheer scope of this site is amazing; the magazine reviews 2,500 children's books a year alone. Each issue spotlights a different subject, such as cookery, religion, sports or first novels. Scan topics by issue, or use the site's search engine. There is also a cumulative index, with alphabetical entries for authors and titles. For the widest range of book reviews, this is the site to visit. ⓐⓐⓐⓐ

BookPage
ONLINE
National Poetry Month
New volumes confirm the power of poetry
An American In Paris
Diane Johnson returns with Le Mariage
PLUS
BALL PARK HITS
BARD'S BIRTHDAY
Jane Smiley's
Horse Heaven

Go to www.bookpage.com for reviews of more mainstream books.

THE NEW YORK REVIEW OF BOOKS
www.nybooks.com/nyrev
This is the intelligent reader's ultimate literary guide, with essays and reviews by writers who hold books and the arts to the highest standard of critique. The print version has long been a source of debate on American life, culture and politics, and this site opens the discussion to Net users as well. Its lone drawback: The Archives currently post the full text of reviews since 1996, but the site is working to put all 37 years of reviews and articles online. You can search the index back to 1963. ⓐⓐⓐⓐ

THE NEW YORK TIMES BOOK REVIEW
www.nytimes.com/books
The Times is the grande dame of book reviews, and its Web site carries on in the same vein. With more than just advice on good reads, this venerable institution offers critical essays on contemporary writing. The reviews, which can often be considered literature themselves, are divided into Fiction and Non-Fiction (with first chapters of some books available for perusal). Plus you get an Expanded Bestseller List, editor's picks and past reviews. ⓐⓐⓐⓐ

BOOKPAGE ONLINE
www.bookpage.com
A great mainstream review site, BookPage Online is neither overly academic nor hyper-specialized. It has sections for Oprah Winfrey's latest recommended reads, author interviews and audio book reviews. There is a variety of feature topics from which to choose, including Biography, Children's Books, Journalism and Medicine. And don't miss Burning Questions, where you can ask about all things bookish. ⓐⓐⓐ

THE BOSTON BOOK REVIEW
www.bookwire.com/bbr/bbr-home.html
Another online companion to a printed journal, this site has a more academic flavor than many others. The BBR staff reviews contemporary books it considers important. Intellectually and thoughtfully written, this site showcases the best of both the latest issue and past editions. With nifty graphics and sections on Poetry, Essays, Interviews and Literary Awards, this diverse site has something for everyone. Check out the Literary Quiz in Bookbag. ⓐⓐⓐ

HUNGRY MIND REVIEW
www.bookwire.com/hmr
This national quarterly magazine's electronic version is literary but not in an elitist way. With a remarkable section where writers recommend books for young adults and a similarly compiled list of Millennium Books, this site stands out. Look for its list of 100 Best 20th-Century American Books—you may be surprised. The only downside is the chaotic homepage. ⓐⓐⓐ

THE MYSTERY READER
www.themysteryreader.com
Mystery fans need look no further for reviews on the latest chills and thrills in print. Using the star system, volunteer reviewers decide which books are worthwhile and which books should be passed up. The mysteries are divided into categories: Historical, Suspense, Cozy, and Police and Detective. There is an archive and

special features, such as Author Freebies. Write to various authors for autographed bookmarks, writing tips and other good stuff. If you like to read romances, too, then visit The Romance Reader, a companion site that offers more than 2,500 reviews. ⓐⓐⓐ

Clip Art

(originally reviewed October 1999)

ANIMATION LIBRARY
animationlibrary.com
This site delivers more than 4,000 free animations, a collection of animated postcards, and hundreds of free letters to help you spell out your message. Fourteen animated alphabets range from elegant Gothic characters to ultramodern and whimsical font styles. There's also a jukebox, so visitors can enjoy their favorite music while surfing the site, a monthly newsletter and a healthy list of links to other clip art sites. ⓐⓐⓐⓐ

MILLANIMATIONS
www.millan.net/anims/giffar.html
Everything moves at Millanimations, a collection of animated clip art by a cartoon artist. You won't find that tired old flickering candle GIF here; instead, the artist has created hundreds of kinetic cartoon images. Visitors will find animations for every holiday under the sun—from Christmas to Deepavali—as well as a clever and sometimes lovable cadre of hugging snakes, beer-drinking aliens, sleeping dogs and other images to get your Web site moving. ⓐⓐⓐⓐ

3RD SHIFT GIFS
www.kevdebin.atlnet.com
There are many collections on the Web that try to incorporate every graphic out there, but 3rd Shift GIFs is more selective and exciting to browse. 3rd Shift has a modern edge, offering metallic textures, buttons and bars, with a very pretty (yet still modern-looking) selection of floral borders and backgrounds. But the real draw here is the relatively small but positively beautiful animated collection of GIFs, with some wonderful birds and Harley-Davidson images. ⓐⓐⓐⓐ

DANCING MOUSE STUDIOS
www.dancingmouse.com
Best for the beginning webmaster looking for graphics to brighten a page, Dancing Mouse's collection contains hundreds of textured backgrounds, buttons and lines. Each image appears as a thumbnail, which makes for quick and easy loading and browsing. Also, you can change the background color to better preview how it will look on your page. ⓐⓐⓐ

AAACLIPART.COM
www.aaaclipart.com
The site is festooned with enough ads and money-making offers to make it a little annoying, but it is still a solid source for thousands of graphics. Pick your category from the menu on the left—buttons, people, sports, food and more—and click to find image after image. AAA is a good clearinghouse for graphics, and it's updated frequently. Just watch where you click to avoid the numerous ad banners. ⓐⓐ

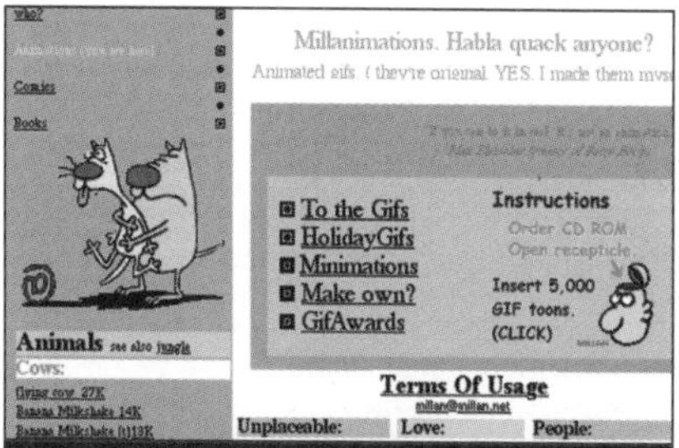

Bring your site to life with animated clip art from Millanimations.

OVER THE RAINBOW
www.gini-net.com
This site requires some scrolling, but it's worth it for the original backgrounds—from solids to batik, rainbow, denim and leopard-spotted designs. There are also blank banners to spruce up Web page headers or ads. A link takes you to Gini's Connoisseur Collection, a commercial site run by the same artist that offers a good selection of free clip art samples in the Art Collections area. ⓐⓐ

Dance

(originally reviewed November 1999)

DANCE ONLINE
www.danceonline.com
This site examines the dance world in all of its gritty beauty. The Dance News section, updated weekly, presents current events and developments in dance, including festivals and grants. The highlight of the site is the small but intriguing Features section, which has commentary by dancers and videos of performances. Also offered are the Photo Exhibit of artists' work and the "Chronicles of Dancer X"—kind of a soap opera about dancers. ⓐⓐⓐⓐ

VOICE OF DANCE
www.voiceofdance.org

This site's design echoes the sleek, simple lines for which many modern choreographers strive. The Insights section is a wonderful resource of dance images, interviews with artists, transcripts of the site's weekly celebrity chats and reviews available for visitors' comments. If that isn't interactive enough, the Community section sponsors message boards that include topics from auditions to yoga. Check the Calendar for dance performances in your area and links to buy tickets. ⓐⓐⓐⓐ

DANCE MAGAZINE
www.dancemagazine.com

This online edition of one of the dance world's most established magazines is not as extensive as the newsstand version. It does have a Young Dancer section, reviews and dance-related artwork from current and back issues. The Calendar is the best feature here, with state-by-state listings and an international database. ⓐⓐⓐ

DANCEART.COM
www.danceart.com

Whether you are beginning ballet, aspiring to dance on Broadway or teaching small children, this dense site has information for you. An extensive forum list and chat room allow connections with other dancers, while expert advice is available in the Features section. Some highlights include advice on living and dancing in New York, facing eating disorders and making your art a business. In addition, the site features interviews with working dancers and an animated ballet dictionary. ⓐⓐⓐ

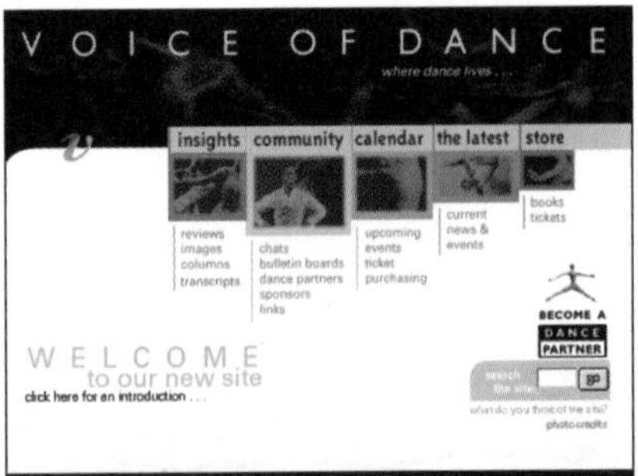

Sleek design makes Voice of Dance a well-choreographed site.

JAZZART
www.jazzart.org

Jazz is one of the most recognizable forms of contemporary dance. It is found in musicals, in movies and on video, as well as in a variety of offshoots, such as hip hop. This site offers articles on the history of jazz dance and many of the major figures in it. Read about the roots of American Vernacular dance, or brush up on the careers of renowned choreographers Jerome Robbins ("West Side Story") and Bob Fosse ("Cabaret"), among others. ⓐⓐ

Drawing

(originally reviewed December 1999)

DRAWING MATERIAL AND DRAWING TECHNIQUES: A GUIDE AND GLOSSARY
www.nyu.edu/classes/miller/guide/contents.html

Consider this a virtual classroom where you can learn about art materials and techniques. Information on everything from graphite to mounting to detail study is at this site, which is often adorned with color pictures of famous works of art. Because it is the digital accompaniment to a New York University class, visiting this site is like taking a college-level course for free. ⓐⓐⓐⓐ

FARP
elfwood.lysator.liu.se/farp

The Fantasy Art Resource Project is a solid guide to drawing figures, faces and fantasy creatures. Amid the gnomes and superheroes is an incomplete but useful collection of tips on materials (pencil sketching, inking) and techniques (tone, depth, lighting). There are also message boards. The community feel here gives visitors the sense that a team of artists is waiting to help them. ⓐⓐⓐ

SAU DEPARTMENT OF ART
www.saumag.edu/art

This site from Southern Arkansas University is quite massive. The two areas most worth visiting are the Figure-Drawing Lab and the Art Studio Chalkboard, which includes in-depth analyses of linear perspective, shading and composition. Diagrams, models and color images illustrate each lesson. ⓐⓐⓐ

HIRO2'S OKONOMI STUDIO
susanooh.anime.net

Hiro2 specializes in anime and manga drawing styles, but any artists who want to improve their figure or face drawing skills will benefit from visiting this site. Click on Drawing Class to learn the basics of sketching shapes and facial expressions. Check out some of the artist's character illustrations or link to other recommended Web sites. ⓐⓐ

education

Adult Education

(originally reviewed November 1999)

BACK TO COLLEGE
www.back2college.com
This may be the best adult education clearinghouse and resource center on the Web, with information about internships, online degrees, life experience credit and financial aid, among other subjects. Top Stories and Features highlight recent articles related to older students. Students will also find study tips, advice for relating to professors and book reviews. The Cool Tools has links to forms, financial aid calculators and specific school information. ⓐⓐⓐⓐ

EDUPOINT.COM
www.edupoint.com
Billing itself as an "education resource for working professionals," EduPoint is a well-developed index site focused on continuing education. Select a degree category, then plug your ZIP code and area of study into the search engine; you'll get a list of programs near you. This site isn't all index, though. Articles on work-site training, MBAs and education tax credits will help lifelong learners make the most of their educational experiences. ⓐⓐⓐⓐ

GED
www.gedtest.org
If you are thinking about earning a high school diploma through the General Educational Development test, this helpful official site offers encouraging statistics. Essential tools are easy to find, such as sample test questions, explanations of scores, FAQs and contact details for testing centers. Even better, though, is the specialized information about French- and Spanish-language tests and accommodations for test takers with disabilities. ⓐⓐⓐ

Explore prospective schools with a visit to www.campustours.com.

GRE ONLINE
www.gre.org
Graduate Record Examination takers will find most of their questions about the test answered here. The GRE is required for admission to many graduate schools. Go to Fast Facts for schedules, fees, online registration and details on the new GRE Writing Assessment. Sample Test Questions contains examples of verbal, quantitative and analytical sections of the test. The site also delves into computer-based testing, the scoring process and score reporting. ⓐⓐⓐ

Applying To College

(originally reviewed December 1999)

CAMPUSTOURS.COM
www.campustours.com
For the next best thing to actually visiting a school, go to CampusTours. The site provides virtual tours of hundreds of colleges and universities throughout the United States. From simple point-and-click maps and photos to live images from campus Webcams, this site lets you be your own tour guide. The site also has links to each school's site and other college resource sites. The Financial Aid section is comprehensive. ⓐⓐⓐⓐ

THE COLLEGE BOARD
www.collegeboard.com
Sorting through all of the information here is a bit overwhelming, but this site covers every stage of college preparation. There is ample advice for seventh- and eighth-graders thinking about college. High school students can find out which classes they should take now and try some SAT questions. Plus, they can register online for the test. The College Search database of more than 3,200 schools can be searched by size, major or location. Once schools have been selected, there are step-by-step instructions for filling out applications. ⓐⓐⓐⓐ

COMMON APPLICATION
www.commonapp.org
The only way applying to college could be easier is if the essays wrote themselves. In the meantime, we have the Common Application, downloadable here and accepted atmore than 200 major universities via snail mail or e-mail. The site itself may not be a font of college information, but since it allows students to complete one application for multiple colleges, it's definitely worth a look. ⓐⓐⓐ

EMBARK.COM: GOING TO COLLEGE
www.embark.com/ugrad.asp
Embark.com is a wonderfully organized site. It breaks down the college selection process into three steps: choosing schools, applying to them, and paying for them. Each category includes online articles and advice. To help you find the perfect school, try the College Matchmaker. Another useful tool at Embark.com is the going-to-school checklist. It reminds you of some of the basics that are often forgotten, such as learning how to do laundry before you leave home and packing first-aid supplies for the dorm room. ⓐⓐⓐ

THE COLLEGE BOUND NETWORK
www.collegebound.net
Geared toward the typical high school student, College Bound is a flashy look at the basics of going to college. It includes advice along with a touch of humor, such as tips for keeping off the dreaded freshman 15. Although the site is a little on the fluffy side—one section tells you where celebrities went to college—it does contain valuable tips. If it doesn't have what you need, it likely has links to sites that do. ⓐⓐ

Home Schooling

(originally reviewed September 1999)

ABOUT.COM: HOMESCHOOLING
homeschooling.about.com
About.com is a network of dedicated advisers on a range of topics, including home schooling. The advisers guide you to relevant resources on the Net, and they've clearly done their homework on this subject. Find insightful comparisons between traditional schooling and "unschooling." There is a state-by-state database of legal information, home-schooling organizations and support groups. Also available at this must-see site are knowledgeable answers to FAQs, tips on getting started, games, weekend activities for kids and links to free stuff. ⓐⓐⓐⓐ

HOMESCHOOL.COM
www.homeschool.com
How will my child learn the tough subjects, you ask? This simple, easy-to-navigate site provides a list of its top 10 home-schooling books and offers Book of the Month and Art Project of the Month selections. Homeschool.com is closely integrated with its sister site, The Education Source, also a rich repository of educational wares. Besides the standard features—curricula, books and an e-mail newsletter—the sites offer information and links for gifted students and distance learning. It is updated weekly. ⓐⓐⓐ

THE HOMESCHOOL ZONE
www.homeschoolzone.com
With a cool but busy layout, this family-oriented site offers resources for novice and experienced home educators. Visitors will find an array of educational resources, some of which are free. Aside from books, crafts, curricula and materials, the site has excellent articles about home schooling. The Home-Ed Help section is packed with useful ideas and support for both teachers and students. ⓐⓐⓐ

KALEIDOSCAPES
www.kaleidoscapes.com
Respectful and responsible, Kaleidoscapes' most distinguishing feature is its user-friendly discussion board. For those interested in connecting with other home educators, the site's discussion topics—including subjects such as curricula, science and special needs students—are current, numerous and varied. Need facts on roaches? Bug recipes? Check out Kaleidoscape's eclectic Kids' Place—a page of educational and fun links for kids. ⓐⓐⓐ

THE HOME SCHOOL
st7.yahoo.com/ths99/index.html
Founded by a pair of veteran home educators who have been dishing out home-schooling advice and materials since 1985, The Home School offers one-stop shopping for parent educators. Along with a wide range of curricula—from Alpha Omega to BJU—the site offers a toll-free advice line, a product search engine and an uncomplicated online ordering system. You won't find freebies or inspirational words because this site is strictly commercial, lacking the motivational tone of other home-schooling sites. ⓐⓐ

HOME'S COOL HOME SCHOOL AND FAMILY SITE
www.homes-cool.com
Despite a somewhat dull appearance and clumsy layout, Home's Cool Home School and Family Site scores decently on content and useful links. It has a Web site hosting service, links to home-schooling support groups and a chat and forum area to share ideas and information. If you're a teacher, you can contribute education techniques and information for a book. ⓐⓐ

Homework Help

(originally reviewed January 2000)

HIGH SCHOOL HUB
www.highschoolhub.org

Focusing on the academic needs of teenagers, this site is a good base for homework help, test preparation and general research. Featured site links include daily history tidbits, vocabulary words and SAT questions, as well as crossword puzzles and a news quiz. The Reference Desk connects to a variety of maps, directories, news, search engines and dictionaries. Plus, there are comprehensive sections for math, science, English and social studies. College-bound seniors should check out the college information sites. ⓐⓐⓐⓐ

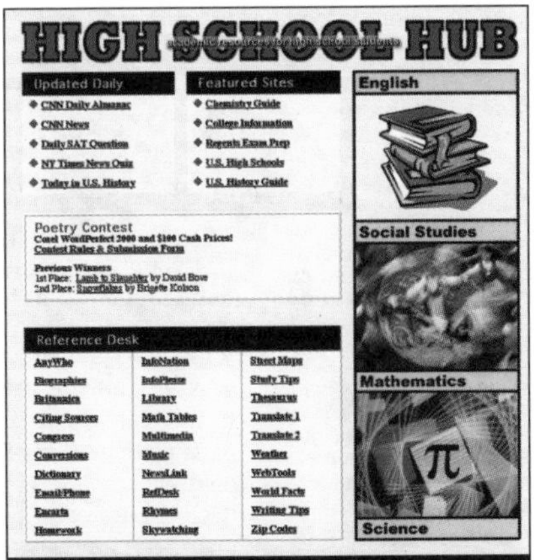

For research tools and test tips go to www.highschoolhub.org.

POWERSCHOOL
www.powerschool.com

Powerschool is a lot more than a homework help site—it's an interactive school management system. Students don't have to be part of the Powerschool system to find help here, though. A click on the Students link brings up a chalkboard of subjects—each offering a small but quality selection of sites—and the Ask Jeeves for Students search engine. There's also a solid reference area, a game section and college prep information. Parents and teachers will also find advice about student development. ⓐⓐⓐⓐ

THE WRITERS' CENTER: RESOURCES FOR WRITERS & TEACHERS
writing.colostate.edu/tools.htm

Published by Colorado State University and intended for its students, The Writers' Center is a valuable tool for learning or fine-tuning writing and researching techniques. The site is organized and extensive, but requires a fair amount of reading (no surprise). It's best suited to high school and college students. Interactive tutorials, demonstrations and writing guides lead students through a variety of subjects, from online research to developing arguments. ⓐⓐⓐⓐ

ALPHABET SUPERHIGHWAY
www.ash.udel.edu/ash

This site offers more than just links to help research and write that unruly term paper; it contains tutorials and guides to help kids become better students. Clean and simple images should keep younger students involved without distracting them. Essential sections for kids include the Library and the Traveling Tutor, which offers reading and writing lessons and links. ⓐⓐⓐ

DAVE'S MATH TABLES
www.sisweb.com/math/tables.htm

Students who need a quick math reference rather than detailed explanations will find all sorts of help here. Ten sections, ranging from general math to linear algebra and calculus, define terms, provide formulas and offer graphs. This makes it easy to brush up on determining the circumference of a circle, converting fractions to decimals and proving calculus theorems. A message board, links, and suggested books and software are also available. ⓐⓐⓐ

SCHOOLWORK.UGH!
www.schoolwork.org

This organized and simple site serves as a homework link library for students in grades seven and up. Topics range from essentials such as math, history and grammar, to the more specialized—law, philosophy, statistics and mythology. The simple nature of the site's design is deceptive; each category is carefully organized and accompanied by helpful commentary. ⓐⓐⓐ

SOCIAL STUDIES SCHOOL SERVICE
www.socialstudies.com

Although this site was designed for teachers, it can be handy for students, as well. Use the Features menu to select a topic, such as Early America, Shakespeare or World Religions. The site brings up suggested essay questions, books and videos to use in class, plus site links. Granted, the site's creators would prefer that you buy the recommended material here, but the links are free, and the book and video listings give students good titles for which to search in the library. To browse Web site links only, click on the Links tab. ⓐⓐⓐ

How To

(originally reviewed January 2000)

FAMILY SHOEBOX
www.familyshoebox.com

Been awhile since you called your mom in Florida? How about Uncle Ned in Arizona? This site offers a smart new way to keep in touch with family members. Set up a free family site at Family Shoebox, and stay connected with relatives around the country. Share family news online, create a calendar to highlight family events, post photos and even set up message boards and chats.

FREE ONLINE LANGUAGE COURSES
rivendel.com/~ric/resources/coursead.html

The Tower of Babel has nothing on this site, a directory of links to free online courses that teach more than 75 different languages. All the standards are here—French, Spanish, German, Italian, Russian—plus less familiar languages such as Icelandic, Hindi, Latvian, Sanskrit and Cherokee. You also can link to online dictionaries, language chat sites and test exercises—handy if you want to try your new Punjabi speaking skills.

LEARN2.COM
www.learn2.com/learn2_everyday.asp

From repairing your car to caring for a new pet tortoise to reading sheet music, this encompassing site teaches you how to do almost anything. The easy-to-follow tutorials cover arts and crafts; business and money; food and drink; health and fitness; style and grace; home and garden; and travel, among others. Shy folks can learn the secrets behind giving a speech, while outdoor enthusiasts can learn the basics of fly fishing, biking, cricket and a number of other sports. The cute illustrations and simple-to-follow instructions are what make this site useful, friendly and fun.

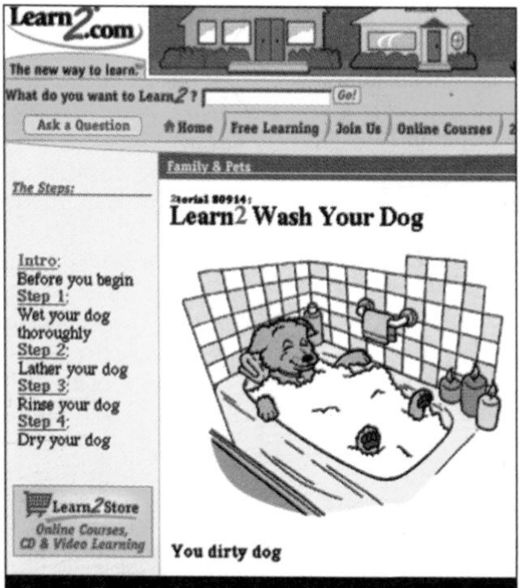

Learn2.com has tutorials on everything from pets to public speaking.

ANCESTRY.COM
www.ancestry.com

Boasting that its genealogical databases contain more than 500 million names, Ancestry.com is a comprehensive resource for tracing your roots. A new database is added each weekday. The catch is that searching Ancestry.com's new databases is only free for 10 days. There are also free online maps and helpful how-to articles, but to enjoy all of the site's services you'll need to pay the $59.95 annual subscription price.

FORWARD MOTION
www.hollylisle.com

If you want to learn how to get a book published—or maybe just learn how to write a book—stop dragging your feet (and your pen). Created by professional writer Holly Lisle, this site exists to "help beginning writers break into print." The site reminds you that all published writers were once unpublished, so don't give up hope. Major sections cover writing techniques, editors, agents and getting published.

GOLF SWINGS
hometown.aol.com/beau1943/golfswings/golf1.htm

Golfers know that the best way to improve a swing, other than practice, is to study how the professionals do it. At this site you can do just that. View video files of more than 20 professional golfers swinging their clubs. Tiger Woods, Greg Norman and Se Ri Pak are a few of the greats who are included. There are also brief bios, as well as links to sports news, golf magazines and a gift store.

HOBBY PLANET
www.hobbyplanet.com

Perhaps you've always wanted to take up a new hobby, such as bird-watching, beer-brewing, stamp-collecting, painting or even glass-blowing. Or maybe you can't quite decide on a hobby and would like to browse a list of possibilities, from crafts to sports to collectibles. Either way, you'll want to head to Hobby Planet. This directory provides links to Web sites for dozens of hobbies, as well as related FAQs, and book and software suggestions in various categories.

education

LYRICAL LINE
www.lyricalline.com

Attention aspiring songwriters: Put down your guitar and surf over here. There are articles, a newsletter, expert advice and an online radio show that offers help with your craft. From keeping the story going to making a demo and getting published, this site covers both the creative and business sides of the process. Post lyrics to have them critiqued by other visitors, or try the Rhyming Dictionary at the bottom of the page. ⓐⓐⓐ

PIANO ON THE NET
www.artdsm.com/music.html

Musician and composer Clinton Shirley Clark created this free online multimedia tutorial. It's a step-by-step piano lesson. Begin with the basics in the 13-lesson Starter Studies, then progress to the Intermediate and Advanced Studies. Each lesson takes about 35 minutes, and many are enhanced with QuickTime audio. ⓐⓐⓐ

HOW TO GIVE A SPEECH
www.augsburg.edu/depts/infotech/present

If public speaking is your greatest fear, you're not alone. This site will teach you how to write and give a great speech. The easy-to-follow tutorial is stellar. The 16 lessons cover types of speech, introductions, organization and how to finish with a strong ending. ⓐⓐ

THE ROSE TEA ROOM
thetearoom.8m.com

Where does the steak knife go? Silverware placement may not be as precise as it used to be, but proper etiquette is just as important today as it was during Queen Victoria's reign. The Rose Tea Room has etiquette tips for all situations, from business meetings to formal dinners to Internet encounters. There are even Historical Etiquette Tidbits and Manners for Children. Oh, and the steak knife goes between the dinner plate and the butter knife. ⓐⓐ

Music Instruction

(originally reviewed October 1999)

DANSM'S HOME PAGE
www.dreamscape.com/esmith/dansm

Created by Cornell University student and acoustic guitarist Dan Smith, this is an excellent site for guitarists of all levels. Beginners should start with the colorful guitar diagram to learn the parts, then tackle reading music and finger-picking lessons. With the basics covered, Smith meticulously leads visitors through chord theory, beginning with the basic open chords and progressing to more complex ones. Novices will love the archive of easy songs. All guitarists will appreciate the warm-up exercises and extensive FAQ page. ⓐⓐⓐⓐ

GITARRE SPIELEN
www.guitarplaying.com

If you play (or hope to play) a guitar, you'll love this site. Clearly presented lessons will help you with everything from learning scales to refining your arpeggio techniques to tuning your guitar. The cool Java chord locator will instantly show you what any chord looks like on the fretboard. Audio and video licks, equipment reviews, profiles of and interviews with legendary guitarists, and a huge tablature archive are just some of the many other features that make this site a must-see. ⓐⓐⓐⓐ

THE PIANO EDUCATION PAGE
www.unm.edu/~loritaf/pnoedmn.html

This is the ultimate online resource for piano students, teachers and parents. At this comprehensive site, students can read inspiring interviews with artists and educators, listen to hundreds of MIDI files of solo piano music in the Audition Room and get tips on practicing and playing better. Interviews with famous composers will help kids understand the human dimension of music. Parents will appreciate the useful guide to choosing the right teacher. ⓐⓐⓐⓐ

JAVA MUSIC THEORY
academics.hamilton.edu/music/spellman/JavaMusic

Even the most motivated students sometimes find music theory tedious. But this interesting site, which offers animated tutorials to enhance students' grasp of theory, does a good job of solving that problem. Whether students want to increase the speed with which they read music or deepen their understanding of scales, the gamelike drills offer a fun way of doing it. ⓐⓐⓐ

THE WOODWIND FINGERING GUIDE
www.sneezy.org/wfg

This is an invaluable resource for woodwind players. The Woodwind Fingering Guide is a tightly focused site offering basic, alternate and trill fingerings for the flute, recorder, clarinet, saxophone, oboe and bassoon. Thanks to frequent submissions from users, the site offers more than 2,000 fingerings and is expanding continually. Students can also use the popular Woodwind Fingering Forum to ask questions and give advice.

PRIVATELESSONS.COM
www.privatelessons.com

Students who visit this site can search for teachers by instrument, style of music or composition. Want to find a teacher in your area who offers bagpipe or polka instruction? Look no further. The online forums under Knowledge Center offer a lively and supportive community for music teachers. Find advice on motivation, fees, techniques and recitals.

Special Education & Learning Disabilities

(originally reviewed October 1999)

LD ONLINE
www.ldonline.org

This well-organized guide walks through the basics of learning disabilities and leads to in-depth discussions of specific disorders and topics. These topics range from family relationships to technological aids. Resources here include: the Ask the Expert bulletin board, a state-by-state resource guide, information on where to find help and the ABCs of LD. The KidZone has artwork by kids with learning disabilities. Kids can use the audio and visual tools to find out about learning disabilities.

BORN TO EXPLORE! THE OTHER SIDE OF ADD
www.borntoexplore.org

This site takes a new approach to attention deficit disorder and attention deficit hyperactivity disorder. Based on research and current articles, the site claims that ADD and ADHD aren't disorders but simply different temperaments—even gifts. Read about Jungian-based temperament theory—people with ADD and ADHD may have different types of creativity and intelligence than others. Biological theories based on observations of nonhuman communities are offered, as are alternative treatment ideas.

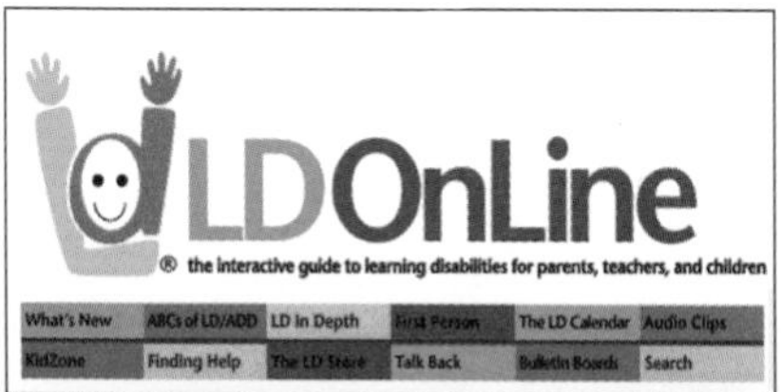

There is information and support for both parents and kids at www.ldonline.org.

CHADD
www.chadd.org

This site provides support and education for individuals with ADD and ADHD, which is the founding goal of Children and Adults with Attention Deficit/Hyperactivity Disorder, a nonprofit organization. Legislative updates and research developments will keep you on the cutting edge of advances in dealing with the disorder. The FAQs and fact sheets answer initial questions about diagnosis, treatment and legal rights. The online selections from the organization's print magazine explore the broader topics that families must consider, include parenting and work issues.

THE COUNCIL FOR EXCEPTIONAL CHILDREN
www.cec.sped.org

Primarily an advocacy site, CEC provides in-depth analysis of current public awareness campaigns and pending legislation, as well as contact information for senators and representatives. You can link here to other CEC sites, such as the Foundation for Exceptional Children and the ERIC Clearinghouse on Disabilities and Gifted Education. These sites provide additional information about grants for educators, scholarships for students and a database of related educational materials.

NATIONAL CENTER FOR LEARNING DISABILITIES
www.ncld.org

This site is a practical guide and resource for people living with learning disabilities. General information alone makes the site worth a visit; however, the NCLD Tips for Parents, Teachers and Adults section in the Resources section requires a stop. Whether struggling to work with your child's teachers or within your work environment, there is down-to-earth advice available here.

TEENS HELPING TEENS
www.ldteens.org

This site for teens with dyslexia and other learning disabilities provides study tips, advice for adapting to college life, questions to ask college recruiters, and a place for teens to express themselves and ask questions. Drop into Study Help for tips on note taking and organizing work, plus lists of common problems that may help teens recognize and cope with their learning disability. E-mail questions to Lee Ann, a dyslexic woman with a master's degree in special education.

entertainment

American Film Classics

(originally reviewed September 1999)

AMERICAN MOVIE CLASSICS
www.amctv.com
This site provides interviews, programming schedules and background information for the 24-hour movie network that features classic films from the 1930s through the 1980s. Browse celebrity interviews, or read bios of dozens of Hollywood greats. Explore an entire section devoted to Romance Classics, or download movie trailers. Film buffs can search the AMC Movie Database for industry gossip, star bios and descriptions of more than 2,000 classic movies from Hollywood's Golden Age. There are also trivia games and contests. ⓐⓐⓐⓐ

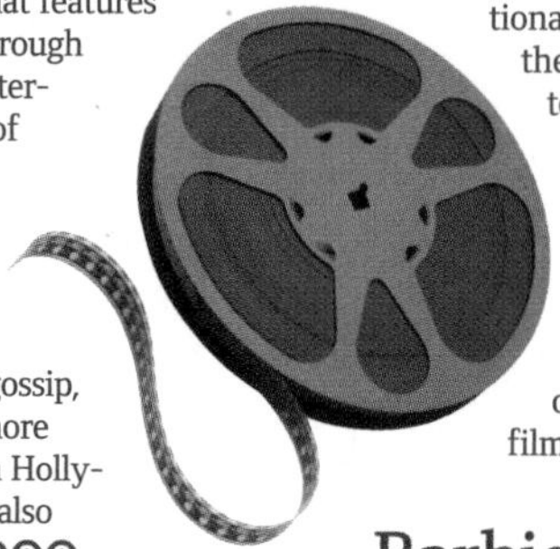

THE FILM 100
www.film100.com
From John Wayne to Jean-Luc Godard, The Film 100 uses dual screens that together form a unique list of the film industry's 100 most influential people. Most of the profiled stars and directors are from Hollywood, but there are top-notch articles on the international heavyweights who did make the list—Vittorio de Sica, Ingmar Bergman and Akira Kurosawa, to name a few. Learn more about the personalities who shaped and continue to shape Hollywood. ⓐⓐⓐⓐ

THE ASTOUNDING B MONSTER
www.bmonster.com
Do you count among your guilty pleasures films like "Forbidden Planet," "I Married a Monster from Outer Space" or "The Incredible Shrinking Man"? This enthusiastic fan site showcases interviews with such B-movie legends as cult film director Jack Hill. First-timers should check out "Ten B-movie names you should know," as well as other fun articles and interviews. The colorful and bold graphics practically burst through the screen—just what you'd expect to see on a B-movie poster. ⓐⓐⓐ

THE PALACE
www.moderntimes.com/palace
The black and white format and art deco-style typeface exude classic movie elegance. The Palace is devoted to film history from the 1920s through the 1950s. Click on a decade for a photo spread of some of that period's memorable films and links to star information. B-movies and film noir have special sections. Midnight Ramble explores black Hollywood and the portrayal of blacks during the first half of the 20th century. Be sure to check out the fabulous movie posters. ⓐⓐⓐ

TURNER CLASSIC MOVIES
tcm.turner.com
TCM claims to have more than 5,000 classic movies, including silent screen and international pictures, from the 1920s through the 1980s. Read interviews with directors such as John Frankenheimer and George Romero, or download movie trailers. Film buffs should submit a review for the monthly contest or check out Between The Scenes, a smorgasbord of movie gossip, trivia and photos that is streamed on the Web while the corresponding film is airing on TCM. ⓐⓐⓐ

Barbie Doll

(originally reviewed September 1999)

BARBIE.COM
www.barbie.com
The official Barbie Web site contains many strategically placed purchasing opportunities, but Mattel, the doll's manufacturer, wraps it all up in a pretty package. There's a lot to see and do at this polished site, including shopping for dolls and browsing collectable items and Barbie software. Sift through nifty postcards, profiles of female athletes, recipes and fairy tales. Did we mention that you can design your own Barbie? ⓐⓐⓐⓐ

BARBIE BAZAAR MAGAZINE
www.barbiebazaar.com
A digital teaser for the monthly print publication, this site delivers a feature story, a place to buy special edition books and back issues of the magazine. If you're ready to play Barbie and you don't mind looking at a few items for sale in the process, point those perpetually high-heeled feet here. ⓐⓐⓐ

BARBIE: THE IMAGE OF US ALL
www.people.virginia.edu/~tsawyer/barbie/barb.html
A virtual dissertation on the Barbie doll as a cultural phenomenon, this site really cuts through the fluff, covering Barbie's origins, evolution and role in our daily lives. Well-written, thoroughly researched and accessible, it will interest doll lovers and collectors, critical feminists, wary parents, Net theologians and academics. ⓐⓐ

The Beatles

(originally reviewed December 1999)

THE BEATLES ONLINE
www.beatlesonline.com
This entertaining site tackles the fun aspects of Beatlemania: a trivia quiz, audio files of interviews and songs played backward. The message board is as lively as "Yellow Submarine," and there are lyrics to 13 Beatles albums. You will also find a limited amount of news. The most amusing section has to be Paul Is Dead; look here for the story and clues from the albums. ⓐⓐⓐⓐ

THE INTERNET BEATLES ALBUM
www.getback.org
This clever, artfully designed site lets fans surf through an eclectic mix of Beatles topics. The homepage features an image of a vinyl record with popular Beatles song titles, each an allusion to the site's topics. For example, "I Should Have Known Better" leads to a page about Beatles myths. Don't miss side two by clicking on the number. The other topics include band history, record typos and the flap over John Lennon's controversial claim that the band was "more popular than Jesus." Click on each Fab Four name for entertaining bios, photographs and audio clips. ⓐⓐⓐⓐ

THE BEATLES PHOTO SESSIONS
www.sigma.net/nems/beatles
Fans looking for Beatles photos should check out this site. It has a bevy of publicity and candid shots from 1964-1969. It's a fascinating glimpse of the wild evolution of the band's public image over five short years. Included are the famous Life magazine photos from the summer of 1968, group photos from the Sgt. Pepper's promotional party and the final photo session of the fabulous foursome at John Lennon and Yoko Ono's house. ⓐⓐⓐ

THE BEATLES ULTIMATE EXPERIENCE
www.geocities.com/~beatleboy1
Explore the compelling story of one of the world's most popular bands through its members' eyes. This creative site guides you through Beatles history with quotes, interviews, photos and animations. From the initial giddiness over publicity to tension and arguments to the transition to independent lives, the information is interesting and well presented. There is also a database of photos and full-length interviews, plus an FAQ page. ⓐⓐⓐ

UBL.COM: THE BEATLES
www.ubl.com/ubl_artist.asp?artistid=001031
For those people who aren't Beatlemaniacs, this page provides a thorough introduction to the band that "introduced more innovations into popular music than any other rock band of the 20th century." The article featured here is long but worth reading. Included here are links to fan sites, lyric sites and audio/video clips. It's a shame that some of the links are broken, but most of them work and help make for an interesting piece of music history. ⓐⓐ

Chat

(originally reviewed September 1999)

GO NETWORK: CHAT
www.go.com/Community/People?topic=chat
The ever-expanding Go Network has an excellent selection of chat rooms categorized by age and interest. Registering with Go is quick and easy, although chatters under the age of 12 need parental permission to sign up. Once logged on, stop by the message board, visit the coffee house, or check in on business, arts, travel or other conversations. Go Network also offers free homepages and e-mail accounts. ⓐⓐⓐⓐ

ICQ
www.icq.com
The busy homepage reflects the ICQ service—there's a lot to do here. But don't let the clutter stop you; ICQ is easy to use. Download the free ICQ software, register, type in your list of

For a visual history, peruse The Beatles Photo Sessions.

friends and associates, and you're in business. Each time you log on, ICQ will let you know if any of those people are also logged on to the Web. If no one you know is online, ICQ's networks will help you find a new chat partner to talk about topics such as art, games, money and travel.

CHAT 101
www.ker95.com/chat101
This site lays out the basics of chat in simple terms—it's perfect for beginners. Chatiquette gives helpful hints on the dos and don'ts of chat, from introducing yourself to the room to addressing other chatters. Chat terms and abbreviations are spelled out to clear up that online jargon.Click on Etc., then Places to Chat and take what you've learned to some starter sites. You'll be chatting in no time.

THE GLOBE.COM: CHAT
www.theglobe.com/chat
Co-founded by 25-year-olds Todd Krizelman and Stephan Paternot, this progressive site has offerings for teens to fiftysomethings, but those in their 20s and 30s are best served here. The site tells you how many people are in each of the rooms and which rooms are most popular. The Mute and Matador features let you block postings from offensive participants. This safety-conscious site also allows you to create your own chat community and offers a free newsletter, listing celebrity and special guest chat sessions.

TALK CITY
www.talkcity.com
Loaded with 20 topic categories, this site is as smooth and diverse as its layout—and it's all talk. Talk citizens can design their own chat rooms or join one of the special chats of the day, from Friday Breakfast Club to CosmoGIRL! to Rush Room where you can tune in to Rush Limbaugh's show and talk about it. If your computer isn't running Java, fix your browser setting when you log in to "EZ Talk Web."

SPORTSCHAT!
www.4-lane.com/sportschat
SportsChat! offers 18 rooms for sports fans of all kinds, from football devotees discussing the latest game, to runners seeking advice about foot injuries. Other rooms feature tennis, biking, backpacking, golf, soccer, NASCAR, rock climbing and skiing. The site is easy to use; just type in your screen name and start talking—no registration required.

YAHOO! CHAT
chat.yahoo.com
Listing information and links to the day's top chat events around the Net, Yahoo presents a wide variety of both Java- and Web-based chat options. The featured rooms are displayed at the top of the page; click on Complete Room List for more options. The depth of offerings and clear instructions make this a solid starting point for newcomers. Specific instructions are available for AOL members under Help to make their systems compatible with Yahoo! Chat.

Classic Games

(originally reviewed October 1999)

THE FOOSBALL SOURCE
www.foosball.com
This site proves that foosball is much more than "that game in the bar where you spin the rods." You'll find Foos History, Official Rules, a Glossary of Terms and videos of basic shots, tricks and championship games. There are also video clips of foosball appearances in movies and TV shows, such as "Friends." Once you master your five-bar pass and your aerial shot, use the tournament database to find a game near you.

THE HOUSE OF CARDS
www.thehouseofcards.com
Self-described as "the best in card games and playing card information," The House of Cards has rules for hundreds of games as well as links to meeting places where card-lovers can play online. Follow the links to classic games such as bridge and cribbage, or more exotic games such as hanafuda. You'll also find kids' games, links to the history of card games and resources for playing-card collectors.

Play classic word games online at www.wordplays.com.

HURRAH MAD LIBS
www.hurrah.com/madlibs
Everyone's favorite fill-in-the-blanks car or slumber party game has come to the Internet—and you don't need a partner to play. There are several Mad Libs sites on the Web, but this one is especially fun. It butchers well-known documents and works of art, such

as the Beatles' "Eleanor Rigby" (Ah ... look at all the vitriolic cheeses!) and "The Catcher in the Rye." The selection is limited, but the site accepts suggestions. ⓐⓐⓐ

WORDPLAYS.COM: INTERACTIVE WORD GAMES
www.wordplays.com
One of the better word game sites on the Web, WordPlays.com includes regularly updated interactive versions of boggler, crossword puzzles, word finds and anagrams. Race against the clock and compare your results with others' scores. Less competitive but just as much fun—the site's pig Latin generator. Type in a phrase for a translation to e-mail a friend. ⓐⓐⓐ

ROSHAMBO RAMPAGE
www.brunching.com/toys/toy-psr.html
Elegant in its simplicity, this site offers online, networked games of rock-paper-scissors. Enter e-mail addresses for you and someone you would like to challenge, along with your choice of the three attack strategies. Once notified of the challenge, your opponent has two days to respond. The winner is notified immediately. The loser is informed that he or she was "defeated in battle." ⓐⓐ

See the many faces of Elvis at the excellent Elvex Pages.

Elvis

(originally reviewed January 2000)

ELVEX PAGES
www.geocities.com/~arpt/eplns.html
The first thing you'll hear at this deluxe Elvis site are tunes from the King himself. Elvis fan Lex Raaphorst presents enough information to keep Elvisologists busy for hours. Rare recordings and seldom-seen photos are in the I Gotta Know and Memories sections. Check out the Edge of Reality for the scoop on Elvis' Hollywood career. Want the lyrics to "Clambake"? You got 'em, along with the words to every other Presley recording. ⓐⓐⓐⓐ

ELVIS LIVES IN EVIL LEVIS
www.people.virginia.edu/~acs5d/elvis.html
What's the connection between Robert De Niro and Elvis? The Oracle of Elvis knows. A variation on the Six Degrees of Kevin Bacon game, this section of one passionate fan's impressive site connects actors to Elvis through their movie roles. (Here's a hint: She was in "Once Upon a Time in America" and "Wild in the Country.") You'll also find a good biography and genealogy report, photos, lyrics and a guide to Graceland. ⓐⓐⓐ

ROLLINGSTONE.COM: ELVIS PRESLEY
rollingstone.tunes.com/sections/artists/text/artistgen.asp?afl=&LookUpString=2024
When they're not busy fawning over the latest pretty young thing to come along, the editors at Rolling Stone magazine do an unparalleled job of writing about rock music. The essays here about "the first real rock & roll star" survey Presley's career in the context of his influence on music and society. Well-written analysis and biographical pieces treat Presley as a serious musical force and avoid taking easy shots at his tragic decline. If you're thinking of buying some Elvis albums, especially posthumous compilations, check out the album guide from Rolling Stone first. ⓐⓐⓐ

WON'T YOU WEAR MY TCB RING
www.casema.net/~arpt/tcbring.html
One of the easiest ways to explore Elvis pages is by following this Webring, which is a chain of related sites. Scroll through the long list of more than 150 sites and pick the links that look interesting, or click on Random Site and hop from stop to stop. One click might take you to The Memphis Mafia page, the next click to a fan's reverent tribute, the next to a site about Elvis and aliens. Some are good, some are not, but they're all Elvis. ⓐⓐⓐ

YAHOO! MUSIC: ELVIS PRESLEY
musicfinder.yahoo.com/shop?d=p&id=presleyelvis&cf=10
If you're looking for music, you've come to the right place. From the 1956 albums that got rock 'n' roll all shook up to 1999's "Artist of the Century" jumbo compilation, you'll find just about every available Elvis recording listed here, including a few rare singles. Even if you're not shopping, the discography is a valuable reference. Or if you just need a shot of the King's music, listen to the sound clips in RealAudio or Liquid Player formats that are available here. ⓐⓐⓐ

Ghost Stories and Hauntings

(originally reviewed October 1999)

HAUNTED AMERICA
www.hauntedamerica.com

If you're looking for the nearest haunted house, this is the site for you. Almost every haunted activity or Halloween attraction in the United States is listed here. Select your state for local listings, addresses and phone numbers—some even have maps. Shop the Halloween store or click on Ghost Stories for spooky stories and a list of ghost tours. Dagon's Fright Site offers make-up tips, scary movie picks and a graveyard gallery. ⓐⓐⓐⓐ

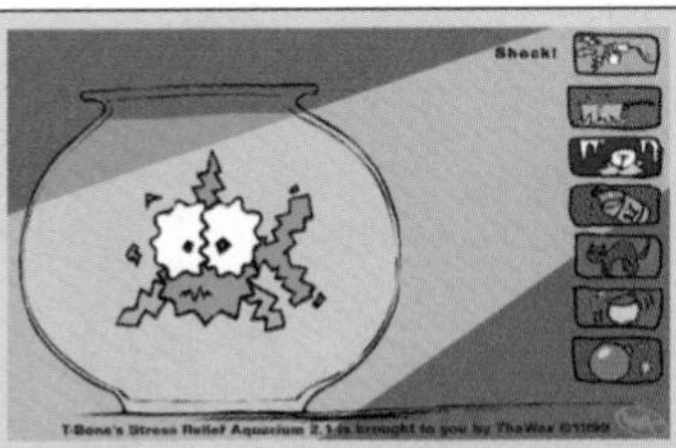

Scare a fish at www.amused.com. (It's OK—they're only virtual fish.)

HALLOWEEN NET
www.halloweennet.com

Everything you need for a macabre Halloween bash is here: party treats, ghost stories posted by readers, ideas for creating your own haunted house and safety tips. Plus, when Halloween is close you'll find a good list of horror flicks that are scheduled for airing on television. For an authentic haunted house, download the MP3 and WAV audio files of horrifying sounds. There are some spooky links listed as well. ⓐⓐⓐ

VIRTUAL HAUNTED HOUSE
www2.ncsu.edu/ncsu/cep/ligon/haunted96/haunted96.menu.html

This site is part of MidLink Magazine, "the digital magazine for kids," created by kids aged 8 to 18. The simple graphics—they're not too gruesome or scary—make it a good site for younger children, but there's still plenty of fun and spookiness. Do the scavenger hunt on the tour of the haunted house, or visit the 3-D haunted house. Kids can send in their own "gruesome graphics" to be added to the site. ⓐⓐⓐ

CASTLE OF SPIRITS
www.castleofspirits.com

This Australian site claims to have more than 1,000 ghost stories. People all over the globe submit ghoulish tales about their encounters with mysterious ghosts. Spook yourself by reading Classic Ghost Stories, such as "The Black Cadillac" and "The Whistling Tea Kettle." Or go to Paranormal Events to find out the truth behind "The Blair Witch Project" and read about the Bermuda Triangle, Ouija boards and werewolves. ⓐⓐ

HALLOWEEN ON THE WEB
www.halloween.com

This spooky, links-based site is neatly divided into various ghoulish topics, including witches and werewolves, vampires, ghosts and cemeteries. Plus, the site has links to costumes, props and games. There's plenty here to induce goose bumps. The Cemeteries links, for example, include a pet cemetery and a site with pictures and scariness ratings. For those with a goofy funny bone, check out Halloween Humor. ⓐⓐ

SPIRIT
www.ghosthunter.org

This site takes ghosts seriously, covering mysticism and folklore from around the world, traditional ghost stories, paranormal activity and ghost documentation. You can read about bone-chilling close encounters in Field Reports. The Toolbox tells you everything you'll need in your utility belt when you go ghost hunting. A link to ghost photographs lets you in on what's fake and what's inexplicable. ⓐⓐ

Humor

(originally reviewed October 1999)

CATBERT'S ANTI-CAREER ZONE
www.dilbert.com/comics/dilbert/career

You say that your human resources director is evil, but is he as cute or as funny as Catbert? This site featuring Dilbert—the popular comic strip character devoted to the mediocrity of work—is incredibly funny. There are work-survey spoofs, real résumé bloopers and weekly career tips. (Tips, mind you, that may end your career.) The best part is the Mission Statement Generator, which spits out an official-sounding, ready-to-use statement for dull meetings and sales pitches. ⓐⓐⓐⓐ

THE CENTRE FOR THE EASILY AMUSED
www.amused.com

Unless you are really jaded, this site is definitely good for a laugh or two. There are tons of great games, riddles and jokes at your disposal, some of which require specific plug-ins. The silly interactive animations take the cake. Try the Rugrats Dance, or test your humor savvy with one of the site's quizzes. Definitely check out the Time-Wasting Calculator and Take My Webpage, Please!, a page devoted to comedians. Before you leave, visit some of the many merry links.

CYBERCHEEZE
www.cybercheeze.com
CyberCheeze's claim that it's the "No. one humor source" is a little strong. However, this site can definitely muster up a few guffaws. It's easy to navigate, and the Joke of the Day mailing list is one piece of junk e-mail you may actually read before deleting. Plus, the jokes are carefully categorized.

COLLEGE HUMOR
www.geocities.com/CollegePark/Hall/2239/humor/college/home.html
The creators of this site—who probably spend most of their time on the Web instead of at the library—do have a slightly twisted sense of humor. Sift through this collection of lists and you'll be sure to find at least a few collegiate chuckles. From 100 Ways to Annoy Your Roommate, to You Might Be a College Student If ..., the humor here will appeal to a select group.

HUMOR SEARCH
www.humorsearch.com
Consider this site a humor portal. Check out the joke of the day or search the humor archive. Asinine Storylines lets you and your fellow netizens create a nonsensical story. The site provides the title and opening line, then visitors keep the story flowing. Joke Machine feeds you a new joke every time you go to the link and gives you the chance to enter one. Please note: Visitors must be 18 or older to subscribe to the humor archive.

A JOKE A DAY.COM
www.ajokeaday.com
OK, so this site isn't going to win any layout awards anytime soon. The navigation is confusing, and the design is not the most aesthetically pleasing, despite the colorful joker. However, if you're looking for a cheap laugh every day, this is the right spot. The site "guarantees to keep all jokes and humor clean," which makes it, along with the joke-a-day e-mail service, good for anyone of any age. Plus, you can send in your favorite joke.

Jazz

(originally reviewed November 1999)

ALL ABOUT JAZZ
www.allaboutjazz.com
Run by a dedicated collective of jazz enthusiasts, All About Jazz is an amazing resource about the genre. There are hundreds of excellent articles and reviews of CDs and concerts. Interviews, biographies and profiles give visitors a chance to get to know jazz artists such as Jackie King, Gary Peacock and Sonny Rollins. The On the Road section allows users to interact with musicians on tour. Check out Festivals for a guide to upcoming shows in your area.

THE JAZZ REVIEW
www.jazzreview.com
This site excels at providing substantive reviews of the latest jazz releases. Jazzviews offers in-depth and illuminating interviews with numerous contemporary jazz artists, such as Andre Bush and Jeffery Smith. Be sure to check out the photographs of musicians in action in the Jazzography section. Guest Reviews lets fans post their own critiques, and there are links to sites that let you listen to jazz over the Net.

DOWN BEAT JAZZ
www.downbeatjazz.com
This hip print magazine's online companion is full of interesting stories and features. Download dozens of MP3 files or read profiles of jazz greats such as John Coltrane, Miles Davis and Betty Carter in Hall of Fame. Visitors will also find CD reviews, audio files of interviews and concerts, and a jazz festival guide.

J-A-ZZ: JAZZ-FROM-A-TO-ZZ
www.geocities.com/BourbonStreet/9555/Jazz-from-A-to-ZZ.html
With links to more than 15,000 jazz-related sites, this Web site purports to be the most comprehensive jazz database online. Whether you want to learn more about the history of Big Band, join a guitar newsgroup or find that rare Swedish jazz record that nobody seems to carry, this site has a link for you. Be sure to read Navigation

Guidelines for help getting around. Note: As of our last visit the site is in the process of renovating its database; so skip the search engine and watch out for some broken links.

JAZZ ONLINE
www.jazzonln.com
Hot Picks, Fresh Reviews and advice from the resident jazz expert will delight faithful fans. Newcomers will appreciate Jazz 101, a brief introduction to 13 styles of jazz, and Starter Kit, a list of recommended CDs that should be in everyone's collection. Read interviews with musicians, listen to audio samples or watch video clips of performances. An active message board and an archive of previous features complete this deserving site.

Magic

(originally reviewed October 1999)

MAGIC SHOW
www.allmagic.com
This weekly guide to all things magic offers columns, the Magicalendar of shows and events around the nation, information on magic props and answers from Mr. Magic. Visit the Arcade section for pointers from top magicians, a card encyclopedia and video demonstrations of magic acts. Of course, there are plenty of lessons here to soak up. Don't miss the spinoff sites, in particular the All Magic Guide.

MAGICTRICKS.COM
www.magictricks.com
Although its retail aspect is pushed hard here, an extensive magic library is only the beginning of the fun at this site. You'll also find one-liners to stop hecklers, magic trivia, an expansive Magic Museum and links to sites that teach you how to perform tricks. Read famous magicians' biographies or articles on getting started, or locate a magic club in your area. The shop sells instructional books, videos, magic kits and a big selection of card and close-up tricks.

CONJUROR
www.conjuror.com
With free trick instructions and a well-stocked shop, Conjuror is a terrific starting point for those just getting familiar with the world of magic. Hook up with a pen pal to exchange encouragement and tips, or pick up advice from professional magicians at The Conversation Corner. Information on stage magic and an archive of magic history and articles add substance to this well-designed site.

HOUDINIANA.COM
www.houdiniana.com
The man who was arguably the world's most famous magician is commemorated on this vast site. It boasts a gigantic collection of Harry Houdini art, videos, articles and movies. Listen to rare audio clips of the master performer, or view photographs and newspaper clippings of some of his most masterful escapes. Little-known facts and a historical account of the man formerly known as Erich Weiss are also available at this interesting site.

EMPIRE MAGIC
www.frontiernet.net/~empirema
Providing supplies for amateur and professional magicians since 1992, Empire Magic offers a convenient online forum for finding the props to make your act go "abracadabra!" Add the Tricks of the Week to your repertoire, or search the Alphabetical Trick Finder for hundreds of magical maneuvers. From illusions and juggling to books and videos, this site has everything you need to become a spellbinding magician.

MAGIC TIMES
www.magictimes.com
This online magazine about magic includes the latest industry news and feature articles on upcoming shows and top magicians. If you're looking for live entertainment, there is a schedule of magic shows nationwide. The TV News section lists TV magic programs, and Club News tells you where to find upcoming magic lectures and teaching forums. An archive of past issues rounds out this straightforward site.

Top magicians offer pointers in the Arcade section of www.allmagic.com.

Movie Guides

(originally reviewed December 1999)

SCREEN IT! MOVIES
www.screenit.com/search_movies.html
The husband and wife team behind this site help parents choose movies that the entire family can enjoy. In addition to a plot synopsis, each review has a chart that details the levels of profanity; sex and nudity; violence; smoking; alcohol and drugs; and blood and gore. Each is ranked as mild, moderate, heavy or extreme. Plus, there are descriptions of scenes that include objectionable material to help you decide if the content is inappropriate. Another standout feature analyzes whether a movie's characters are good or bad role models for children. ⓐⓐⓐⓐ

VIDEOSEEKER: MOVIES
www.videoseeker.com/movies
Don't let the name fool you—this is not a video game or a video store locator. This giant movie site primarily offers the latest downloadable, full-length movie trailers, clips, behind-the-scenes features and interviews with stars and directors. You won't find reviews here, but watch the trailers and be your own critic. You'll need Windows Media Player, QuickTime or RealPlayer. ⓐⓐⓐⓐ

XOOM.COM: MOVIE REVIEWS
xoom.com/visit/entertainment/movies
The Movies section of XOOM.com, a massive e-commerce site, has a hefty selection. There are sharp movie reviews, a calendar of upcoming releases and interviews with everyone from action film legend Jackie Chan to Alexander Payne, director of the film "Election." People who want short movie recommendations can visit Quickies for capsule reviews of many current films. ⓐⓐⓐⓐ

FILM.COM
www.film.com
This elegantly designed site is packed with a lot of useful information, including reports from film festivals, interviews and video picks. In Kid Picks, parents can browse recommended children's films and some reviews written by youngsters. Visitors should have a pleasant time at the site, which lets you play soundtrack music and watch new clips and trailers while surfing; RealPlayer is required to enjoy these extras. ⓐⓐⓐ

MOVIEFONE.COM
www.moviefone.com
Like Moviefone's automated phone service, its Web site searches for films and sells tickets for local theaters. The site also offers some services you can't get over the phone. Moviemail will e-mail you notices of film release dates. Moviefone.com offers synopses, video trailers and links to reviews. In Reality Check, real-life experts comment on the level of realism in current films. ⓐⓐⓐ

PREMIERE ONLINE
www.premiere.com
Features and articles from the print magazine fill this site. Read about upcoming movies and stars. The articles are thorough and compelling. Lush photographs accompany interviews of stars like Vince Vaughn, Claire Danes and Will Smith in Features. Check out the On Video and In Theaters reviews. Archived issues are also available online. ⓐⓐⓐ

Pokémon

(originally reviewed December 1999)

POKÉMON TRADING CARD GAME
www.wizards.com/pokemon
This is the official site from the creators of the Pokémon trading card game—also known as Pokémon TCG. Read up on the various versions and expansions first; then, if you're daring, delve into the virtual community of players, traders and strategists. Learn the finer points of attack damage and drool over the latest and greatest card packs. New players will find an Online Rulebook, Checklists and instructions on how to read cards. This site is a sure bet if you want to become a better trainer. ⓐⓐⓐⓐ

POKÉTECH
www.poketech.com
This self-described School of the Experts provides a virtual course catalog of Pokémon information. Although the content is written by a team whose command of the English language pales compared to its command of a joystick, the site is well designed. Get game-playing tips, download sounds and images, read about the TV show and the movie, or peruse questions and answers in Ask A Master. ⓐⓐⓐⓐ

KIDS DOMAIN: POKÉMON FUN
www.kidsdomain.com/kids/pokemon
Although it doesn't offer cheat codes or information on card collecting, this site is a playground for young Pokémon enthusiasts. Try the Online Games and Poké Printables, which include riddles, word searches, anagrams and mazes. Crafty kids can put together some of the projects on the site; we particularly like the Pikachu Yarn Bug. Pokémon-related Downloads for Windows computers and Macintoshes are available, as well.

POKÉMONLINE NETWORK
pokemon.vgf.net
For die-hard Pokémon video-game players, this site is a feast for the eyes. The site features an impressive, up-to-the-minute news section (This just in: "Pokemon falls from top Lycos spot"), as well as an active, moderated forum, a chat area and links to other Pokemon sites. Fans can submit fiction, drawings and mail in the Fans section.

POKÉMON: THE FIRST MOVIE
www.pokemonthemovie.com
Kids begin their exploration of this colorful site by selecting a Pokémon character as their site "host." They can then pick and choose from a range of activities and freebies. Kids in the mood for games can try the quiz or play a Shockwave memory teaser. Those seeking information can use the PokéDex to check out characters or read up on the Pokémon craze. Pokémon Goodies include computer backgrounds and movie posters to download, plus a small selection of Web cards. Last, but not least, the site offers a movie trailer and still photos for fans who just can't get enough of these little creatures' cinema debut.

POKÉMON WORLD
www.pokemon.com
This official site from Nintendo is a great place to start if you are a bit behind on the latest news. Delve into some of the many branches of the Pokémon world—Pokémon Snap, Pokémon Pinball, Pokémon League—and check out the various versions of the video game. You can also read the dire warnings about the multitude of pirate versions of Pokémon and learn how to differentiate impostors from the real thing.

THE ULTIMATE POKÉMON PAGE
pokemon.therpgn.com
This independent site houses introductory and advanced information on the GameBoy and Nintendo 64 versions of the video game, the card game and the television series. Additionally, there's a chat room, a Pokémon quiz, little-known facts, images and a gallery of fan art. For those who have heard of Pokémon but are a little skeptical about entering the world of pocket monsters, this site is a great launching point.

POKÉMON-TRADE.COM
www.pokemon-trade.com/index.cfm
Serious Pokémon card enthusiasts will enjoy this site, but video players may want to go elsewhere. Wander the virtual trading bazaar of cards culled from the basic game and both its current extensions, Fossil and Jungle. Visitors can purchase U.S. and Japanese card packs. Players and card dealers can register their information on the site.

The Magic 8 Ball is ready to solve life's dilemmas for you.

Quirky

(originally reviewed October 1999)

THE COSMIC BASEBALL ASSOCIATION
www.clark.net/pub/cosmic/cba1.html
Both inscrutable and educational, the CBA describes itself as "a baseball league of the imagination." At this home plate of eclectic home pages, the emphasis is on poetics, not athletics. Rosters include left fielder Jack Kerouac, shortstop Andrew Jackson and rookie pitcher Vanessa Williams. The point? CBA founders hope you'll view the site as "an art exhibit or as an educational resource."

UNUSUAL MUSEUMS OF THE INTERNET
www.wooden-nickel.net/museum
Are you snake-bit by the Smithsonian? Down on the Guggenheim? Well, maybe those museums are just too vast. You need focus. The Wooden Nickel Historical Museum presents Unusual Museums of the Internet, which offers links to 50 idiosyncratic collections, from sugar packets to corkscrews to pocket calculators. Highlights include the Virtual Toilet Paper Museum, the Cyber Toaster Museum and one of those Web sites that really sucks—the Cyberspace Vacuum Cleaner Museum. It's all there, the Hoover, the Electrolux, and the mighty Sears-Roebuck Energex.

THE MAGIC 8 BALL
8ball.federated.com
For those tired of consulting chicken bones and tea leaves, this site has a new spin. Ask the Magic 8 Ball a question: "Should I get a new job?" The 8 Ball is shaken by a Lego robot and presents its answer: "Outlook not so good." Unlike ersatz computer simulations, your query is sent to a real Magic 8 Ball. A video camera displays the oracle's answers in real time—as many as 400 per hour. The mechanics are complicated, but creator Jim Studt posts a detailed explanation for anyone who is interested. ⓐⓐⓐ

NEWS OF THE WEIRD
www.newsoftheweird.com
For more than 10 years, Chuck Shepherd's News of the Weird column has been chronicling the best—or is it the worst?—bizarre-but-true stories about inappropriate or stupid things that people do. There is a vast archive of stories about such topics as dogs and drunkenness. It's all here, from dwarf tossing to the man who ate 10,000 macaroni and cheese dinners. A handy feature lets you e-mail news items to friends. ⓐⓐⓐ

THE OFFICIAL FRENCH FRIES PAGES
www.tx7.com/fries
This fast food-style site is ground zero for fry freaks the world over. Learn everything there is to know about fry history—are they really French, or are they Belgian? Also: fry manufacturing, using fries to fill small, drafty cracks and, most important, eating fries. True addicts will especially appreciate the results of rigorous testing of various brands of microwaveable french fries. ⓐⓐⓐ

TRACY AND MIA'S PEEP-O-RAMA
www.critpath.org/~tracy/new.html
Marshmallow Peeps, those sticky "gods of the Easter candy aisle," are what this site is all about. Peep fanciers far and wide come here to trade information on Peep gastronomy and science, research topics such as Peep ripening and debate the best Peep color. Literary Peepaholics have contributed stories and poetry, including the poignant Gedichte der Peeps—Poem of the Peeps. Browse the Peep Galleries for hilarious photos of Peeps engaged in fun activities such as rock climbing and camping. ⓐⓐⓐ

INTERNET ANAGRAM SERVER: I, REARRANGEMENT SERVANT
www.wordsmith.org/anagram
An anagram is a word or phrase formed by reordering the letters of another word or phrase. Aficionados know that anagrams contain a certain amount of truth. "Clint Eastwood," for example, is an anagram of "old west action." The best feature here is the anagram generator, which will help you find the truth by offering every possible anagram of the word or phrase that you enter. ⓐⓐ

THE REAL LEVITATION
www-hfml.sci.kun.nl/hfml/levitate.html
Diamagnetism is a property of nearly all materials that allows objects to emit an external magnetic field. Scientists at the Nijmegen High Field Magnet Laboratory in the Netherlands have found a neat way to levitate things using diamagnetism. This "real levitation" can even be performed with living organisms—the scientists have been levitating frogs, fish and mice since 1996. The images and video clips of levitating frogs are fascinating. ⓐⓐ

Royalty

(originally reviewed October 1999)

THE BRITISH MONARCHY
www.royal.gov.uk
This is the official site of the British crown, so you won't find any sensationalism here. Aside from the usual fare of royal press releases and tributes to Diana, this site offers bios of the royals, family trees, a great section about the royal collection of art and jewels, and an extensive history of the monarchy. Learn about the coronation process, the rules of succession and how the royal family got its name. Profiles and photos of the royal palaces and visitor information round out the site. ⓐⓐⓐⓐ

THE UNOFFICIAL BRITISH ROYAL FAMILY PAGES
www.etoile.co.uk/Royal.html
There is a refreshingly wide array of options at this site, from sending electronic postcards to tracing genealogy to talking in a chat room. You'll find official press releases from Buckingham Palace, current

newspaper articles, text of speeches by royals, a collectors' page where you can buy and sell memorabilia, and a page devoted to Princess Diana. An outline of the succession to the throne and links to recent royal celebrations such as the queen's 50th wedding anniversary give a historical twist. ⓐⓐⓐⓐ

EUROPEAN ROYAL HISTORY
www.eurohistory.com
The companion site to the print publication, the European Royal History Journal, this site contains many articles about royalty throughout history. Some of the more interesting articles include "Bourbon Weddings," "The Red Queen" and "The Lost Honor of a German Prince." The bookstore is also a standout feature. It offer rare and out-of-print books. The site design is basic, but it's quick-loading. ⓐⓐⓐ

GARY DAVIS

JOHN LEE HOOKER

The Mudcat Cafe: lyrics database

ROYAL FAMILIES OF THE WORLD
www.royalfamily.com
Links to everything and everyone royal—from Prince Rainier of Monaco to the Japanese Imperial family—are on this easy-to-navigate site. No country is too small: Tiny Luxembourg is even included. This site is a good first stop for a variety of information about royal families in Europe, the Middle East, the Far East and even Canada. Note: Most links go to outside sites—some official, some unofficial—and the depth of information varies from site to site. ⓐⓐⓐ

REGALIS
www.regalis.com/intro.htm
This site presents royalty, nobility and heraldry from diverse cultures around the globe. The Romanovs of Russia are highlighted, as is the Imperial Family of Ethiopia. There is also an exhaustive yet thorough glossary of related terms. Topics are intentionally broad, focusing on the whole monarchy of a given country, but the information is good. The downside: no photos. ⓐⓐ

ROYAL INSIGHT
www.royalinsight.gov.uk
The online edition of a monthly magazine covering the British monarchy focuses on the royals' official duties. From tournaments to statue unveilings, you get a grand glimpse of the range of activities a monarch must attend. There is also a place to ask questions about the royal family, but watch your spelling—the question might be posted on the site. ⓐⓐ

ROYALTY MAGAZINE
www.royalty-magazine.com
This modified version of the printed journal that covers British royal misadventures is just as gossipy as the original. The photos are excellent and the pages load quickly, but there isn't always much substance to the content. ⓐⓐ

Song Lyrics

(originally reviewed November 1999)

HARRY'S BLUES LYRICS ONLINE
blueslyrics.tripod.com
Bluesman Harry's love for his subject is visible on every page of his handsomely designed and thriving Web site. Both newcomers and lifelong blues enthusiasts are assured they'll find "No Britney Spears" here, and guaranteed a worthwhile visit. Besides lyrics, the site offers blues history, chords and tablature pages. But if it's lyrics you want, there are more than 1,500 songs here. First-time visitors should click on Blues Language to learn the meanings of unique words and phrases, such as "killing floor" or "hot foot powder," contained within the songs. ⓐⓐⓐⓐ

THE MUDCAT CAFÉ
www.mudcat.org
This outstanding lyrics database of blues and traditional folk songs boasts a search engine and resources to help lyric-searchers find background material. The Mudcat Blues Museum contains photographs and articles on such legends as Leadbelly and Mississippi John Hurt. For answers to more obscure questions, visit the Forum, where adults can follow the eclectic topic threads that *usually* relate to music. The Mudcat Café for Kids explains how to make simple instruments such as Dooley sticks and gourd rattlers. ⓐⓐⓐⓐ

LYRICS WORLD
www.summer.com.br/~pfilho/summer.html
The most surprising aspect of this site is the number of decades it covers. We expected to see Top 40 hits for 1965, but 1932 was a pleasant surprise. The archive offers a few search options: Browse Top 40 songs by year, No. 1 songs by year and top singles by decade. Not all the Top 40 listings have lyrics attached, but just

finding rare 1930s information is enough of a pleasure for us.

ULTIMATE '80S SONGS
www.afn.org/~afn30091/80songs.html
This extensive compilation of nearly 500 tunes from the Reagan era includes such pop chestnuts as Def Leppard's "Photograph," Taco's "Puttin' on the Ritz" and Murray Head's "One Night in Bangkok." The idiosyncratic selection might remind visitors of a personal mix tape, but there's enough here to please most '80s fans. The archive can be searched by artist or song title.

BBHQ: MUSIC ROOM LYRICS
www.bbhq.com/lyrics.htm
BBHQ stands for Baby Boomer HeadQuarters. As you might expect, this site focuses on lyrics of baby-boomer favorites—the Mamas & the Papas, the Rolling Stones, the Drifters, Eric Clapton and the Beatles. The layout is very basic—pick a song off the list and click to see a text page of lyrics—but it's an amusing walk down memory lane.

Star Trek

(originally reviewed October 1999)

THE GREAT LINK
www.greatlink.org
This Trek site is described as "the home of the Founders," a key alien race of Shapeshifters from "Star Trek: Deep Space Nine." The site contains current interviews, news, gossip and episode reviews in both spoiler and non-spoiler form—for those who want to be surprised when they see an episode. There's also an extensive section on the various alien races.

STARTREK.COM
www.startrek.com
Paramount Television's official "Star Trek" site offers some impressive features, including episode lists from all four Trek series, the latest news, interactive games, daily trivia and occasional online chats with cast and crew members. The Library contains an amazing collection of information, such as Klingon rituals and character bios. The official Star Trek Store sells everything from action figures and posters to a life-size replica of Borg bombshell Seven of Nine.

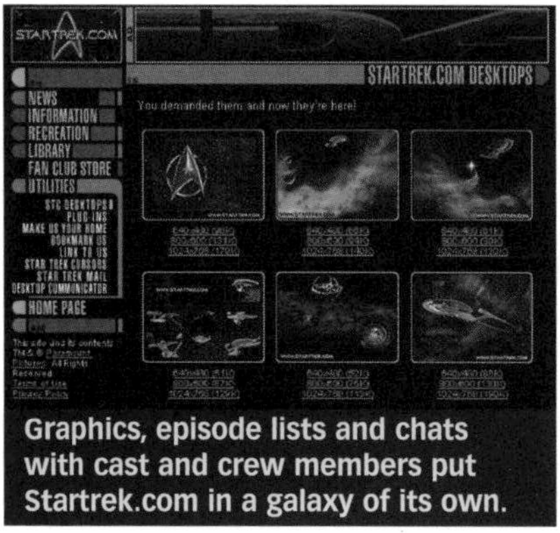

Graphics, episode lists and chats with cast and crew members put Startrek.com in a galaxy of its own.

TREKWEB.COM
www.trekweb.com
"Star Trek" fans love good gossip, and there's no better place to find the latest movie rumors and episode spoilers than this plucky site. Some fans consider this to be one of the more reliable sources of behind-the-scenes secrets, and its news section often previews upcom-ing episodes long before they air. There are episode reviews, cast and character bios and a bulletin board where Trekkies exchange rumors and opinions. Or write your own Trek script by following the site's screen-writing guidelines.

THE KLINGON LANGUAGE INSTITUTE
www.kli.org
Don't tell the devotees of this site that the Klingon language is a nonsensical jumble of words and sounds made up for science fiction. Klingons, as any Trekkie knows, are the cantankerous allies/enemies of "Star Trek." This site strives to teach the language by starting with the basic sounds. Students can also purchase books and audio tapes to learn spelling, grammar and pronunciation, or order a free at-home Klingon language course. Qapla'! (Good luck.)

USS JAGUAR
www.worldkids.net/jaguar
"Star Trek" has always appealed to kids, so a trip aboard the USS Jaguar (run by the United Federation of Kids) should interest young Trekkies.This graphics-rich site serves a younger age group without talking down to it. It offers a deck-by-deck tour of the fictional starship, games and information on features such as the EMH (Emergency Medical Holographic) System. Sign up for a tour of duty, but be prepared to pass a "Star Trek" trivia quiz first.

STAR TREK NEXUS
members.aol.com/treknexus
Some of this site's information is slightly outdated—such as the reviews of episodes—and the navigation is sometimes confusing, but don't complain too much. The big attraction

is the more than 1,500 links in 48 categories to other Star Trek sites, including pages of Trek humor and sites devoted to the actors and characters. As you boldly go from link to link, be forewarned: Many are broken, and the quality varies wildly. Great graphics and interactive features put www.startrek.com in a galaxy of its own. The Web offers plenty of supplemental information about Capt. Picard and the other "Next Generation" characters. ⓐⓐ

Webcasts

(originally reviewed November 1999)

LIKETELEVISION
www.liketelevision.com/starter
As the name suggests, this site is set up kind of like your television, with a variety of channels and types of shows. The main difference: The programming here is viewed via your browser's video plug-in. Classic TV tops the list, with episodes of "Dragnet," "Gumby" and "The Three Stooges." Also look for movies such as "D.O.A." and "The James Dean Story." Sci-fi, sports and weather channels are also available. ⓐⓐⓐⓐ

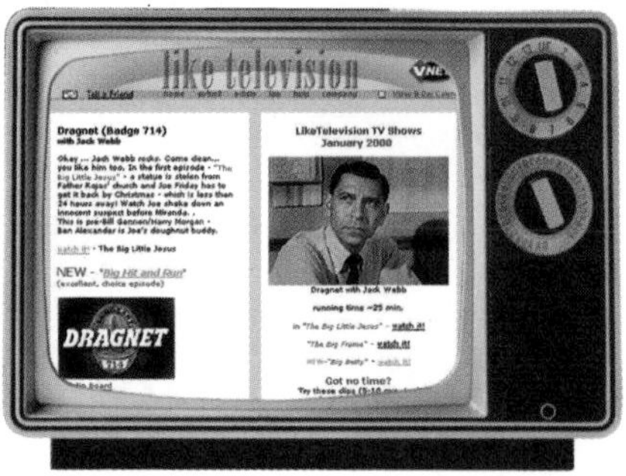

LIVECONCERTS.COM
www.liveconcerts.com
This site claims to be the Internet's largest library of live concerts. That may or may not be true, but it certainly has one of the most entertaining mixes of artists around. The archive has Big Bad Voodoo Daddy, Willie Nelson, Melissa Etheridge and Buckwheat Zydeco concerts. In addition to the performances, you can also listen to in-studio interviews and clips featuring a variety of artists. ⓐⓐⓐⓐ

NATIONAL PUBLIC RADIO
www.npr.org
NPR fans who traditionally listen to the famed radio broadcast in their cars now have a new way to get their daily fix. Listen to the regular news show, or pick from the archive of features from programs such as "All Things Considered," "Morning Edition" and "Car Talk." Listening is simple: Click on the black Audio button on each page to use your RealPlayer or Windows Media Player plug-in. The site also has station listings and a current events discussion forum. ⓐⓐⓐⓐ

family & home

Container Gardening

(originally reviewed November 1999)

WINDOWBOX.COM
www.windowbox.com
The creators of this site are devoted to bringing people and plants together, even if the people are on the 22nd floor. Consult the Floracle for plants that suit your environment and needs, or see what the experts have to say about design, care and use of your garden. Those who already know what they need can go straight to the Balcony Store for container-friendly plants and products for "the balcony lifestyle." This site's humorous style makes even pest control fun. ⓐⓐⓐⓐ

CONTAINED GARDEN
www.anet-chi.com/~kmguise
This small but lovely site is centered around four container garden designs. If you want a patio garden that glows in the moonlight, attracts butterflies, blossoms in early spring or has a tropical flair, this is the place to look. Explanations, good photographs and information about specific plants make the designs here easy to follow and enjoy. ⓐⓐⓐ

GARDENGUIDES:CONTAINER GARDENING
www.gardenguides.com/TipsandTechniques/container.htm
The highlight of this section from the GardenGuides site is a list of annuals and vegetables that grow well in pots. You'll find detailed descriptions, photographs and care tips for the recommended plants. The site also offers basic advice about containers, soil, fertilizing and watering. Don't forget to click on the articles at the top of the page to read about flowering gardens, hanging baskets and eight rules for container gardens. ⓐⓐⓐ

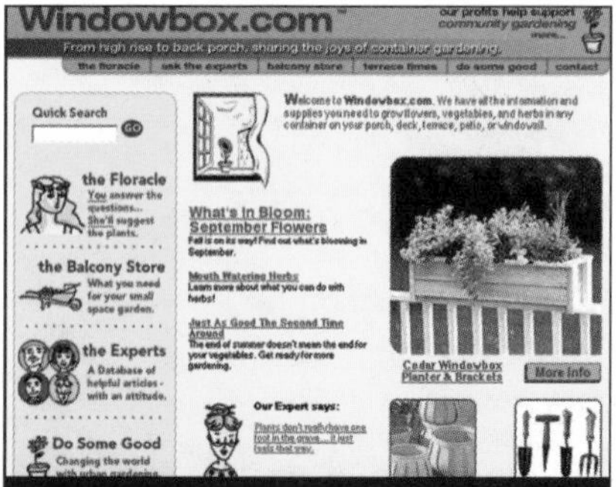

Gardening tips from Windowbox.com can help your balcony bloom.

URBAN GARDEN
www.urbangarden.com
Journey through the year with this container gardener as you peruse her scrapbook site. Click on a month for a lovely photograph of a city garden; plus, hints, ideas and plant descriptions. Each month's Plants section recommends annuals, shrubs and vegetables that thrive during that particular month. To keep the plants—and the entire garden—in shape from season to season, don't forget to read the monthly chores. ⓐⓐⓐ

VEGETABLE GARDENING IN CONTAINERS
aggie-horticulture.tamu.edu/extension/container/container.html
This simple page from the Texas Agricultural Extension Service uses drawings and diagrams to explain how to raise your own vegetables on a porch or even on a windowsill. Although the whole page is useful, the list of vegetable types and the planting and common problem charts are indispensable. Whether you're trying to nurse a thin and unproductive plant back to health, or trying to figure out when to harvest cucumbers, this site takes the guesswork out of vegetable gardening. ⓐⓐ

Family e-zines

(originally reviewed December 1999)

HOMEARTS: FAMILY TIME
homearts.com/depts/family/00dpftc1.htm
Targeting both moms and dads, this site offers lots of edifying material on children's behavior, education and creative projects. Find tips and advice from Dr. Joyce Brothers and other experts on balancing a career and family, stimulating kids' learning and development, and dealing with kids when they lie or steal. Pick up parenting tips in Dad's Corner, The Whole Nine Months, Care Guide, Mom's the Word and Babynamer.com. ⓐⓐⓐⓐ

PARENTS.COM
www.parents.com
With toy reviews, parenting advice and craft ideas for all ages and abilities, the whole family will benefit from a visit to this site. Users must register for free or log in as a guest to access the site, but the people who bring you Parents, Child, Family Circle and McCall's magazines make it worthwhile. There are also health, beauty and medical tips, product recall lists, safety issues and chat sessions with experts. The great ideas here will help keep your family healthy, wealthy and wise. ⓐⓐⓐⓐ

THE FAMILY CORNER
www.thefamilycorner.com
Topics here range from how to talk to your kids about sex to how to throw a really fun pizza party. Along with featured products and kids' crafts, there's the Frugal Mom newsletter, holiday tips and a guide to a better home and garden. If you're planning leisure activities, these experts will guide you through the road or camping trip, or the evening spent together in the living room. ⓐⓐⓐ

FAMILYFUN MAGAZINE
www.familyfun.com
This well-known monthly publication has taken to the Web with the same fervor and ingenuity found within its printed pages. Search for holiday ideas, crafts and activities that parents and kids can share together. Readers can participate in monthly contests, look for local events or chat about parental challenges. Special praise goes to its Craft Finder, where users can search for projects by materials, holiday or season. ⓐⓐⓐ

THE F.U.N. PLACE
www.thefunplace.com
This grassroots effort offers something for everyone on the family home computer. Parents can cruise the bulletin boards and chat rooms and get some advice from other moms and dads. Get tech help and tips for maximizing computer time, learn simple, inexpensive home improvement methods, or peruse beauty and health ideas. Share thoughts for holiday events, discuss parenting strategies or plan dinner from the Recipe Box. Overall, this is a comfy, homey place to visit. ⓐⓐⓐ

HAPPY FAMILIES
www.happyfamilies.com
So you think you have the weirdest family on the planet? Take a look at this collection of stories and anecdotes from other visitors. Read funny, off-the-wall stories about weird relatives, funny things kids say, vacation disasters, embarrassing mishaps between spouses and amusing tales about family pets. Don't forget to share some of your own family's folklore. ⓐⓐⓐ

PARENTSPLACE: FAMILY
www.parentsplace.com/family
Bringing families together across the globe is the goal here. Select a chat session or message board tailored to your needs—Buddhist Parenting, Adoption, Stepfamilies and Feminist Moms, to name a few. There are also resources to help find local child or elder care, special ideas for dads, expert parenting advice and news. ⓐⓐⓐ

Grandparenting

(originally reviewed September 1999)

FOR MY GRANDCHILD
www.mygrandchild.com
For My Grandchild serves as a source of practical information to help grandparents build and sustain special relationships with their grandchildren. Visitors can share stories of special moments, interact with other grandparents or ask questions in The Grandparent Forum. Of particular interest are feature articles about grandparents' roles in the '90s and household dangers—such as electrical outlets and steep stairs—that grandparents need to address before the kids visit. ⓐⓐⓐⓐ

GRANDSPLACE
www.grandsplace.com
This site is dedicated to the grandparents, aunts, uncles, stepparents and foster parents raising children whose biological parents are unable or unwilling to care for them. The site offers a compassionate online forum where caregivers can exchange stories and advice. There's a monthly newsletter and a children's section with games and coloring books. Visitors should check out Every Day Living tips and the excellent Legal Resources database. ⓐⓐⓐⓐ

NATIONAL GRANDPARENTS DAY
www.grandparents-day.com
This fun site sponsors art, essay, poetry, photo and songwriting contests for children to help them learn to appreciate grandparents. Visitors should first browse the Activities for Groups & Families section. It's brimming with project suggestions such as photo and history preservation, family tree creation and grandparent interviews. The site also offers grandparent-related articles and a history of how Grandparents Day began. ⓐⓐⓐ

ASK GREAT-GRANNY
www.mbnet.mb.ca/crm/granny/granny.html
As a great-grandmother with a degree in psychology, Rosaleen Dickson is uniquely qualified to offer practical advice on all sorts of family-related topics here. There are special sections on grandparents and grandchildren where you'll find answers to questions about visita-

tion, sharing and abusive situations. Other sections on children contain equally helpful information about childhood and teen issues about which grandparents may need a refresher, including picky eating habits, lying and rebellion.

THE FOUNDATION FOR GRANDPARENTING
www.grandparenting.org
"Every time a child is born, a grandparent is born, too!" Established with these words in mind, The Foundation for Grandparenting helps grandparents to get involved in their grandchildren's lives. This site offers reading lists of the latest senior guidebooks, a bulletin board and in-depth analysis of the 1998 Visitation Rights Enforcement Act. There are also helpful articles about long-distance grandparenting and mistakes that grandparents sometimes make. Also find out about the grandparent-grandchild summer camp that is run by the foundation.

Family.com can help you dress up your kids, house and yard for Halloween.

OFF OUR ROCKERS
www.sonic.net/thom/oor
No, they're not nuts. These grandparents are up and at 'em, raising a second generation of children. This site features a chat room, a message board filled with incredible stories and a list of recommended reading. To add a light note to a serious topic, don't miss Quippersnappers, a collection of hilarious observations from children. A sample: "No matter how hard you try, you can't baptize cats."

Halloween Crafts

(originally reviewed October 1999)

FAMILY.COM: WORLD'S GREATEST HALLOWEEN GUIDE
family.go.com/Features/family_0000_01/dony/halloween
A family-friendly Halloween starts here. This idea-packed site is a great resource to help parents create fun Halloween costumes, make party treats, carve a pumpkin, decorate the house and send kids safely out the door. Tops on the list here are the 26 photographs of Halloween costumes, followed by recipes for such mouth-watering dishes as worms on a bun and putrid punch. For the well-decorated house, we highly recommend the Crashed Witch and Super-size Bat.

HALLOWEEN ONLINE
www.halloween-online.com
Grown-ups deserve a little Halloween fun, too. Adults who visit this atmospheric site can find out how to get in on the fright-night fun. It gives the details on how to pull off complicated and creepy Halloween tricks and treats. Special FX & Props (under Halloween Online Magazine) gives instructions for how to create skeletons and spooky lighting. But don't stop there—check out Pumpkin Carving 101, Halloween Ghost Stories and Labyrinth of Links, which offers hundreds of links to other Halloween sites.

CAROLYN'S 1999 HALLOWEEN SITE
mystuff.snet.net/halloween99
Visitors will find a nice mishmash of Halloween activities and lore here. Investigate the recipes section for scary concoctions such as swamp slime, bloody fingers (ack!) and graveyard pudding. There are also party games, directions for making pumpkin lanterns and papier-mâché paste, some good decorating ideas, a brief history of Halloween and safety tips for trick-or-treaters. Another plus: a small selection of creepy clip art.

MAKESTUFF.COM: THE HALLOWEEN PAGE
www.makestuff.com/halloween.html
The projects here are more cute than scary, but they are easy on small fingers. Recycle milk bottles and small pompoms into skeletons and spiders. Transform round vases into pumpkin candy dishes and old chair legs into all sorts of easy-to-handle figures. The few recipes here sound good and look simple—we particularly like the idea for "cat litter treats."

MAKE YOUR OWN HALLOWEEN MAKEUP
www.osweb.com/kidzkorner/makeup.htm
The content here is limited, but very important. After all, what self-respecting monster or witch doesn't need fake scabs, hairy warts or dripping blood? These recipes are simple and made from ingredients found in most pantries—food coloring, corn syrup and cornmeal. They're also nontoxic—but don't eat the special effects. ⓐⓐ

Holiday Crafts

(originally reviewed November 1999)

CRAFT CENTRAL STATION
www.craftcentralstation.com/christmas
The fun holiday projects here are sure to put you in the Christmas spirit. With easy-to-follow instructions, they include a Fish Bowl Snowman, a recycled Light-Bulb Reindeer, Cotton-Swab Snowflakes and a whole treeload of ornaments. Plus, there are articles on making gift tags, wrapping paper and gift baskets. ⓐⓐⓐⓐ

CRAFTNETVILLAGE.COM: HOLIDAY PROJECTS
www.craftnetvillage.com/projectlibrary/holiday.cfm
The 100 holiday projects on this site will help you decorate your tree, your house and your yard for the season. The projects use materials such as Styrofoam and wood, and recycled items that might otherwise be thrown away, such as coffee cans and soda bottles. The Santa Wobbler, Paper-Tube Tree, Rag Ball Santa, Felt Penguin Can and Porch Pals are good projects. This site is no-frills, but it's loaded with fun projects. ⓐⓐⓐⓐ

Make a wreath at Craftnetvillage.com.

ABOUT.COM: CRAFTS FOR KIDS: CHRISTMAS CRAFTS
craftsforkids.about.com/kidsteens/kthobbies/craftsforkids/msubchmas.htm
This is a useful collection of links to ideas, patterns and directions for hundreds of fun Christmas projects that require little or no adult supervision. What is also nice is that many of these crafts use supplies that are often found around the house, such as baby food jars, paper towel rolls, cloth napkins and can lids. Perhaps every household should have a Fruit Loop Christmas Tree this year. ⓐⓐⓐ

CROCHET COLLECTION: CHRISTMAS PATTERNS
members.aol.com/SAG55/christmas.html
They say that no two snowflakes are alike, but anyone who has seen crocheted snowflake ornaments might think otherwise. These pretty ornaments can be almost as identical as Pringles. This site rescues Christmas from that same old snowflake. There are 71 patterns for ornaments in the shapes of stockings, gingerbread men, bells, angels and snowflakes. Each pattern includes a photograph so you know how the finished project is supposed to look. ⓐⓐⓐ

FAMILY.COM ACTIVITIES: HAPPY HANUKKAH
family.go.com/Categories/Activities/Features/family_1997_12/famf/famf127hanukah
Although you'll find more Hanukkah recipes than crafts on the Web, you can learn how to make your own menorahs, candles and Stars of David. This site offers several ideas for these and other Hanukkah projects. The Cellophane Candles are a particularly innovative creation. If you have forgotten how to play the Dreidel game, you'll find the rules here. There are also recipes for those traditional Hanukkah treats: latkes and applesauce. ⓐⓐⓐ

READER'S DIGEST: CHRISTMAS
www.rdchristmas.com
For decades Reader's Digest has packed a bundle of information into a small printed magazine. Its Christmas site is no exception, save for the fact that there's much more room online for the host of great ideas. The Crafts & Home Projects section includes a cloth advent calendar, a gingerbread cottage, christmas party favors and novelty gift tags. The site also features Recipes and a holiday chat group so readers can share ideas. ⓐⓐⓐ

SANTALAND: CHRISTMAS ARTS & CRAFTS
www.santaland.com/arts.html
This clearinghouse of Christmas craft links will take you to sites that have instructions for making stained glass, ideas for homemade gift wrap, quilt patterns, directions for making ornaments out of citrus fruit and even a recipe for doggie biscuits. Plus, there are details for several gift projects, such as creating scented bath salt and button jewelry. The site does advise that some

of the crafts require adult supervision, but it's more fun to do it together anyway. Note: A few of the links are outdated.

BEN AND JERRY'S: WINTER HOLIDAY CRAFTS
www.benjerry.com/yule
The guys who brought you Cherry Garcia ice cream now offer crafts. This site should appeal to kids everywhere, no matter which winter holiday they celebrate. The Winter Crafts—of the print-'em-out, cut-'em-out and color-'em-in variety—include paper cutouts of Ben and Jerry on sleds, snowflakes and an entire New England village. As expected, you will need a printer for these crafts.

Family.com Activities: Happy Hanukkah has holiday craft and game ideas.

CHANUKAH ON THE NET
www.holidays.net/chanukah
The highlight of this site is a large pattern to make your own dreidel. Print it on heavy paper, cut it out, fold it up, then color it in as your heart desires and spin away. There is also a virtual dreidel for those who'd rather skip the scissors. If you like to sing, there's music to accompany you. Plus, you can make your own wrapping paper or print out pictures for the kids to color.

KWANZAA: KWANZAA ACTIVITIES
members.dca.net/areid/activity.htm
Though it's plain, this site offers useful ideas and activities for celebrating this cultural festival. Kids will probably like Oware the best. Also known as Mankala, Ohoro or Ayo—depending on the part of Africa—Oware is a traditional African game that involves moving stones and counting skills. In America, the game is often played as part of a Kwanzaa celebration. This site has directions for how to make a homemade Oware board using an egg carton as well as instructions for playing the game.

Holiday Traditions

(originally reviewed December 1999)

CLAUS.COM
www.claus.com
Pay a virtual visit to Santa's home in the North Pole. The colorful, snowy town features an Elf School, where kids can play games online to earn an elf diploma; a Toy Workshop, where you can make your own virtual toy Mrs. Claus' Kitchen of tasty recipes; and the Post Office, where you can send e-mail to Santa. The Santa Spotter keeps tabs on Santa's route on Christmas Eve. Visit the Naughty or Nice Archives for Santa's report on your behavior during the year.

HAPPY CHRISTMAS
www.happy christmas.com
This slick, seemingly simple site recalls holiday hilarity in its Catastrophes section. Remember when the cat ate all the tinsel and spent the next few days as a walking ornament of sorts? The Useless Gifts section will make you forget those ugly, too-small shirts with its lineup of partially eaten cookies, a pack of gum with a nickel taped to it, cheap underwear wrapped in toilet paper and Q-tips. After browsing these items, you might realize that fruitcake isn't such a bad gift.

URBAN LEGENDS REFERENCE PAGES: CHRISTMAS
snopes.com/holidays/xmas
There are lots of weird facts and Christmas myths we all vaguely remember on this decidedly nonreligious site for Generation X-mas-ers. Was Rudolph the Red-Nosed Reindeer really invented by Montgomery Ward? Was Jesus really born on Dec. 25? And where did those yule logs and poisonous poinsettia plants come from, anyway? Find all the answers as well as witty and irreverent holiday commentary here. The articles may be few in number, but they are expansive, well-written and thoroughly researched.

RAMADAN
www.ifgstl.org/html/basics/ramadannf.htm
Ramadan sites are still fairly rare on the Net. This site by the Islamic Foundation of Greater St. Louis gives a good overview of this Muslim holiday, explaining the month-long fast and the three-day celebration that follows, Eid-Ul-Fitr. You will also find a thorough explanation of the Islam faith and its Five Pillars, Shahada (the oath), Salat (prayers), Siyam (fasting), Zakat (alms) and Haji (pilgrimmage).

KWANZAA INFORMATION CENTER
www.melanet.com/kwanzaa
The MelaNet organization has created this site to help continue spreading the word about Kwanzaa. The ever-expanding site explains the history of this African-rooted holiday created by Dr. Maulana Ron Karenga. Newcomers to the celebration will discover the principles behind one of America's newest and fastest-growing nonreligious holiday feasts through resources that include a Kwanzaa chat room, calendar, helpful links and a holiday shop. ⓐⓐ

Home Repair

(originally reviewed September 1999)

DOITYOURSELF.COM
www.doityourself.com
Need a little motivation to get around to those run-of-the-mill home repair jobs? Then take a look at this site, which offers advice on many helpful topics, from appliance repair to installing insulation to painting. The How To's topics are well presented and have clear instructions. If you can't find what you need there, visit the Community bulletin boards to post your question. The site also offers a searchable directory of contractors and suppliers for jobs that require outside help. ⓐⓐⓐⓐ

HOME DOCTOR
homedoctor.net/main.html
Every Mr. and Ms. Fix-it should bookmark this site. It's well organized and has a lot of important information on everything from home safety and security to health and allergies. Various sections on the site explain how to fix simple plumbing problems, keep your home free from pests and avoid lead hazards. The site also features an Ask the Home Doctor section and a free newsletter, so do-it-yourselfers can keep up with the latest in home improvement. ⓐⓐⓐⓐ

THE NATURAL HANDYMAN
www.naturalhandyman.com
This site combines great information with a good dose of humor—a recent article on insulation was titled, "I've got your love to keep me warm ... but extra insulation sure helps!" There is a small archive of several dozen articles that covers everything from adhesives to water heaters. If you have a home repair question that hasn't been addressed in any of the articles, send it in and then check back later to read the answer in the Natural Handyman Newsletter. ⓐⓐⓐⓐ

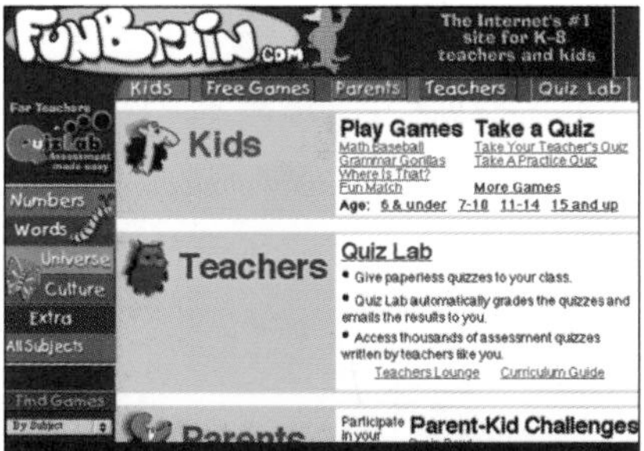

Funbrain.com will fill kids' heads with fun and learning.

HOME REPAIR ENCYCLOPEDIA
homearts.com/helpers/homecare/00homcc1.htm
Starting with instructions on how to handle such emergencies as gas leaks and power failures, the Home Repair Encyclopedia gives a brief rundown on how to tackle some common household problems. Learn how to thaw frozen pipes, relight a pilot light, replace rotted deck boards, clear a jammed garbage disposal and more. ⓐⓐ

TOILETOLOGY 101
www.toiletology.com/index.shtml
You've got to give the creators of this site some credit: They've zeroed in on an unusual area of study and covered it well. This might not be the most attractive site, but it's clear and thorough as it runs through a lesson plan about one of the most basic and necessary household fixtures. The lessons explain how a toilet works, how to fix common toilet problems, and how to properly clean and sanitize your toilet. ⓐⓐ

Kid Fun

(originally reviewed December 1999)

BOOWA & KWALA
www.boowakwala.com
Children will be singing and laughing their way through this inventive site from funny 'toons Boowa and Kwala. Among the play activities are coloring, mazes and guessing games. Kids can send in drawings to be displayed in the club gallery—the club membership is free—or take a trip to the land of the funny dance. Our favorite part of this site: the animated "Chocosong." Note: You will need Macromedia's free Flash plug-in. ⓐⓐⓐⓐ

FUNBRAIN.COM
www.funbrain.com
Featuring dozens of educational games in subjects such as Numbers, Words, Universe and Culture, this vibrantly animated site is a fun place for kids in kindergarten through high school to improve their math and

language skills. The Kids Center (click on Kids on the homepage) constitutes the heart of FunBrain.com, but the resources for parents and teachers take this site to another level. Our favorite is The Translator Alligator in the Words section, which walks kids through the basics of learning Spanish. Who knew learning could be all fun and games? ⓐⓐⓐⓐ

FUNSCHOOL.COM
www.funschool.com
With children's activities designated according to grade level, funschool.com makes it easy for parents to find material suitable for their child's ability. This site's strength is its balance of educational games with activities that are just plain fun. Teachers can surf Funcorner for free downloadable classroom activities. ⓐⓐⓐⓐ

AFRO-AMERIC@: KIDS ZONE
www.afroam.org/children
Blending interactive activities with culturally rich insights, this site is both a fun and informative resource for children in the lower elementary school grades. The Brainteasers and word scramblers sharpen young minds, while the fables, myths and profiles of African countries enlighten them. Kids will enjoy exploring this site's stimulating offerings. Many of the games require the Shockwave plug-in to play them. ⓐⓐⓐ

CTW FAMILY WORKSHOP: PRESCHOOL PLAYGROUND
www.sesamestreet.org/preschool/games
This virtual playground run by Bert, Ernie and the rest of the "Sesame Street" gang makes learning as fun as recess. Parents can click on characters for simple educational games to share with their children, from Conductor Cookie's train to Big Bird's camping adventures. Next to each game are links for parents to more activities and ideas. Bonus: This site's craft projects will come in handy when computer time is done. ⓐⓐⓐ

HARINGKIDS
www.haringkids.com
This official site of the late modern artist Keith Haring is intended to inspire in children a love for the arts. With brilliantly animated sections devoted to books, games and, of course, art, this site encourages creativity at a young age. HaringKids also includes lesson plans and projects for teachers and parents. But there is a small inconvenience: Viewing this site requires a free download of the Flash plug-in. ⓐⓐⓐ

SEUSSVILLE: GAMES
www.randomhouse.com/seussville/games
Fashioned in the creative style of Theodor Geisel, a k a Dr. Seuss, this site's activities combine doggerel verse with zany artwork and a lot of fun. From Diffendoofer Day to Horton's Who Hunt, the Seussville games are as original as the tykes who will play them. Several of the games require the Shockwave plug-in. Some of the other games, including old standbys Connect the Dots and The Cat's Hat Maze, need to be printed out to play. ⓐⓐⓐ

Kids e-zines

(originally reviewed October 1999)

CYBERKIDS
www.cyberkids.com
There's so much to do here, it's hard to know where to start. Magic tricks, contests, quizzes, puzzles, chat, music and interactive games will keep kids occupied long after bedtime. There's also the supercool KidZeen zone, a fantastic collection of art, articles, fiction and poetry created by kids. If visitors to the site are inspired, they can submit their own work. ⓐⓐⓐⓐ

GIRL ZONE
www.girlzone.com
At Girl Zone, girls are encouraged to share their stories and connect with other young voices around the Internet. Learn about health and the body or managing negative thoughts and feelings. Girls can also plan a career, learn about a new sport or go shopping. Sift through music reviews, personal stories of accomplishments and obstacles, and tips on how to network with new friends. Oh yeah, some of this stuff will be of interest to guys, too. ⓐⓐⓐⓐ

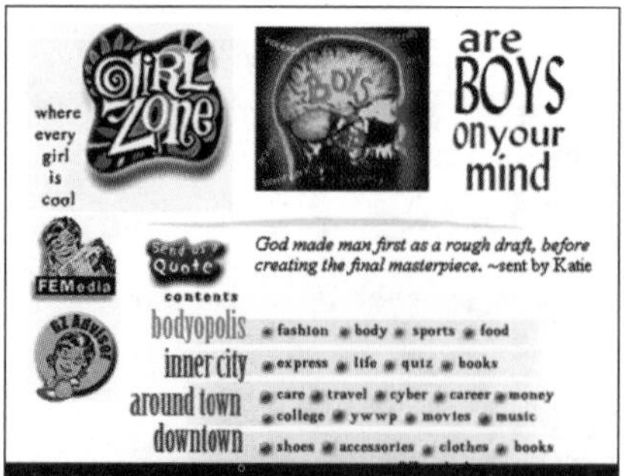

Girl Zone serves up a feast of music reviews, quizzes and career planning.

TOO COOL FOR GROWNUPS
www.tcfg.com
It is too cool, but grownups will enjoy this colorful e-zine as much as kids will. Tune in for facts about ancient civilizations, online science experiments, games, puzzles and kid fiction. There are also helpful tools such as The Homework

Wizard, a top 10 Web site list, and explanations and lists of search engines and portals. Teachers will appreciate the vast selection of worksheets and lesson plans they can find at this site. ⓐⓐⓐⓐ

NATIONAL GEOGRAPHIC.COM/KIDS
www.nationalgeographic.com/kids

National Geographic is known for its take-me-there photography and journalism, and this site for kids brings them the world with the same vivid colors and storytelling. Get up close with bottlenose dolphins, or find a pen pal. There's even an opportunity to save the planet with the help of a planetary pal named Spin; check in the Really Wild Animals section. Links to cool stories and interactive features about animals make this an interesting read for kids and their families. ⓐⓐⓐ

BHG KIDS
www.bhg.com/bhgkids
This site by Better Homes and Gardens magazine features fun activities, facts and projects. On our last visit, we read cool dinosaur trivia, jotted down the recipe for peanut butter dino cookies and learned how to create dinosaur duds with some yarn, paper plates and construction paper. The site, formerly the online companion to Crayola's print magazine, has scaled back a bit in the past year, but it still provides fun activities for kids. ⓐⓐ

THE KIDS REPORT
kids.library.wisc.edu
Published biweekly during the school year, this is one of the few good e-zines that is done by kids for kids, with just a little help from their teachers. Each issue, readers get a selection of recommended Web sites chosen for overall interest and educational value. Students write brief reviews of their selections. Although this is only a directory, its intentions are admirable and the content valuable. ⓐⓐ

Knitting

(originally reviewed October 1999)

KNITNET
www.knitnet.com
This fantastic Canadian knitting e-zine provides a plethora of patterns, handy how-to video clips, articles and personal profiles of knitters around the globe. An organized table of contents and numbered pages allow readers to flip through the 'zine as if looking at a printed version—your fingers can almost feel the pages. Archived editions supply even more information. The KnitNet LYS—jargon for local yarn store—is a great place to order yarn, hand-knit garments and even knitting software. ⓐⓐⓐⓐ

THE KNITTING UNIVERSE
www.knittinguniverse.com
This well-organized Web site is a companion to the print version of Knitter's Universe. A handy site map helps you navigate the many articles and features that put knitters in touch with each other via shared patterns or upcoming conventions. Use the ShopFinder for store information in the United States and Canada. Check for tips and lessons in KnitU. ⓐⓐⓐⓐ

KNITTING
www.geocities.com/Paris/9197/pattern.htm
A kind of knitter's Yellow Pages, this is a carefully organized directory, but not visually stimulating. It contains nearly 200 original and vintage patterns, as well as stitch techniques. To translate from U.K. or Australian measurements, there is an invaluable conversion table in Hints and Tips, listed under Special Techniques. The site is geared toward those who are old hands at knitting, but there are also links for beginners. ⓐⓐⓐ

WOOL WORKS
www.woolworks.org
Founded in 1994—pretty old by Internet standards—and maintained by a few knitting hobbyists, this site is a grand repository of information for the large and enthusiastic online knitting community. Lists of Stores around the world, recommended knitting books, knitting guilds, patterns and photos of visitors' creations add to the excitement. ⓐⓐⓐ

YARN FORWARD
www.yarnfwd.com
The online counterpart to a Canadian yarn and knitting store of the same name, this site is great for ordering yarn, needles and hard-to-find accessories. Spend some time looking through more than 1,400 yarns by brand or manufacturer.

Purchase unusual presents, such as mohair socks, or play it safe with a gift certificate. ⓐⓐⓐ

KNITLIST HOME PAGE
www.kniton.com/knitlist

This site is ground zero for an online community of 2,200 knitters. Newcomers should refer to the Frequently Asked Questions for a complete rundown of KnitList rules, terms and etiquette, as well as popular patterns. Exchange knitting tips and projects with other craft enthusiasts. Or, continue in the KnitList tradition of posting gift ideas in the Knitting Sources section for other members to enjoy each holiday season. ⓐⓐ

Parenting

(originally reviewed January 2000)

AMERICANBABY.COM
www.americanbaby.com

Appearances are often deceiving: Behind this simple interface is a great resource for parents. Articles are updated daily and cover a wide range of topics for moms and dads, including pregnancy, infant care and family. With articles that address pregnancy's physical and emotional changes, and how-tos on bathing, burping and breastfeeding, consider this a survival guide for new parents. You can even sign up for a free subscription to the print magazine. Now that's service. ⓐⓐⓐⓐ

FATHER'S WORLD
www.fathersworld.com/fatherhood

Moms deserve a lot of credit, but being a father is hard work, too. Scan the menu bar on the left side of the page for helpful articles and tools. Career Coach offers practical advice on balancing work and home life, and Dad's Home chronicles the adventures of a real Mr. Mom. Parent Toolbox offers a Parents Bill of Rights and tips on doling out constructive criticism. Plus, there are recipes and crafts you can whip up with your kids. ⓐⓐⓐⓐ

KIDSOURCE ONLINE
www.kidsource.com

This vast collection of in-depth child-rearing articles offers something that is ideal for a parenting site—a search engine. Here, information on specific topics—including everything from health concerns to discipline to finding child care—is right at your fingertips. The data can also be browsed by topic, which is especially nice if you don't know exactly what you're trying to find. ⓐⓐⓐⓐ

ABC'S OF PARENTING

Americanbaby.com has answers about pregnancy and caring for a newborn.

www.abcparenting.com

Whether you're looking for information on pregnancy, toy safety, education, discipline or single parenting, this collection of links has nearly every aspect of parenthood covered. The well-organized homepage makes it easy to find the right information. Share stories and advice on the message boards or in the hosted chat room—each day of the week has a full lineup of topics. There's also a free e-newsletter with tips and articles. ⓐⓐⓐ

SINGLE PARENT CENTRAL
www.singleparentcentral.com

When there's only one parent in the household, outside support can be a welcome relief. This site's helpful articles and pages cover government resources for low-income families, child support, divorce, careers and money. There's also a useful checklist to help you choose a child-care provider, as well as child safety tips and articles on successful single parenting. Soak up the advice here and show critics what you already know: An informed single parent is better than two uninformed parents. ⓐⓐⓐ

Pet Care

(originally reviewed October 1999)

ANIMALHOSPITAL.COM
www.animalhospital.com

This site's presentation of dog and cat health issues is comprehensive. From dentistry and nutrition to immunizations and surgery, it should answer all of your questions. A detailed article on the birth cycle of dogs is a must if you're considering breeding your pet. If your pet is approaching its golden years, read this site's section on how to care for senior pets. ⓐⓐⓐⓐ

AVMA CARE FOR PETS
www.avma.org/care4pets/default.htm

Dog and cat owners will especially appreciate the resources here, but owners of horses and other pets will find guidance as well. The site offers general advice on health, safety and travel. The Paws for Pets section has seasonal care information and general tips for puppies and kittens. In the Kid's Korner, young pet lovers will find veterinary advice, pictures to color, activities and animal safety tips. ⓐⓐⓐⓐ

FRESHWATER FISH FAQ'S
members.tripod.com/~Boeing_Dude/welcome.html
The creator of this site, known here as DaFishDude, is a human encyclopedia of fish facts. He advises visitors on shopping for fish, setting up tanks and feeding various species. There is also extensive information about diseases and treatments, including a chart to help you diagnose illnesses. In the rare case you don't find your answer to a fish question here, DaFishDude accepts questions via e-mail. ⓐⓐⓐⓐ

ALTVETMED
www.altvetmed.com
The alternative medicine craze has spread to veterinary medicine, and this site explores alternative ways to care for your pet. The site is designed to be easily loaded by all browsers, so it's not big on graphics—but it is dense with information. The helpful articles cover herbs, dental care, natural flea control and cancer management. Best of all, there are links to directories of practitioners. ⓐⓐⓐ

HEALTHYPET
www.healthypet.com
An online newsletter and an animal hospital search engine are two bonuses at this informative site. The FAQs and Pet Care Library sections have a lot of advice for dog and cat owners, nutrition information for various pets and preventive care tips. Helpful topics include hip dysplasia, the danger of chocolate to pets and ways to help your pet adjust to the arrival of a new baby. ⓐⓐⓐ

AVIANVET
www.avianvet.com

A Texas veterinarian is in the process of developing this wonderful Web site about pet birds. The site provides characteristics of popular species to help you select a bird, tips on what makes a good cage, nutrition information and grooming hints. Medical updates and potential signs of illness are also listed, with the warning that birds are good at hiding disease. The chat room and event calendar were under construction on our last visit. ⓐⓐ

Quilting

(originally reviewed September 1999)

QUILTERSBEE
www.quiltersbee.com
Boasting more than 1,000 members, this virtual quilting guild offers opportunities to learn about quilt history, fabric care and quilting tricks. Learn new tips every Friday, or share your work through Good Works, a listing of ways to donate your quilts to people in need. For a smile, visit Odds and Ends, a collection of quilting-related, Letterman-style top 10 lists. The swap section tells quilters how to make and swap quilt blocks for projects outlined on the site. ⓐⓐⓐⓐ

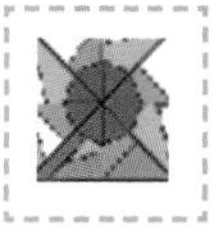

QUILTERS ONLINE RESOURCE
www.nmia.com/~mgdesign/qor/index.html
This handy site explains techniques varying from fabric dyeing to crafting 3-D quilts, and it is geared toward both novices and experts. The site reviews quilt-design computer software, holds quilt swaps and showcases eight quilt styles, including Amish, classic, crazy quilt and Hawaiian. Visit Quilt Projects for information about Project Linus, an organization that provides security blankets to children in need. ⓐⓐⓐ

QUILTING ARTS FORUM
www.delphi.com/quilting
Quilting Arts Forum is nicely designed on all levels. The homepage is attractive, and the resources are organized and varied enough to appeal to quilters of all types. Tips and tricks from award-winning quilter Candy Goff anchor the site, supported by block-of-the-month instructions, message boards, links to fabric shops, mystery quilts and swaps. Don't miss the scrapbook, which has photos of stunning quilts. ⓐⓐⓐ

REMEDIAL QUILTERS
207.27.153.3/remedialquilters
If you have quilt dreams or have ever fantasized about making your own quilt, visit this attractive site. It caters to beginners and those who have little time to spend with needle and thread. There is a Quilting Basics section to get you going, an easy starter project to build your confidence and a variety of patterns to keep you busy. ⓐⓐⓐ

YOUR FREQUENTLY ASKED QUESTIONS ANSWERED
www.reddawn.net/quilt/quilting.htm
This lighthearted but serious quilting site answers a slew of questions so as not to leave you guessing. It is a complete resource offering advice on everything from getting started to finding a quilt guild to treating sore fingers. Pick up equipment and fabric tips, find patterns, learn how to care for antique quilts or play a quilt game. Bookmark this site—it is an excellent resource. ⓐⓐⓐ

QUILTART
www.quiltart.com
If you're a contemporary art quilter or have notions of becoming one, this is a great place for you to get started. Examine the photographs of contemporary quilts in the gallery, then, if they've caught your fancy, sign up for the Quiltart online critique and discussion group. Upcoming exhibits and quilting-related events can be found in the News and Features section. ⓐⓐ

WORLD WIDE QUILTING PAGE
www.quilt.com/mainquiltingpage
Despite the lackluster layout, this site is a good resource for quilters. Scroll down the page for choices ranging from quilting how-tos to patterns to supplies. New features are highlighted at the top of the homepage, where you'll also find photographs of quilts submitted by site visitors. The site's prominent search engine conducts an advanced search for more quilting sites on the Web using Alta Vista, but you'll still have to scroll through 1,200 matches. ⓐⓐ

Relationship Advice

(originally reviewed November 1999)

ASK BREAKUP GIRL!
breakupgirl.oxygen.com
Despite her name, Breakup Girl gives advice about more than just the fallout from a crashed relationship. There are wise words here for both the coupled and uncoupled. For example, Breakup Girl devotes a healthy amount of space to the subject of snooping, advising that the sneaky deed is not only wrong, it doesn't help your relationship. The answers are smart and practical, with just the right amount of tough love and wit thrown into the mix. ⓐⓐⓐⓐ

LOVE & LEARN
www.loveandlearn.com
This amusing site gets a thumbs-up for its witty style and talk show feel. Mr. Sensitive is your

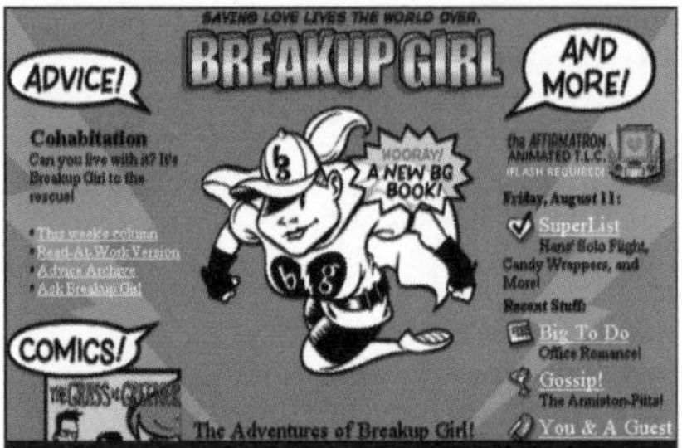

If you need relationship answers, you might Ask Breakup Girl!

animated host, and his panel of regular folks is ready to give its two cents. Read opinions on current questions, or browse the answers to previous questions for wisdom on maintaining relationships and finding new partners. If you're short on time, try Virtual Mr. Sensitive, an interactive program that lets you describe your relationship by moving graphics (such as a woman, a man, a heart, the word "trust" with a slash through it) onto a diagram. The site searches its archive for relevant advice. ⓐⓐⓐⓐ

MARRIAGE BUILDERS
www.marriagebuilders.com
The thoughts and theories of a marriage counselor form the core of this site. Start with Basic Concepts for an outline of traits that contribute to and detract from a healthy marriage. For specific problems, visit the Q&A archive, where you will find detailed—but sometimes long-winded—answers to questions about emotional needs, sexual compatibility, infidelity, negotiation and resolving conflicts. Or go to Quick Clicks for easy-to-find advice on common marital problems. ⓐⓐⓐⓐ

WOMEN.COM: SEX & ROMANCE
women.com/sex/experts
Although this site starts out with the Sexpert advice column at the top of the page, the content is much more practical than racy. There is advice for everyone here—from female psychology to the perceptions of the married male. The Sexpert doles out matter-of-fact suggestions on a variety of subjects, including romantic excursions and rebound relationships. The Marriage Doctor is always in, and there are plenty of games and quizzes to analyze your love life. ⓐⓐⓐⓐ

ADOLESCENT ADULTHOOD
www.adolescentadulthood.com
Consider this to be a primer on the basics of dating—you know, those rules that most people picked up in college but which are easily forgotten. First, study up on effective and

appropriate flirting in the Flirting Manual. Then skip on over to the Dating Guide, which explores how to ask out a potential mate, dining etiquette and mistakes to avoid. If your date goes well, Kissing Explained and the 3 Step Guide may be useful tools. If the date is a failure, however, take the Dumping Tutorial.

RELATIONSHIP CENTRAL
www.valhallamoon.com
With section titles such as Pretty Good Advice and Pretty Good Philosophy, this site hides its light under the proverbial bushel. Look here for thoughtful commentaries on love, power, friends and family. The Pretty Good Advice section is particularly strong, with answers from a real-life couple. Also, check out the Adventures of Enlightened Man and tips for long-distance relationships.

Sewing

(originally reviewed December 1999)

HOME SEWING ASSOCIATION
www.sewing.org
Slick as a new needle and as nimble as a thimble, this site gives great advice for all sorts of sewing projects. There is an emphasis on parent-child activities to get your children involved in a new hobby. Get patterns and tricks of the trade, and read through Guidelines for tips on how to sew with fleece or interfacings. There's a Kid's Page, and also a page just for teens. You'll also find links to chats and educational question-and-answer sessions online. Think of this site as the ultimate family-friendly sewing headquarters.

THREADS MAGAZINE
www.taunton.com/th
From sewing buttons to designing pants, Threads Magazine offers a bevy of instructions for sewers of all skill levels. Check out 20 Ways to Improve your Sewing to make sure your garments don't get left on the cutting room floor. Not all of the print magazine's content is available on this site, but articles and discussion boards addressing alterations, fitting and fabrics should be enough to get users stitching, basting and hemming.

The Sew News site is anchored by a wide-ranging archive of articles.

SEW NEWS MAGAZINE
www.sewnews.com
This monthly publication has been spinning out sewing news and instruction for 18 years. Its site's strength is its extensive library of articles—some authored by top-line designers—covering fashion, fabrics and sewing techniques. Chat, message boards and a listing of craft and sewing events nationwide complete this thorough, interactive guide.

SEWNET
www.sewnet.com
An elegant site featuring Online Classes, a swap section and links to companies selling goods, this site is constantly expanding to include a wider range of sophisticated designs and resources. The pages load quickly with hyperlinks to other professional and amateur craftspeople who are eager to share their knowledge.

SEWINGLESSONS.COM
www.sewinglessons.com
This text-rich site has a great teaching network for those looking for students and those looking for lessons. Join frequent chat sessions hosted by experts, or get help from other visitors at the Message Board. For $25 a year, you can get discounts for online lessons and access to special features. Even if you choose not to pay, you will still get the lowdown on all of the basic techniques and best machines.

Thanksgiving

(originally reviewed November 1999)

THANKSGIVING WITH READER'S DIGEST
www.readersdigest.com/features/thanksgiving
Reader's Digest has assembled a fantastic offering at its festive Thanksgiving site. Click on Projects & Crafts for great woodworking projects, decorating ideas and tips for choosing, cooking and carving the turkey. Or visit Holiday Host for information about dinner-planning, etiquette and entertaining small children. Traditional, not-so-traditional and vegetarian recipes are here, as well as a varied selection of Thanksgiving stories.

BETTER HOMES AND GARDENS' HOLIDAY SURVIVAL GUIDE
www.bhg.com/food/holiday
For total holiday planning, recipes, cooking tips and table-setting ideas, run to this site. Better Homes & Gardens' well-organized selection includes online videos that will show you how to stuff a turkey, make potatoes, bread and eggnog, and bake some traditional desserts. Take a look at the Holiday Article Archives for more ideas and recipes from the past, or browse the Cooking Encyclopedia for more detailed help. If all else fails, join the Holiday Discussion Group and get advice from other visitors. ⓐⓐⓐ

HAPPY THANKSGIVING FROM EVERYONE AT BEN & JERRY'S
www.benjerry.com/thanksgiving
In addition to delicious dessert recipes and games, this site exemplifies Ben & Jerry's socially minded business. It includes plenty of Native American links and information on indigenous cultures. There are pages to color and links to Mayflower and American Indian sites. Of course, there's a section on incorporating ice cream into the Turkey Day feast. ⓐⓐⓐ

KID'S DOMAIN: HAPPY THANKSGIVING!
www.kidsdomain.com/holiday/thanks
This kids site has assembled a wide selection of Thanksgiving stories, legends and historical facts and figures. Kids will enjoy the Online Thanksgiving Games: Personalize a silly Thanksgiving Story, take a Turkey Day trivia quiz or work through mazes. Also available are Crafts and Recipes, downloadable clip art and a suggested reading list. ⓐⓐⓐ

MACY'S THANKSGIVING DAY PARADE
www.nyctourist.com/macys_menu.htm
One of America's favorite Thanksgiving traditions is this 2-mile parade in Manhattan. Follow the virtual tour of the route, complete with pictures of floats, clowns, performers and balloons from last year's event. Listen to giant parade balloons as they're being filled with helium. And check out photos and facts in the Parade's History section. ⓐⓐ

NATIONAL TURKEY FEDERATION
www.eatturkey.com
According to this organization, 91 percent of Americans eat turkey on Thanksgiving. From thawing and stuffing to cooking and carving, the Thanksgiving guide here will help you make the perfect bird, whether it's roasted, deep-fried or grilled. This site thinks beyond the big day, too: its recipe database has more than 500 ideas for leftover turkey. Watch cooking demonstrations by celebrity Virtual Chefs. ⓐⓐⓐ

PLIMOTH ON THE WEB
www.plimoth.org/Museum/museum.htm
History buffs will love this official site of the Plimoth Plantation Museum in Plymouth, Mass. Learn the historical explanation of how Thanksgiving grew from a run-of-the-mill Puritan religious ritual. Then click on The 1621 Bill of Fare, which you'll find under The First Thanksgiving: Facts and Fancies, for insight into which foods made up the first Thanksgiving feast. Also find out why popcorn has caused such a stir among historians. ⓐⓐⓐ

AN AMERICAN THANKSGIVING
www.night.net/thanksgiving
Maintained by a public school teacher, this site offers lots of stuff for kids and some information for adults, too. Find Thanksgiving poems, low-fat recipes and plenty of links for kids. The text of several historical documents, such as the Mayflower Compact, are here; these are interesting, but a tad advanced for small children. Click on Thanksgiving Fun for games and a selection of MIDI audio files to play and sing along with the songs. ⓐⓐ

ARISTOTLE'S THANKSGIVING ON THE WEB
www.aristotle.net/thanksgiving
Do you have a particularly entertaining Thanksgiving story? Then type it up and submit it for posting to this site's Favorite Thanksgivings section. The stories here range from hokey to funny to touching. For a look at Mother Nature's metamorphosis, stop by Fall Colors. You will find links to Webcams in the Northeast. ⓐⓐ

Kids Domain
Craft Exchange
A Gaggle of Thanksgiving Geese
Decorate your table with some funny geese by adding clove eyes to crookneck squash. This project is simple, but requires an adult's help with the sharp knife!
Parental supervision is recommended.
This project is rated EASY to do.

There's a full spread of activities for children at Kid's Domain.

government

Animal Rights

(originally reviewed September 1999)

THE ANIMALS' AGENDA
www.animalsagenda.org

The Web edition of The Animals' Agenda magazine furthers the print version's nonmilitant yet forceful protest of animal suffering; its motto is, "helping people help animals." Through interviews with such celebrity activists as Paul McCartney, in-depth articles and details on events such as vegetarian food festivals and national rallies, The Animals' Agenda lets readers decide how to contribute to the cause. Visitors can also subscribe to the magazine from the site. ⓐⓐⓐⓐ

THE HUMANE SOCIETY OF THE UNITED STATES
www.hsus.org

The remarkable thing about this site is that it offers a comprehensive selection of articles and news without the rabid tone associated with many animal rights groups; be aware of photos of caged animals, however. HSUS focuses on being a "voice for animals" in Washington, D.C., so you'll find excellent updates on current legislation. Of special note: the Animal Disaster Relief section, which finds new homes for animal victims of disasters, and the Animal Channel sections, which showcase animal stories and issues in the news. ⓐⓐⓐⓐ

ANIMAL CONCERNS.ORG
animalconcerns.netforchange.com

This site looks plain but has great depth. Animalconcerns.org offers recent newspaper headlines, background on a variety of issues, lists of organizations, a calendar of events, bulletin boards and educational resources. Before browsing, be aware that deeper in the site are unpleasant photos of animal injuries and testing, which are used to illustrate the organization's arguments. ⓐⓐⓐ

PETA ONLINE
www.peta-online.org

Before you go to this page, be warned: This site contains distressing photos of, and language about, abused animals. That said, this is a gold mine of information about animal rights. News, articles and current campaigns are easy to find, thanks to snazzy graphics and clear links. There's also a kids section with no graphic photos, lists of companies that do or do not test on animals, an extensive catalog for "cruelty-free living" and a PETA bookstore. ⓐⓐⓐ

INTERNATIONAL SOCIETY FOR ANIMAL RIGHTS
www.i-s-a-r.com

Founded in 1959, ISAR focuses primarily on the practice of spaying and neutering cats and dogs. It also provides information covering relevant legislation, current and back issues of the society's newsletter, and free reports on subjects such as kennel overpopulation, euthanasia and puppy mills. ⓐⓐ

Crime

(originally reviewed September 1999)

APBNEWS.COM
www.apbnews.com

Updated regularly, APBnews.com should be a bookmark for anyone wanting to keep up with crime news in the United States. Whether you want to find out why police arrested your favorite TV star or keep abreast of local crimes, you won't be disappointed. The site is divided into subjects ranging from Breaking News to Action Video. A live police scanner tracks close to 30 cities and reports incidents with RealPlayer. Get a taste of detective work in Unsolved. Examine evidence and leads of cases that haven't been solved, then post your conclusions or tips on the discussion board. You'll be contacted if the information has merit. ⓐⓐⓐⓐ

FEDERAL BUREAU OF INVESTIGATION
www.fbi.gov

Obviously, the FBI is not going to divulge all of its activities on its official Web site. But you will find captivating and useful information about the Ten Most Wanted, current letter bomb investigations, stolen art and other federal crimes. Check out the fugitive photos to see if you recognize anyone. The site also features especially informative crime statistics and a cool kids page to teach aspiring agents how the FBI fights crime. ⓐⓐⓐⓐ

CRIME MAGAZINE
www.crimemagazine.com

As its tag line, "an encyclopedia of crime," suggests, Crime magazine documents crimes and related issues in a methodical manner. The curious can read about Martin Luther King Jr.'s assassination, the progress of the JonBenet

Ramsey investigation, the controversy around capital punishment and gun control, and the evolution of crime films.

NATIONAL CRIME PREVENTION COUNCIL'S ONLINE RESOURCE CENTER
www.ncpc.org
Home of McGruff the Crime Dog, the NCPC's mission is "to help America prevent crime and build safer, stronger communities." The information for adults and children covers everything from forming neighborhood action groups to avoiding danger on the playground. Everything on the site promotes safe, proactive behavior, and many of the suggestions are valuable. Readers who live in crime-ridden neighborhoods may find some of the ideas a bit naïve.

LA COSA NOSTRA
www.geocities.com/CapitolHill/Lobby/9880
Fans of "The Godfather," check this out. La Cosa Nostra takes a reverent look at the Mafia, despite the B-movie-esque dripping-blood effect on some of the text. This site includes a history of the crime organization, basic dossiers on famous Mafiosi, a map of the Mafia chain of command, reviews of Mafia movies, a mobster's glossary and even a Mafia chat room.

SOCIOREALM: CRIMINOLOGY AND CRIMINAL JUSTICE
www.geocities.com/~sociorealm/criminology.htm
Here's a good starting place for doing sociological research. The criminology page links to hundreds of resources on crime prevention, corporate crime, statistics and theory. Each link features a picture of a tiny flag, so you know from which country the information is coming. The page plays a digitized version of "The Godfather" theme.

Human Rights

(originally reviewed December 1999)

AMNESTY INTERNATIONAL USA
www.amnesty-usa.org
If you want to learn more about this serious subject, stop here first. International news goes beyond television sound bites, with in-depth reports, updates and event and campaign specifics. Campaigns & Actions sorts the information into manageable categories by issues such as Children's Rights and Death Penalty; and by countries such as East Timor and Nigeria. This site makes it easy to be involved and informed.

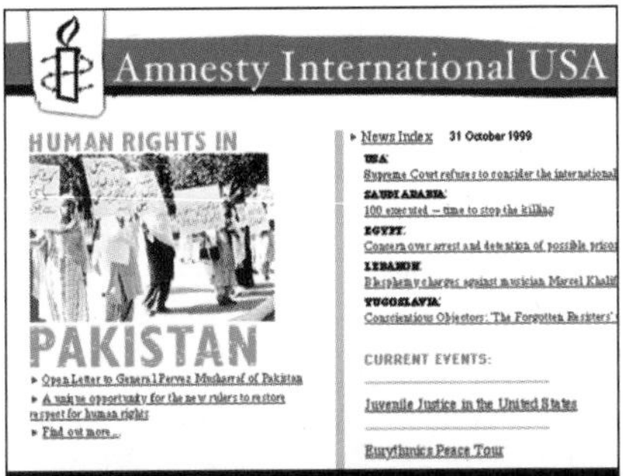

Amnesty International covers human rights issues by topic and country.

HUMAN RIGHTS WATCH
www.hrw.org
Available in seven languages, HRW provides striking photo essays, Breaking News and Commentary. The coverage ranges from neglected Russian orphans to the search for thousands of missing Kosovar men. Those interested in specific regions should use the Clickable World Map to find reports for that area. There's also ample information here on HRW's campaigns.

RELIEFWEB
www.reliefweb.int
ReliefWeb focuses on relief efforts involving political and natural disasters. Floods in New Mexico and political unrest in East Timor are among those discussed. There's a Directory of Humanitarian Organizations and links to disaster warning sites.

U.S. STATE DEPARTMENT: BUREAU OF DEMOCRACY, HUMAN RIGHTS, AND LABOR
www.state.gov/www/global/human_rights
This site is from the U.S. State Department, which has the mission of fostering worldwide democracy and devising U.S. human rights policies. Recent updates give details of committee activity in Congress. Information on the U.N. Commission on Human Rights is also here.

Immigration

(originally reviewed September 1999)

UNITED STATES IMMIGRATION & NATURALIZATION SERVICE
www.ins.usdoj.gov
The INS is the federal agency that does double duty as both a welcome wagon and a border

guard to everyone who wants to enter the United States. The agency's Web site is a great first stop for prospective immigrants. You'll find laws and regulations, official reports and studies, plus downloadable forms and fee charts. A new, especially helpful feature is a naturalization eligibility worksheet that helps to determine the likelihood that an immigration applicant will become a U.S. citizen.

ATLANTIC UNBOUND: IMMIGRATION
www.theatlantic.com/atlantic/election/connection/immigrat/immigrat.htm

The Atlantic Monthly is among the country's oldest magazines of literary journalism and political commentary. This Web site from the journal compiles many of the publication's best articles about immigration and naturalization from the last decade. Be sure to check out "One Nation, Inhospitable?" This is a roundtable discussion about the role immigration plays in America today. The site also includes links to several information resources for people considering a move to the United States.

NATIONAL VISA OFFICE ON-LINE
www.nationalvisaoffice.org

Each year the U.S. Diversity Immigration Program—a k a the Green Card Lottery—offers 50,000 permanent residence visas to those applicants who meet certain eligibility requirements. This site explains those requirements and enables hopeful residents to apply online for green cards. After signing up for a user name and password, applicants can check their application status periodically and find out if this is their lucky year.

VISALAW
www.visalaw.com

Siskind, Susser, Haas & Devine are attorneys who specialize in immigration and naturalization law. Their site includes a monthly newsletter with updates about these laws, which is useful since the laws tend to change frequently. Helpful links from the homepage include Siskind's Green Card Lottery Center, Siskind's Immigration Forms Center and the site's collection of government documents.

AMERICAN IMMIGRATION LAWYERS ASSOCIATION
www.aila.org

The American Immigration Lawyers Association is a national bar association of more than 5,200 attorneys who practice and teach immigration law. While much of this Web site focuses on the association itself, the About Immigration section is extremely informative and debunks several myths about immigrants.

IMMIGRANTS' RIGHTS
www.aclu.org/issues/immigrant/hmir.html

The American Civil Liberties Union's immigration site highlights recent court decisions and pending congressional bills that are likely to affect immigration laws and regulations. Some of the briefings on immigration issues date back to 1996, but News Updates can keep you informed about immigration-related developments. A rather self-congratulatory archive of the work the ACLU has done to further the cause of immigrants' rights is also included.

THE VIRTUAL ELLIS ISLAND TOUR
www.capital.net/~alta

Created by students at a New York middle school for other students around the world, this site follows four fictional immigrants from their departures in their respective homelands to the lines and questions at Ellis Island. Complete with audio files and diary entries written by the students, the site offers a simple history of Ellis Island procedures. A teacher's guide explains the story behind this school project.

Veterans Resources

(originally reviewed November 1999)

THE VETERANS ADMINISTRATION
www.va.gov

This site gets a four-star rating for content, if not for design. This official site from the Veterans Administration is one small way for the government to repay American veterans for their service. The main draw is the Benefits section, with information on education, disability, burial, insurance and home loan services. Many of the forms for these services may be down-

A crisis hotline at www.nvf.org connects veterans with assistance.

loaded. Also included: background on the VA's structure, helpful contact information for VA facilities in each state and a separate listing of medical services.

THE AMERICAN LEGION: VETERANS ISSUES
www.legion.org/vetissue.htm

The Legion's 80-year tradition of providing quality services to American veterans is enhanced by this online offering. The resources include background data on common illnesses such as from Agent Orange exposure, information on post-traumatic stress disorder and a contact number for a nationwide listing of VA health care and benefits offices. Veterans who need financial assistance for their families can find it here. It's available through the Family Support Network in the Support of Troops in Bosnia section.

NATIONAL VETERANS FOUNDATION
www.nvf.org

This informative site is devoted to the humanitarian needs of veterans and their families. The information about the foundation's educational outreach programs is helpful and often healing for veterans who are looking to share their experiences. Outlets for contributing to the NVF are available on the Our Veterans Legacy page. A key element: A toll-free crisis lifeline that connects veterans with assistance for everything from treating mental illness to résumés to benefits.

VETERANS ALLIANCE SERVICE CENTER
www.vets.com

With more than 20 departments for assistance, The Veterans Alliance Service Center is an all-encompassing resource. This site provides insight on every subject, from obtaining lost military records to sorting through the Veteran Administration's many offerings (see review above). Vets who can't find what they need on the site can always Ask Sarge—through an e-mail. Some areas require free registration for access.

DISABLED AMERICAN VETERANS
www.dav.org

America's 2.1 million disabled veterans and their families can get information about the DAV's free services at this site. Established in 1920, the DAV has 69 offices nationwide, which are listed in a directory here. Services include transportation to VA medical facilities to guidance on disability compensation and related programs. This patriotic site includes DAV membership applications as well as information about the National Voluntary Service Program.

Voter Education

(originally reviewed October 1999)

THE DEMOCRACY NETWORK
www.dnet.org

This site is a premier guide to staying educated about elections and politics, offering voter information and party and candidate positions in all 50 states. Plus, there are extensive links to coverage of the 2000 presidential race. One-stop shops for all 50 states present a plethora of state election information, including a list of candidates and their statements, as well as the unique opportunity for citizens to contact candidates with questions.

PROJECT VOTE SMART
www.vote-smart.org

Touted as "a voter's self-defense system," Project Vote Smart offers an incredible compilation of biographies, contact information, position platforms and voting records of more than 13,000 candidates and elected officials. The Vote Smart Classroom provides election activities for students, while Congress Track keeps citizens abreast of representatives' stances on current legislation. Listing credentials on politicians from the president down to local officials, this site is a complete resource for staying politically literate.

VOTENET
www.votenet.com

As "America's active political community," Votenet harnesses the power of the Internet to serve as an informative meeting place for politicians, candidates and citizens alike. Listing candidates by party and election results by state, this site covers both the local and national political scene. With information on Advocacy Groups and outlets to contact elected officials, this site not only educates citizens on political affairs, it encourages and facilitates their involvement.

ABCNEWS.COM: POLITICS
www.abcnews.go.com/sections/politics

Through its extensive array of features and

comprehensive coverage of government and key campaign races, ABC News' Political Nation deploys daily reports that inform the voting public. Don't miss "This Week Roundtable," hosted by Cokie Roberts and Sam Donaldson, which promotes informed decision-making via healthy debate. Congress Watch and current poll results also help to make this a center of political enlightenment. ⓐⓐⓐ

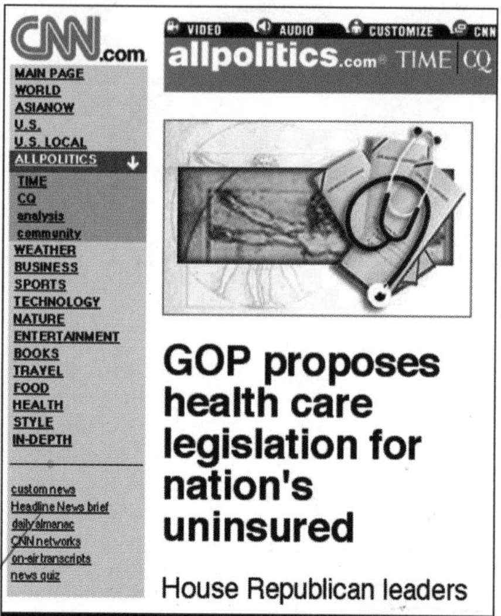

CNN's All Politics can help you stay informed with news, analysis and chat.

CNN.COM
www.cnn.com/allpolitics
Serving a daily smorgasbord of news stories and election reports in its typically thorough style, CNN's All Politics site is sure to keep political junkies well-fed. Chat sessions with candidates provide an easy means of examining their platforms; if you miss them you can read the transcripts on the site. Message boards allow a forum for voters to discuss issues. Cartoon strips provide humorous and insightful commentary on the latest political happenings. Voter polls and links to Time magazine cover stories complete this well-designed, professional site. ⓐⓐⓐ

POLITICS.COM
www.politics.com
Posting the latest stories and news, this site is a guide to all things political. Select from the list of prominent political columnists, or find out about campaign finance results in each state. The site's forums are spirited. (A recent topic: "Dems current and future." With its organized layout and links to top political magazines as well as the sites of 13 political parties, the Political Junkie supplies readers with the substantial fix of data they need to stay informed. ⓐⓐ

health

Addiction Resources

(originally reviewed September 1999)

ARIZONA COUNCIL ON COMPULSIVE GAMBLING, INC.
www.azccg.org
Although it doesn't get as much press as, say, alcoholism, compulsive gambling can destroy lives just as easily. This compassionate site gives detailed information to help gamblers and their loved ones identify and confront the problem. Offering targeted information for male and female gamblers, as well as "action" and "escape" gamblers, ACCG zeros in on psychological needs. The site also offers techniques for families who need to challenge a loved one. ⓐⓐⓐⓐ

CLOSE TO HOME: MOYERS ON ADDICTION
www.wnet.org/closetohome/home.html
This Web site is based on the acclaimed PBS documentary "Moyers on Addiction: Close to Home," which aired in March 1998. Although the show is not new, the information is timeless, covering the science behind addiction, prevention, treatment and related politics. The QuickTime clips from the series are a great touch, and true stories illustrate the devastation of addiction. A tremendous number of addiction resources are available on this site. For younger visitors, there is Overboard, a soap opera/comic book about teens making choices about drugs, alcohol and tobacco. ⓐⓐⓐⓐ

DR. KOOP.COM: TACKLING TOBACCO
www.drkoop.com/tobacco
This is an excellent resource for those thinking about kicking the cigarette habit. It gives a great deal of information on the medical problems associated with tobacco, plus solid information on how to quit, from emotional preparedness to physical resources such as nicotine patches. It also offers smoking-related health news and thought-provoking articles on tobacco advertising. ⓐⓐⓐⓐ

PREVLINE: THE NATIONAL CLEARINGHOUSE FOR ALCOHOL AND DRUG INFORMATION
www.health.org
This site, which is a service of the federal Substance Abuse and Mental Health Services Administration agency, has a plethora of great information about how to treat alcohol and drug addictions, as well as how to prevent them. Health care and education administrators can get helpful information and ideas to keep kids off drugs, and kids can go to their own section for advice and safety tips. There are also resources for people who are recovering from addictions, and help for runaways who are hooked but want to get clean. ⓐⓐⓐ

QUITSMOKINGSUPPORT.COM
www.quitsmokingsupport.com
Thanks to this site, smokers who are trying to quit don't have to do it alone. Aside from the latest in tobacco research and legislation, self-assessment tools and a special section for teen smokers, this site features chats and forums for people who need some you-can-do-it encouragement. For added inspiration, check out What Are The Benefits Of Quitting, where visitors can see how their bodies recover after 20 minutes to 15 years. ⓐⓐⓐ

ANOTHER EMPTY BOTTLE
www.alcoholismhelp.com
This site for alcoholics, their families and their friends uses a clear and simple format to direct visitors to a quality selection of resources. From drunk driving to damaged relationships to college drinking, this site is an excellent stop for people trying to find ways to cope with alcoholism. In Our Words in the Interaction section features submissions from visitors who are dealing with alcoholism or alcoholic family members. Readers can post responses to the submissions. ⓐⓐ

DRUGNET
www.drugnet.net
Drugnet provides a concise array of drug and alcohol abuse information. Its Treatment and Prevention sections highlight surprising statistics while sprinkling useful links throughout easy-to-scan articles. An assessment questionnaire, while not a substitute for professional help, may lead respondents toward recognizing problems and finding help. ⓐⓐ

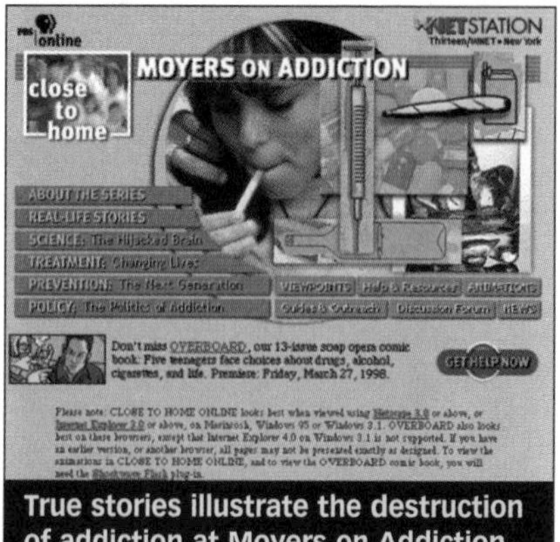

True stories illustrate the destruction of addiction at Moyers on Addiction.

Alternative Medicine

(originally reviewed October 1999)

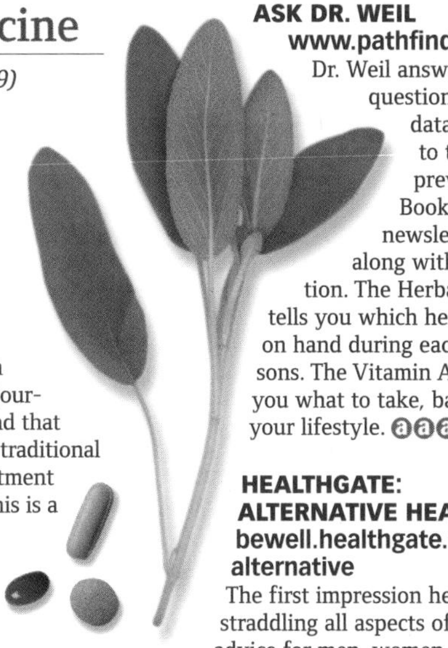

ALTERNATIVE HEALTH NEWS ONLINE
www.altmedicine.com
Here is an excellent resource for comprehensive information about diet and nutrition, mind-body control, manual healing and alternative medical systems such as Chinese, ayurvedic and homeopathic. Keep in mind that the site is maintained by journalists, not doctors—who recommend that alternative practices be balanced by traditional medicine. That said, for specific treatment information or the latest research, this is a site you can use with confidence. ⓐⓐⓐⓐ

PREVENTION
www.prevention.com
The name says it all: Cooking, nutrition, health and fitness tips presented on this site can help readers head off problems before they happen. There's a nice blend of conventional and alternative medicine here. It's an excellent starting place for those people who are new—or are looking for a moderate approach—to alternative therapies. ⓐⓐⓐⓐ

THRIVEONLINE
www.thriveonline.com

This site aims to inform and empower readers by offering self-care options and health and wellness advice from experts. Friendly and easy-to-use, it has a good, searchable health library. Topics cover six major themes: Medical, Fitness, Weight, Nutrition, Sexuality and Serenity. Features include an interactive questionnaire that builds your health portrait, a recipe finder, a body fat calculator, a vitamin guide and alternative medicine resources that are listed in the Serenity section. ⓐⓐⓐⓐ

ALTERNATIVE MEDICINE
www.alternativemedicine.com
The brainchild of Burton Goldberg, the controversial publisher of Alternative Medicine magazine and several books, this site offers numerous useful features. You'll find taped audio programs, alternative health news, essays, a calendar of events and extensive lists of practitioners. The site features one of the largest searchable databases of alternative medical information on the Web. There is a lot of information here, but the emphasis veers toward quantity over quality. ⓐⓐⓐ

ASK DR. WEIL
www.pathfinder.com/drweil
Dr. Weil answers one consumer question each day, but a database allows visitors to troll for answers to previous questions. Books, bulletins and newsletters are offered, along with self-help information. The Herbal Medicine Chest tells you which herbs you should have on hand during each of the four seasons. The Vitamin Adviser tells you what to take, based on your lifestyle. ⓐⓐⓐ

HEALTHGATE: ALTERNATIVE HEALTH
bewell.healthgate.com/healthy/alternative
The first impression here is of an e-zine straddling all aspects of healthy living—advice for men, women, athletes and parents. You'll find drug and medical information alongside natural healing topics such as flower essences and reflexology. Read up on medical tests, surgeries, vitamins, magnet therapy and aromatherapy. The Travel & Health page offers plenty of useful advice. ⓐⓐⓐ

HEALTHWORLD ONLINE
www.healthy.net
Combining conventional and alternative approaches, this site offers a broad array of information on wellness, fitness, nutrition, illnesses, alternative medicine, self-care and family health. It provides links to organizations, a practitioner referral network, newsletters and discussion groups. In short, it's extremely comprehensive. The emphasis is on traditional medicine from around the world. This is a good place for empowered consumers to explore self-health. ⓐⓐⓐ

Alzheimer's Disease

(originally reviewed November 1999)

ALZHEIMER'S ASSOCIATION
www.alz.org
This site takes a gentle approach to a painful topic. Whether you are looking for general information about the disease, treatment options, research advances or caregiving tips, the information is thorough and easy to understand. Patients, family members and health care professionals will appreciate the resources here. The site's primary concern is expanding awareness. ⓐⓐⓐⓐ

ALZHEIMERS.COM
www.alzheimers.com
Providing the most current Alzheimer's information in comprehensible terms is the goal of this site from PlanetRx. Medical professionals can benefit from features in the Health Library about behavioral studies, medical advances and specific drug information. Families and friends of people with Alzheimer's will be particularly interested in articles on the history of the disease, prevention, warning signs and links to community outreach programs. ⓐⓐⓐⓐ

ALZHEIMER'S DISEASE EDUCATION & REFERRAL CENTER
www.alzheimers.org
Visitors here will find the most up-to-date information that has been published about Alzheimer's and other age-related diseases. The resources are impressive, both in size and in content. Read fact sheets, find out about research news from The National Institute on Aging or scan the Clinical Trials Database. A calendar keeps visitors abreast of nationwide conferences and meetings about Alzheimer's. ⓐⓐⓐ

COPING
www.bhoffcomp.com/coping
This informative, inspiring site is for caregivers of patients with Alzheimer's and other dementia. Both professional and family caregivers can share experiences, give advice and support, and keep each other informed. Featured items include everything from personal short stories and poems by patients' family members to clinical instructions on dealing with specific symptoms. ⓐⓐⓐ

THE ALZHEIMER PAGE
www.biostat.wustl.edu/alzheimer
This is a companion site to an Alzheimer's e-mail discussion group. It's a forum for patients, family members, health care providers, students and public policy makers. In addition to the topics and FAQs, there are links to other sites on aging and dementia. The site could make more of a visual splash, but the text is concise and to-the-point. The Alzheimer Archive is a monthly index of list submissions from the past five years. ⓐⓐ

Arthritis

(originally reviewed October 1999)

THE ARTHRITIS SOCIETY
www.arthritis.ca/home.html
This Canadian research organization is focused on informing the public and helping arthritis sufferers. The site offers the latest news on clinical research in the Canadian medical community and tips on participating in experimental trials. Take advantage of the online bulletin board, or watch videos of experts discussing such topics as psoriatic arthritis and resurfacing joint cartilage in the Programs & Resources section. You can also shop at the Arthritis Storefront and learn Tips for Living Well. ⓐⓐⓐⓐ

ARTHRITISWEBSITE.COM
www.arthritiswebsite.com
Devoted to informing and connecting arthritis sufferers, their families and friends, this site's 300-plus pages offer something for everyone. For example, did you know that there are 171 different types of arthritis? Track the latest news about the disease, share questions and answers with other visitors, and get informed about medications and treatments. There is also a comprehensive section for children. ⓐⓐⓐⓐ

DOCTOR'S GUIDE TO ARTHRITIS INFORMATION & RESOURCES
www.pslgroup.com/arthritis.htm
The doctors are in, and they've culled the best data from the Net for arthritis patients. Fact Sheets in the Arthritis Information section give the lowdown on juvenile arthritis, exercise, living with the disease and how it affects the body. There are also links to related sites and newsgroups, a periodic mailing about clinical trials and news, and a huge archive of Medical News and Alerts. ⓐⓐⓐ

MCW HEALTHLINK: ARTHRITIS
healthlink.mcw.edu/arthritis
This site continues to grow, adding new information regularly. Although not well-organized, the overall quality of the articles on the site is superb. You'll find articles on polymyalgia rheumatica, lupus and joint replacement. Rest assured that the information is trustworthy: Most is from the Health Care Information Journal, and it is all backed by the expertise of the Medical College of Wisconsin Physicians & Clinics group. ⓐⓐⓐ

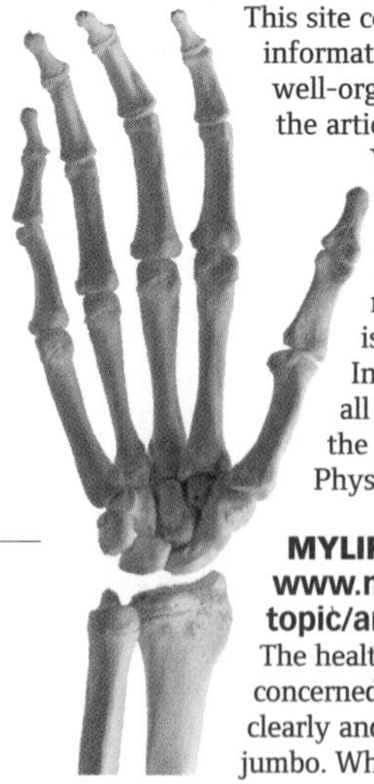

MYLIFEPATH.COM: ARTHRITIS
www.mylifepath.com/topic/arthritis
The health experts at this site answer a concerned patient's questions quickly, clearly and without any medical mumbo jumbo. What are the symptoms? When

should you see a doctor? What are the best ways to get relief? You'll find answers to these questions and more, along with current news about the disease, plenty of links to Web resources and journal articles. ⓐⓐⓐ

PLANETRX: ARTHRITIS
www.planetrx.com/condition/cond_detail/info/ 11_Introduction.html
This pharmaceutical site has easy-to-understand information on the latest drug treatments for arthritis as well as on causes and prevention. Readers can get the facts on the many different types of arthritis and related conditions, as well as current treatment options, alternative care and lists of symptoms. Naturally, you'll also find plenty of information on specific drugs. ⓐⓐⓐ

KIDS GET ARTHRITIS, TOO!
home.att.net/~r.drackley/KidsArthritis.html
The elderly are not the only ones suffering from this disease. Kids and their caregivers can share their hopes, fears, stories, wishes and experiences with juvenile arthritis through bulletin boards and chats. Overlook the dowdy appearance and you'll find touching stories and a terrific support network. Check out the links page or nominate your child for the Arthritis Warrior Award. ⓐⓐ

Cancer

(originally reviewed October 1999)

AMERICAN CANCER SOCIETY
www.cancer.org
With lots of hope, progress and answers, the ACS is an advocate for cancer patients and a source of emotional support for their families. This site provides a great deal of in-depth information, including a cancer glossary, statistics, a list of symptoms and treatments for a variety of childhood cancers. The news area carries stories on the latest scientific developments. The ACS also offers free materials about specific issues such as tobacco, breast cancer and radiation therapy. ⓐⓐⓐⓐ

NATIONAL COALITION FOR CANCER SURVIVORSHIP
www.cansearch.org
A nationwide network of support groups for cancer patients and the people who care for them, the NCCS ensures that cancer survivors have a voice. Find out about its latest survivorship programs, public health and policy support, sponsored conferences and events. Also, check out the Cancer Survival Toolbox, a set of audio tapes that visitors can hear or read online. The Toolbox can help cancer patients cope with daily challenges and difficult decisions. ⓐⓐⓐⓐ

The Oncology Nursing Society explores fatigue at CancerFatigue.org.

CANCER CARE, INC.
www.cancercareinc.org
This helpful site offers assistance, information and resources for cancer patients. A free telephone hotline is available for questions, medical concerns and referrals. The organization also runs teleconference and in-person support groups. You'll find plenty of information about many types of cancer, fatigue, pain and clinical trials. ⓐⓐⓐ

NATIONAL CANCER INSTITUTE: CANCERNET
cancernet.nci.nih.gov
Offering reliable and credible cancer information, the National Cancer Institute's CancerNet is compiled by oncology experts and cancer researchers. Clinical trials, the latest research, new drugs and innovations in medical technology are just a few of the topics that are covered in-depth for patients and health professionals. The site also provides easy access to the NCI's CANCERLIT bibliographic database and the cancerTrials information center. ⓐⓐⓐ

ONCOLINK
oncolink.upenn.edu
One of the largest online cancer encyclopedias and resource libraries, this is the place to research the disease, read the latest clinical news or watch cancer-related videos. A massive search engine will facilitate your quest, and deep drawers of resources for patients, clinicians, families and researchers make this effort by the University of Pennsylvania a worthwhile stop. ⓐⓐⓐ

CANCERFATIGUE.ORG
www.cancerfatigue.org

Fatigue is a problem for nearly all cancer patients, no matter the type of cancer or course of treatment. In an effort to improve patients' quality of life, this site from the Oncology Nursing Society explains what causes fatigue and offers practical advice for coping with it. The ONS also notes that caregivers need to monitor their own exhaustion levels. The Ask the Experts message area is available for questions that are not covered.

CANCER NEWS ON THE NET
www.cancernews.com

For those who aren't quite sure what information they need, this site can save dozens of aimless clicks. It gathers cancer news from numerous online publications and press releases and divides them into categories, including skin, breast and lung cancer. In addition to the news, there are other practical directories of prevention resources, support groups, books and events.

MEDICINE ONLINE
www.meds.com

This site will probably be most useful to physicians, but patients well versed in medical jargon may find it helpful as well. Lung cancer, colon cancer and leukemia are the primary focus, but the site also includes informative features such as the cancer glossary and the DoseCalc dosage calculator. Cancer forums, oncology news and abundant links round out the site.

Colds & Flu

(originally reviewed December 1999)

BH&G FAMILY HEALTH GUIDE TO COLDS, FLU, & ALLERGIES
www.bhglive.com/health/coldflu.html

The editors of Better Homes and Gardens have put together a comprehensive treatment guide. An interactive quiz will identify your ailment. Quick clicks take you to reviews of widely used over-the-counter drugs, preventive measures and home remedies. Plus, it tells you how to use the medication, the best times to take it, possible side effects and suitability for children.

Find out what's ailing you at BH&G Family Health Guide to Colds, Flu & Allergies.

HEALTHTOUCH ONLINE
www.healthtouch.com

This site pulls together information from dozens of respected medical and health research organizations. Start on the Health Information page, then select Colds or Flu. In the Colds section, visitors will find general information, prevention tips, treatments (including news about vitamin C) and research. In the Flu section, look for a history of human influenza, news about the flu vaccine and prevention tips.

KAISER PERMANENTE: COLD AND FLU WEBZINE
www.kaiserpermanente.org/toyourhealth/hottopics/coldnflu/coldnflu.html

This colorful, well-designed site from one of the country's biggest HMOs is great for a quick rundown on preventing and treating your illness. It answers common questions, such as "How do I know what I have?" and "What do I do for my symptoms?" Answers are easy to understand and add a dose of humor.

HEALTHWORLD ONLINE: COLDS AND FLU
www.healthy.net/clinic/dandc/colds

If you prefer alternative therapies, try this site. Articles by doctors and other health care professionals discuss homeopathic, naturopathic and herbal treatments. Start with Medical Self-Care for general information and crucial questions to ask yourself before starting self-treatment. Note: Sections marked "premium" are fee-based audio files; however, most of the material is free.

Deafness

(originally reviewed September 1999)

DEAF WORLD WEB
dww.deafworldweb.org

Based in Canada, Deáf World Web is arguably the largest and most comprehensive site for the global deaf community—acting as a news service, reference guide and bulletin board. The

Sign Language Dictionary has an accompanying video of a translator demonstrating how to sign. The Regions section offers information about the deaf in more than 100 countries, and there's also a special section for deaf kids. Check out the anecdotes and opinions in Ask Q, Answer Q.

DEAFNATION
www.deafnation.com
DeafNation aspires to be the most complete Internet service provider for deaf people. The site includes job resource information for deaf people, a Marketplace to buy products and services and a comprehensive news section. While many articles focus on deaf-related technology, the sports section covers everything from the 1999 Deaf Games to regional club tournaments. DeafNation also offers free e-mail accounts, chat rooms and a newsletter.

GALLAUDET UNIVERSITY
www.gallaudet.edu
As the world's premier university for the deaf and hearing impaired, people have always turned to Gallaudet for answers. The school's National Information Center on Deafness provides summer camp listings, pen-pal links, a database of state agencies that offer services for the deaf, information on laws protecting people with disabilities and much more. Learn about the cutting-edge research conducted at the university, or read thought-provoking articles from the school's outstanding publications.

SIGNHEAR COMMUNICATIONS CENTER
library.advanced.org/10202
Originally designed by three high school students for an international contest, this site is a great resource for those who want to communicate with deaf people. SIGNhear strives to teach American Sign Language to the public over the Internet. Included are sketches of alphabet and number signs as well as 200 basic signs. The site also offers tips, such as "never practice signing in a mirror" because you'll see the signs in reverse.

WHERE DO WE GO FROM HEAR?
www.gohear.org
This is a good source of information for parents and caregivers of infants and children who have been diagnosed with hearing loss. In addition to true stories from families adapting to life with a deaf child, the site includes useful information about hearing loss and testing. There are also useful links to a bevy of resources on hearing assistance devices, educational facilities, research centers and much more.

THE DEAFENED PEOPLE PAGE
www.deafened.org
For those born without hearing, deafness can be considered an entire culture in itself. For those who lose their hearing later in life, the situation may feel different. The Deafened People Page is designed for people who become deaf as adults. The site includes articles and debates about subjects such as loud music and cochlear implants, a surgical insertion of electrodes in the cochlea. Despite an awkward design, there is plenty of useful information at this site.

NATIONAL ASSOCIATION OF THE DEAF
www.nad.org
Founded in 1880, the National Association of the Deaf is an advocacy group for the more than 28 million deaf and hearing-impaired Americans. Besides general information about the organization and its offerings, the site includes articles from the association's publications, The NAD Broadcaster and NAD E-Zine, an electronic magazine dealing with deaf issues. Topics include civil rights, education, technology and legislation.

Depression

(originally reviewed November 1999)

DEPRESSION.COM
www.depression.com
This user-friendly site takes an in-depth look at every topic related to depression. There's the standard depression symptoms quiz, but this site digs deeper. It also touches on the different types of depression, therapies and physical effects, such as sleeplessness. The Health Library is the place where you will find the bulk of information here. Visit the Newsroom to peruse up-to-date articles about depression and recent studies on the disease. The online pharmacy is one of the many ventures sponsored by online drugstore PlanetRx.

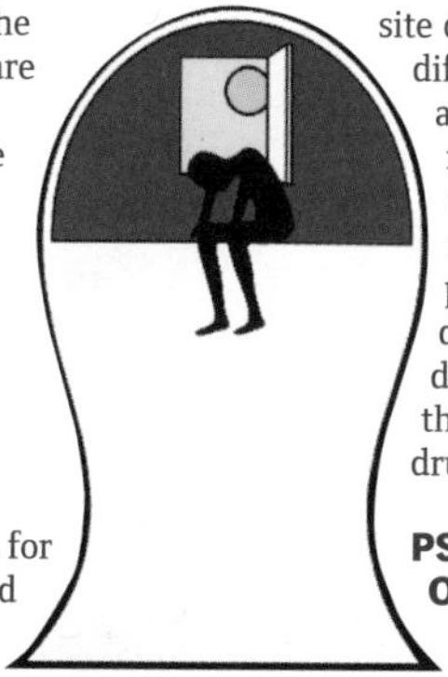

Learn about depression at www.depression.org.

PSYCHOLOGY INFORMATION ONLINE: DEPRESSION
www.psychologyinfo.com/depression
Although this site isn't flashy, it does offer a solid amount of information. The content not

only explains depression and treatment options, it also examines the specific effects the disease has on women, teens and seniors. Seasonal affective disorder, major depression, bipolar disorder and dysthymia are among the types of depression that are covered here. You will also find a comprehensive national directory of psychologists under the Help section. ⓐⓐⓐⓐ

ANDREW'S DEPRESSION PAGE
www.blarg.net/~charlatn/Depression.html
Follow one man's battle with depression at this personal site. Read Andrew's online journal—other depression sufferers will relate to his mood swings, unhappiness with his social life and experiences with anti-depressant drugs. Voices is a collection of moving poems and stories by people suffering from depression. Plus, there are links to more information about the disease, suicide and treatment. The depression questionnaire is designed to track your moods from week to week and can be printed out and given to your doctor. ⓐⓐⓐ

DEFEAT DEPRESSION
www.rcpsych.ac.uk/public/help/depintro/dep_frame.htm
The Royal College of Psychiatrists in London has based this site on a campaign to defeat depression. The site provides a series of articles on various topics, including Depression in the Elderly, Depression in the Workplace and Depression in People with Learning Disabilities. Within each category are additional articles on prevention, treatment and commonly asked questions. For example, the Post Natal Depression section asks and answers questions about hormones, possible harm to children—which the site says is highly unlikely—and how talk therapy and medication can help. ⓐⓐⓐ

NATIONAL FOUNDATION FOR DEPRESSIVE ILLNESS, INC.
www.depression.org
This is a good place to start for general information about depression. It may be most useful to family members or friends trying to get a better idea of what a depression sufferer is experiencing. Brief entries outline what depression is, its major symptoms and how treatment can help. Feeling Better offers practical tips on managing depression once the illness is under control. ⓐⓐ

SA\VE
www.save.org
Suicide Awareness\Voices of Education says the top cause of suicide is untreated depression. This site strives to educate and help. There are symptom checklists to help families and friends identify depression in adults, seniors, children, teens and even infants. There are tips on what to do if someone is suicidal. If the worst happens, there's helpful information about coping and explaining suicide to children. ⓐⓐ

Diabetes

(originally reviewed November 1999)

AMERICAN DIABETES ASSOCIATION
www.diabetes.org
Visitors can register and customize this Web site to match their preferences—sign up for daily tips and recipes or receive the ADA's newsletter and headlines. The site has comprehensive information on diet, exercise and treatment programs as well as petitions and fund-raising sections for activists. Shop the store for magazines and books on the disease. There are also special areas devoted to issues of interest to physicians and other health-care professionals. ⓐⓐⓐⓐ

CHILDREN WITH DIABETES
www.kwd.org
This superb site is designed especially for diabetic children and their parents. It provides current news about products and regulations, good tips for managing diabetes at school, advice for teachers with diabetic students, answers to questions and genuine emotional support for the entire family. Parents and kids will each find their own sections with letters, chats, links and advice. Kids can read profiles of other diabetic children, and there's even a directory of camps for diabetic kids. ⓐⓐⓐⓐ

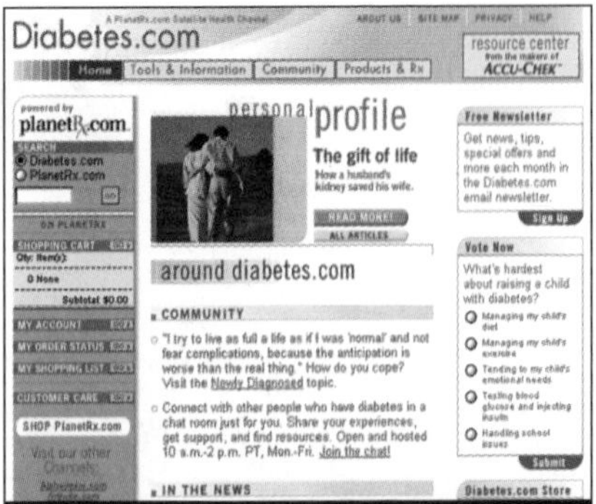

Diabetes.com has message boards for all types of diabetic patients.

DIABETES.COM
www.diabetes.com
Boasting a superb design, this site features recent news about diabetes, prevention information and a special area devoted to those recently diagnosed with the disease. Community message boards provide areas to discuss sugar levels, emotions, medications, men's and women's issues and discrimination. Plus, there's targeted information for children and pregnant women. Be aware that Diabetes.com is produced by PlanetRx, an online pharmacy that sells medical products and supplies. ⓐⓐⓐⓐ

CDC'S DIABETES AND PUBLIC HEALTH RESOURCE
www.cdc.gov/diabetes
The Centers for Disease Control provide interesting statistical information on the disease. A helpful, clearly written FAQ page provides concise, informative responses to basic questions about the illness and its treatments. There are also a modest list of links, a map of Diabetes Control Programs by state and a comprehensive library of clip art. ⓐⓐⓐ

THE HEALING HANDBOOK FOR PERSONS WITH DIABETES
www.umassmed.edu/diabeteshandbook
This virtual handbook is a good resource for essential information about living with diabetes. Chapters cover diet, monitoring, exercise, skin and foot care, family concerns and traveling. The site is plain, but it's straightforward and clearly laid out. Be sure to check out its glossary and list of related links. ⓐⓐⓐ

KIDS LEARN ABOUT DIABETES
www.geocities.com/HotSprings/6935
This site for kids with diabetes was designed by a young Eagle Scout and offers a helpful tutorial. Without using "doctorese," diabetes is explained in terms that young people can easily understand. Though not as comprehensive as other sites that cover the disease, diagrams, simple explanations and an emphasis on feelings make it a useful resource for children. ⓐⓐⓐ

NATIONAL INSTITUTE OF DIABETES AND DIGESTIVE AND KIDNEY DISEASES
www.niddk.nih.gov
Get past the complex first page and you'll find a wealth of resources on diabetes, diabetes-related programs and research funding. Special sections cover diabetes-related eye, kidney and foot problems, as well as options for controlling the disease. Helpful fact sheets and patient booklets about insulin and noninsulin-dependent diabetes are also available. ⓐⓐⓐ

How Many Lawyers Does It Take To End Domestic Violence?
[Answer]
About the
INTERNET WARNINGS:
How An Abuser Can Discover Your Internet Activities
Commission on Domestic Violence
For help call the National Domestic Violence Hotline: 1-800-799-SAFE 1-800-787-3224 (TTY)
The ABA Commission on Domestic Violence is unable to respond to emails regarding specific cases, research, or general matters.
The ABA's site on domestic violence is rich with resources and advice.

Domestic Violence

(originally reviewed November 1999)

ABA COMMISSION ON DOMESTIC VIOLENCE
www.abanet.org/domviol
The American Bar Association maintains this comprehensive site of resources for dealing with domestic violence. It includes a warning that an abuser may be able to track your computer use and an explanation of how to cover your tracks. The ABA runs through emergency plans, legal assistance, statistics and news. It also directs researchers toward legal resources, laws and codes. This is a good stop for victims and for professionals who wish to help them. ⓐⓐⓐⓐ

SAFE HORIZON
www.dvsheltertour.org
This is a powerful tour of a battered women's shelter. Personal stories and photos document the residents' pain and survival. Even more touching is the artwork created by children who have survived domestic violence. For those moved to seek or offer help, there's an abundance of information about abuse and how to prevent or escape it. A map lists help organizations in every state. ⓐⓐⓐⓐ

THE SAFETY ZONE
www.serve.com/zone
This is a solid site for victims and their supporters. It includes thorough articles on the nature of domestic violence as well as the details of finding help and support. Victims can learn what an order of protection is and create a personalized safety plan. A section for helpers lays out guidelines for approaching and assisting a possible abuse victim. The site also explores the possible link between alcohol and abuse. ⓐⓐⓐⓐ

WHEN LOVE HURTS
home.vicnet.net.au/~girlsown

Though it looks more like a page ripped from a teen magazine than a victim's resource, don't let this site's colorful exterior fool you. When Love Hurts is a top-notch primer on date-related violence. It explains what abuse is and offers a list of warning signs and advice on breaking up. There are questions and ideas for teens who may be in abusive relationships. Be sure to read Isabella's Story for inspiration. This clear, nonjudgmental site is a must-read for young women.

MEN FOR CHANGE
www.chebucto.ns.ca/CommunitySupport/Men4Change/index.htm

This positive, forward-thinking site promotes nonviolent, nonracist and nonhomophobic behavior. The Personal section contains advice and thoughts on ending domestic violence and preventing rape, as well as commentary on gender, health and parenting issues. The Political section dives further into the issues of violence and sexism, addressing pornography and assault as well as detailing public outreach initiatives.

VIOLENCE AT HOME
www.sacbee.com/news/projects/violence

This 1997 Sacramento Bee project offers a thorough and startling look at family violence. The 12-part series addresses more sides of the problem than most other sites. It touches on parental abuse by children, special police teams, and the strengths and limitations of courts. The statistics here are a few years old, but much of the information is timeless and extremely valuable.

Dream Interpretation

(originally reviewed November 1999)

ASK THE DREAM DOCTOR
www.dreamdoctor.com

Someone who truly understands the psyche developed this page. It's smartly divided into categories that make sense—Women's Dreams, Men's Dreams, Teen Zone, Romance Dreams, Parent's Page and Senior's Dreams. Concerns, goals and feelings that affect our dreams are addressed from each perspective. Scan visitors' letters and the Dream Doctor's replies. Reading is free, but the doctor charges $20 to analyze your dream.

DREAM CENTRAL
www.sleeps.com/dreams.html

This site is ideal for bedtime browsing. Take a peek at Dream Basics for an introduction to dream interpretation before you hit the hay. Delve deeper into the subconscious by using tips on dream inducement in Analyzing Dreams. Highlight: Each of the 500 entries in the Dream Dictionary lends insight into the symbolic meanings of what we see in dreams.

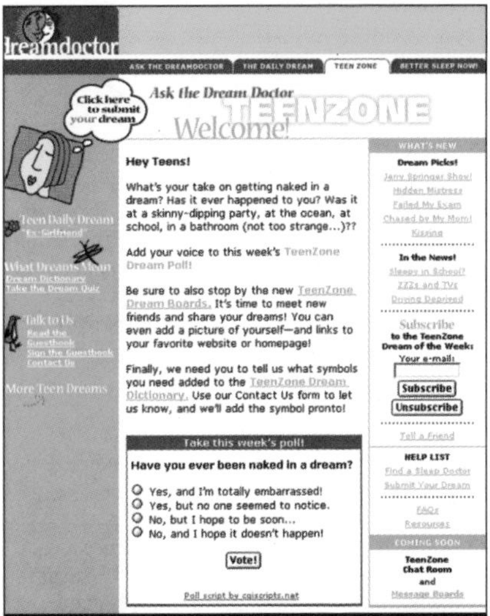

Ask the Dream Doctor interprets dreams from many perspectives.

AISLING—DREAM INTERPRETATION
www.avcweb.com/dreams

By exploring the emblematic roles of numbers, colors and characters in dreams, this solid site helps us understand our subconscious reveries. This site is peppered with useful information designed to heighten dream comprehension. An average layout is bolstered by the enlightening content, which includes insight on the spirituality of dreams and how they relate to our health.

THRIVEONLINE: DREAM ARCHIVE
www.thriveonline.com/serenity/experts/dream/dream.today.html

The Dream Archives of this site skip fancy graphics and let you start reading other people's dreams right away. Dream submissions that span workplace woes to wedding-day jitters are analyzed. Spearheaded by dream guru Charles McPhee, this site helps uncover the symbolic meanings of dreams. Exchange ideas with others in Dream Talk or submit your own dream for a chance at a free interpretation.

TIGER'S NEST
www.frii.com/~tigrnest
Based on the premise that dreams are directly connected to our daily lives, this site highlights the spiritual elements of our subconscious insights. Submit your dreams to the Dream Interpretation Board for analysis by other users and occasionally by an onsite expert. Tiger's Nest also offers a newsletter and book reviews, including commentary on several works by renowned psychiatrist and dream analyst Carl Jung.

DREAM INTERPRETATION
library.advanced.org/tq-admin/month.cgi
Isn't it annoying when you can't remember your dreams? This site, developed by students for the ThinkQuest school competition, has a golden rule of dream interpretation: Always write them down. From ancient dream analysis theories to the more modern ideas of Freud and Jung, this site presents various perspectives on dream comprehension. The main shortcoming is its underdeveloped layout.

SLEEPY BEAR DREAM INTERPRETATION
www.myenvoy.com/sleepybear
This interactive site calls upon users to analyze an extensive collection of real dreams. It's the perfect forum for honing dream interpretation skills. Pick an entry from the Dream Menu. Read the entry and then click on View Interpretations to read how others analyzed it. An asterisk signifies dreams that have yet to be interpreted, so start with those if you'd like to take the first crack at deciphering someone else's nocturnal reveries.

Fitness

(originally reviewed January 2000)

ALLHEALTH.COM
www.allhealth.com
Part of the giant iVillage family, the focus here is on women's health. However, there are also sections for men, children and seniors. The Never Say Diet section scoffs at traditional dieting. Instead, the information focuses on managing exercise, food and self-image. Use the Health Calculator under Interactivities to determine your ideal weight, take the health Quiz of the Day or find a physician in your state. Physical, mental and emotional well-being are emphasized.

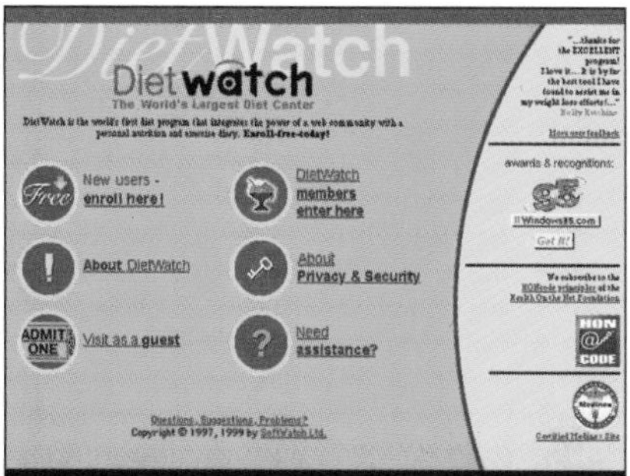

Chart diet and exercise progress with tools at www.dietwatch.com.

CYBERDIET
www.cyberdiet.com
More than just diets, Cyberdiet tells you how to be healthier. Start with the self-assessment tests, such as the Nutritional Profile, Waist-Hip-Ratio and Body Fat Distribution. Then use the Daily Food Planner to start eating right. You'll also find recipes, food facts and nutrition information about fast food. Now it's time to exercise, so hit the Health Club for a free workout program. If you fall off the wagon next week, come back for Support & Motivation.

DIETWATCH
www.dietwatch.com
If you want to lose weight, look no further. Free registration and a supportive e-mail community for encouragement are just some of the features here. Monitor your calories, nutrition and exercise with the daily diet diary, and get graphs and reports of your progress. You can design a personal profile, and set nutrition and weight goals. Join live chats with diet and fitness experts to help stay on track. The Library has articles and links for several health and dieting topics.

ACCENTHEALTH.COM
www.accenthealth.com
The motto here is, "Get well. Stay well." Fill out the confidential Custom Health Profile to assess your health risks and get suggestions on preventative measures. Like many other health sites, the bulk of the personalized information can be obtained upon registration. Learn about prescription drugs, medical tests, healthy aging, nutrition and children's health. The Quick Diagnosis feature can help determine what ails you—just click on a body part of the virtual patient.

AMERICAS DOCTOR.COM
www.americas doctor.com
Here's where you can go online, ask a doctor a medical question and receive real-time answers, 24 hours a day, seven days a week. Get timely information on everything from vaccines to physical fit-

ness. Don't miss the Communities—in-depth sections on a variety of topics, including breast cancer, eating disorders and depression. There are scheduled chats and recommended links for each topic.

THE DAILY APPLE
www.thedailyapple.com
Welcome to the online equivalent of that familiar saying about an apple a day. Register for a free, secure membership and receive weekly mailings. Put your medical records online for easy access and schedule health reminders. Even if you don't sign up, you still can take advantage of the site. There are more than 10 Centers you can visit that contain information on topics such as allergies, exercise, nutrition and diabetes.

EDIETS.COM
www.ediets.com
Plug in your height, weight and the number of pounds you want to lose and get a one-day sample of a personalized diet for free. You can visit the site for no charge as a guest and enjoy a number of the services, such as recipes, an e-newsletter and a list of 100 Best Supermarket Products. But to get all of the benefits, including online support meetings and customized diet plans, it will cost you $30 for three months.

FITNESS ONLINE
www.fitnessonline.com
Choose your fitness priority—a healthy pregnancy, losing weight, adding muscle or just looking and feeling better. Fitness Online draws its resources from several Weider magazines, including Shape, Men's Fitness, Natural Health and Fit Pregnancy. Ask questions of doctors and fitness experts, and find nutritious recipes. You'll also find good information about adventure sports and mental fitness.

NATIONAL INSTITUTES OF HEALTH
www.nih.gov
The NIH works to improve public health through its research. Its Web site is a clearinghouse of health information. Each institute revolves around a certain aspect of health, such as cancer, drug abuse or aging. There are consumer resources, and press releases on news and events. MEDLINEplus is a service developed by medical reference librarians that helps guide you to the best health sites. Much of the information is also available in Spanish.

Headaches

(originally reviewed October 1999)

MIGRAINE AWARENESS GROUP: M.A.G.N.U.M.
www.migraines.org
A nonprofit health care organization conceived in 1993, MAGNUM offers an outstanding array of information for America's estimated 26 million migraine sufferers. Though the site can be slow to load, the bicoastal list of migraine and headache clinics, drug profiles, alternative treatments and questions to ask your doctor are worth the wait. Migraine sufferers should click on Disability & Impairment to read articles on coping with migraines at home and work. Myth & Reality dispels common fallacies about migraines.

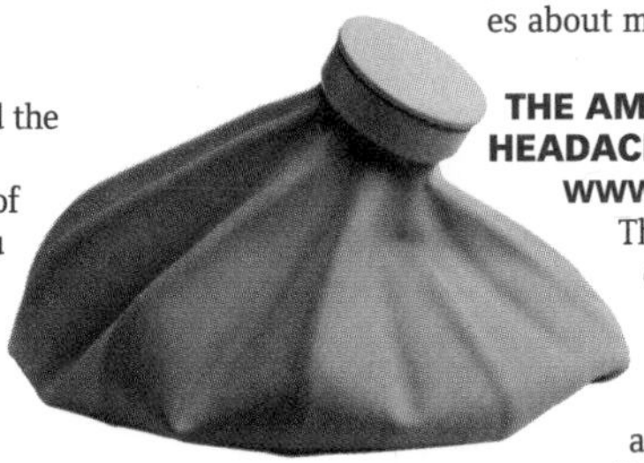

THE AMERICAN COUNCIL FOR HEADACHE EDUCATION
www.achenet.org
This site helps answer crucial questions for headache sufferers by offering tips on prevention and treatment, a migraine disability assessment questionnaire, medication charts and a searchable physician directory for headache specialists in your area. Tune in to find out how to tell the difference between headaches and migraines and why caffeine—which may lead to headaches—is in painkillers.

CLUSTERHEADACHES.COM
www.clusterheadaches.com
There are no doctors here, but this community of cluster headache sufferers provides something just as important as medical information: support from people who understand. Try the Cluster Quiz to see if you really are experiencing cluster headaches—pain that occurs in regular "cluster" periods and may last for minutes to several hours. Questions, comments and personal connections can be found on the message board and in scheduled chats. Keep in mind that this is not a substitute for medical advice.

HEADACHE CYBERTEXT
www.upstate.edu/neurology/haas
Do children have the same kinds of headaches as adults? Could your headache be the result of a brain tumor? Created by Dr. David Haas, this site primarily addresses the diagnosis and treatment of the five most common headache types. Visitors can also investigate an archive of articles on the causes and treatments of less

common headache types, such as exertional and cough. ⓐⓐⓐ

HEADACHES
www.painforum.com/en/1/ngheadache.html

Pain relief is the focus of this appealing site. The Brief History of Headache Treatment is an amusing look at ancient remedies such as trephination—removing small pieces of the skull to let out evil spirits. Today's more fortunate patients can click on any of the site's subsections—which include sinus, cluster, tension, alcohol-induced and migraine headaches—for quick descriptions and potential causes. OTC Medication and Alternative Therapies lay out a variety of possible solutions. ⓐⓐⓐ

THE ELECTRONIC HEADACHE SUPPORT GROUP
www.medsupport.com/survival

This simple site offers quick and helpful strategies to reduce headaches, including lifestyle changes, food sensitivities and other environmental factors as possible culprits. Though the discussion forum has been temporarily shut down, visitors can check out the Headache Survival Guide. This section explains your rights as a sufferer and offers tips for dealing with doctors and insurance companies. ⓐⓐ

Health (General)

(originally reviewed December 1999)

CBS HEALTHWATCH BY MEDSCAPE
cbs.medscape.com

Registering for this site is easy, and if personal health and current information are important to you, it's worth it. HealthWatch offers a daily health diary, nutrition calculators and graphs to chart glucose or carbohydrate levels. You can search databases and dictionaries, ask an expert for answers and, best of all, take a course online from the Mini Medical School sponsored by Emory University. Don't want to register? There are 22 health channels available for non-registered guests. ⓐⓐⓐⓐ

Quizzes and articles make AHealthyMe! both a fun and an informative Web site.

DISCOVERY HEALTH
www.discoveryhealth.com

This online partner to the new Discovery Health cable channel is a good mix of educational information and entertainment. Read health news or interesting features, such as "Anatomy of a Gunshot." There are voluminous sections for women, men, kids and seniors. Interactive features like Ask the Doctor, quizzes and nutrition calculators can help you be more proactive about your health. Don't miss the Fitness Club and Weight Center. ⓐⓐⓐⓐ

A HEALTHY ME!
www.ahealthyme.com

This newsy site from Blue Cross and Blue Shield of Massachusetts is organized around topics such as women's health, parenting and alternative therapies. Each topic includes daily highlights, news articles and a directory of topics. The quizzes and calculators here are useful and fun, assessing your knowledge on subjects as diverse as weight management, pregnancy and hair loss. For answers to common questions, visit Dr. Anne. ⓐⓐⓐⓐ

INTELIHEALTH
www.intelihealth.com

InteliHealth is a joint venture of Aetna U.S. Healthcare and the Johns Hopkins University and Health System. There is an enormous amount of information here. Topics include allergy, arthritis, diabetes, headache, pregnancy, cancer, men's and women's health, and weight management. There's also a Drug Resource Center, discussion groups, a doctor finder, Ask the Doc and special reports on timely issues. ⓐⓐⓐⓐ

Health Insurance

(originally reviewed September 1999)

HEALTHGRADES.COM
www.healthgrades.com

If you've ever been too confused by health insurance gobbledygook to accurately compare competing health plans, click on this outstanding site because HealthGrades.com has done the work for you. It offers report cards on physicians, hospitals, health plans and nursing homes. The search engine makes it easy to find quality care and coverage near you. The site also provides health news and a handy glossary of medical terms and procedures. ⓐⓐⓐⓐ

FAMILIES USA
www.familiesusa.org
Delve into this site's extensive database of articles on Medicaid, Medicare, managed care and children's health care. Visitors can also sign a national petition for a stronger patients' bill of rights or join any of three issue-focused listservs to share health care concerns. The site offers an excellent comparison of health care reform bills passed by Congress as well as e-mail links to senators and representatives. ⓐⓐⓐ

HEALTH PLAN DIRECTORY
www.healthplandirectory.com
This site provides consumers with comprehensive, well-organized directories of physicians, hospitals and health insurance providers. You'll find contact information for the HMOs and PPOs in your state. Or learn more about a doctor's specialty, medical school, residency, board certification and which health plans he or she accepts. Keep in mind that the site is only a directory and does not provide ratings of health plans or physicians. ⓐⓐⓐ

INSWEB: MEDICAL EXPENSE (HEALTH) INSURANCE QUESTIONS
www.insweb.com/insurance101/qa/health-q.htm
This straightforward list of answers to frequently asked medical insurance questions is a component of InsWeb, a free service that lets you comparison shop and, in some states, receive rate quotes for insurance plans. Learn about preexisting condition clauses and copayments. The quiz under Do-It-Yourself Tools will help you determine if an HMO, PPO or traditional plan is best for you. There's also a glossary, articles and informative special reports. ⓐⓐⓐ

MEDICARE HMO
www.medicarehmo.com
This site is a must for anyone who needs more information about Medicare HMOs and PPOs. Browse through a state-by-state list of HMOs or a complete Medicare handbook from the Health Care Financing Administration in the Medicare HMOs section. The site also features excellent links in its Senior Web Center. There are a few broken links, but visitors should be able to enjoy articles on choosing the right health plan or doctor, and on the pros and cons of a Medicare HMO. ⓐⓐ

HIV/AIDS

(originally reviewed October 1999)

AVERT: AIDS EDUCATION & RESEARCH TRUST
www.avert.org
To say this British site contains a wealth of information would be an understatement. It educates the young and the old about HIV and AIDS, using remarkably accessible language and simple yet effective visuals. Topics include the history of HIV and AIDS, answers to FAQs, statistics, prevention advice and information about living with HIV or AIDS. This site gives special attention to young people, women, healthcare workers and those who carry the virus. ⓐⓐⓐⓐ

HIV INFOWEB
www.infoweb.org
Concise, well-organized and, above all, informative, this site could be renamed "Everything You Need to Know About HIV and AIDS." Labeled as an online library, it presents visitors with a seemingly never-ending list of AIDS-related topics. You can find legal resources, view photographic essays and learn about alternative medical approaches for treatment. Despite the bland homepage, everyone can benefit from a visit to this site. ⓐⓐⓐⓐ

HIV INSITE
hivinsite.ucsf.edu
This outstanding site serves as a gateway to one of the world's top research centers for HIV. Learn about the clinical trials underway, treatment guidelines or case studies. Scan the drug database, or find programs that will help pay for medication. Naturally, you'll also find statistics and prevention information, but there's also the latest news on vaccine research and other topics, and plenty of information about such HIV issues as re-entering the workforce. ⓐⓐⓐⓐ

AIDS ACTION
www.aidsaction.org
Designed for the community activist in all of us, this site from the powerful advocacy group AIDS Action explains how to join the fight against AIDS. Visitors can learn more about the purpose and accomplishments of the organization. Everyone is invited to participate in upcoming events. Younger surfers will want to check out the page dedicated to the late MTV

celebrity Pedro Zamora, which highlights education, prevention and minority communities. There's also a report on the presidential candidates and their positions on AIDS funding and research. ⓐⓐⓐ

HIV/AIDS TREATMENT INFORMATION SERVICE
www.hivatis.org

This site provides general guidelines and in-depth details about the treatment of HIV and AIDS. For those people diagnosed with the disease or anyone who knows someone with it, it's helpful to have access to the latest federally approved treatment guidelines. The information is thorough and impressive but may seem a bit dense to a casual reader. For the site's target audience, however, the daily updates are practically essential. ⓐⓐⓐ

HIVPOSITIVE.COM
www.hivpositive.com

Though the two acronyms HIV and AIDS tend to go hand in hand, this site focuses solely on the prevention, diagnosis and treatment of the human immunodeficiency virus. People who are living with it can check in here to receive advice on nutrition, drug therapies and personal finances, among other things. One of the site's most practical features is the link to the American Medical Association database, where visitors can search online for a nearby specialist. Plus, there is a section devoted to women and children who have HIV. ⓐⓐⓐ

Mental Health

(originally reviewed January 2000)

AMERICAN PSYCHOLOGICAL ASSOCIATION
www.apa.org

Offering an excellent selection of consumer information about mental health, the APA leans toward covering everyday issues, such as work stress, raising nonviolent children and controlling anger. The Help Center is the place to go for family and work issues. Learn how to find and use psychological services, how to cope with traumatic stress and how the mind-body connection can help heal. ⓐⓐⓐⓐ

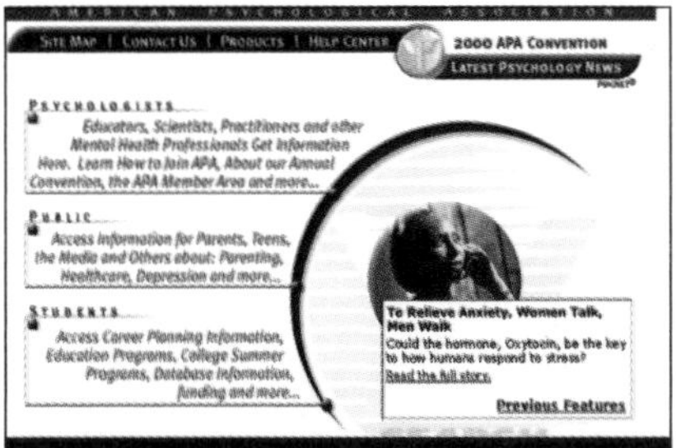

American Psychological Association's site focuses on everyday issues.

THE CENTER FOR MENTAL HEALTH SERVICES
www.mentalhealth.org

In addition to Surgeon General reports, this site offers a host of publications about mental illness, disorder diagnosis, therapy and related issues. You can also read recent coverage of developments in mental health treatment, and professionals can find out about upcoming conferences. There's a good section for kids, complete with educational games. ⓐⓐⓐⓐ

MENTAL HEALTH INFOSOURCE
www.mhsource.com

Choose from a menu of symptoms and disorders to get information about a wide range of mental illnesses. You can read articles from the Psychiatric Times here also, or find detailed case histories and treatment alternatives for schizophrenia, depression or other illnesses. The site also offers an extensive list of treatment centers and mental health professionals, plus an Ask the Expert section. It's an excellent resource for patients and caregivers. ⓐⓐⓐⓐ

ABC'S OF "INTERNET THERAPY"
www.metanoia.org/imhs

Learn how to meet with a psychotherapist online at this site. A thorough guide explains the legal, ethical and practical issues to consider, plus there is a database of more than 100 online counseling services. The site has checked credentials for most of the therapists in the database; read Therapist Credentials for a guide to the symbols used to explain the status of the background checks. You'll also get information about typical fees and payment arrangements. None of the therapists has paid to be included in the guide, so the service is impartial. ⓐⓐⓐ

MENTAL HEALTH MATTERS!
www.mental-health-matters.com

Although this site's design could use some polishing, this is a clearinghouse for a wealth of resources. There are helpful sections devoted to alternative treatments, mental health statistics, self-help and patients' rights. There are also resources and links to hotlines for individuals in need. The Psychobabble section includes links to chats, message boards and mailing lists. ⓐⓐⓐ

MENTAL HEALTH NET
www.mentalhelp.net
If you or someone you know is considering suicide, this site could be helpful. The section on medications has detailed information about a wide range of treatments, as well as Ask the Pharmacists. Read the latest news or peruse articles from the online e-zine Perspectives. Be sure to take advantage of the support forums. ⓐⓐⓐ

Stress Management

(originally reviewed October 1999)

INTERNATIONAL STRESS MANAGEMENT ASSOCIATION
www.stress-management-isma.org
Dedicated to making the world less stressful, the ISMA has created a thorough site for the many stressed-out people around the globe. Its library contains a mother lode of articles and tips on dissipating stress, including "Top ten reasons we should learn to laugh a whole lot." There are lists of suggested books and journal articles, and contact information for ISMA chapters worldwide. ⓐⓐⓐⓐ

MIND TOOLS: HOW TO MASTER STRESS
www.mindtools.com/smpage.html
Are you a perfectionist? An excessive self-effacer? Visit Mind Tools to learn how to better manage those personality traits that generate unhealthy stress. You'll also gain insight into the environmental, lifestyle and job-related factors that can cause tension. This straightforward site contains a treasure chest of helpful techniques, from keeping a stress diary to using imagery and time-management tools. ⓐⓐⓐⓐ

JOB STRESS HELP
www.jobstresshelp.com
The licensed professionals here offer personal consultations via e-mail for $9.95, but there also is plenty of free advice at this well-designed site. From quick tips to relieve job stress to in-depth articles about conflict and management from the newsletter, you'll find plenty of helpful information. Check out the list of 10 most stressful jobs. ⓐⓐⓐ

STRESS FREE NET
www.stressfree.com
This network of health professionals provides a range of confidential services, from diagnosis to advice to referrals to nearby therapists—for anyone suffering from stress. You can e-mail a psychologist with specific questions at Ask the Psychologist, or gain personal insight by offering solutions to other people's problems in You Be The Therapist. Take the Vulnerability Test to check your stress tolerance. ⓐⓐⓐ

TOWNSEND INTERNATIONAL
www.gday-mate.com
This commercial site offers information and products that address stress in today's high-tech, high-pressure world. Learn how to combat computer-related stress and depression. There are a variety of stress tests to analyze your physical, emotional, spiritual, mental and social well-being. Enjoy Creative Leisure features a list of fun activities you can do every day to reduce stress. ⓐⓐⓐ

history

Aviation History

(originally reviewed October 1999)

THE AVIATION HISTORY ON-LINE MUSEUM
www.aviation-history.com
Listen to the roar of airplane engines as you navigate Aviation History's On-line Museum. This site offers technical specifications, history and photos of airplanes from around the world. Visit the Airmen section for photos, bios and stories of history's top fliers. Or take a virtual tour of the enormous Garber Restoration Facility, where historic aircraft are refurbished before being put on display. Gearheads should visit Theory to learn about airfoils and elevons. ⓐⓐⓐⓐ

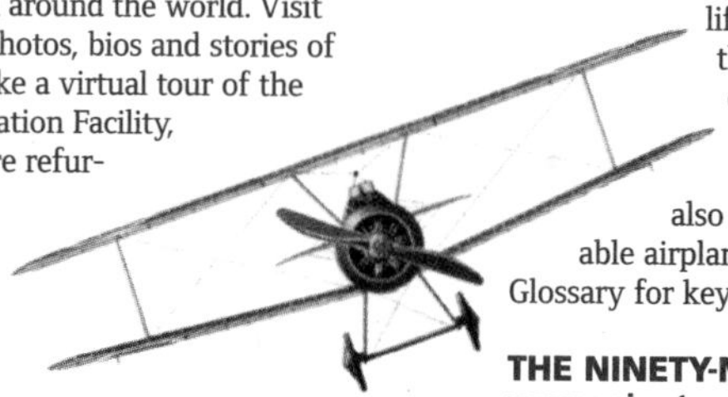

SMITHSONIAN NATIONAL AIR AND SPACE MUSEUM
www.nasm.si.edu
The Smithsonian's National Air and Space Museum is a paradise for aviation fans of all ages, and its Web site is almost as cool as the real thing. Visitors can tour all 23 exhibitions, viewing photos and reading flight histories. The museum covers the major milestones of flight, legends of World War I, aviation of World War II, commercial planes and space flight in an attractive and organized layout. How Things Fly is a great section for kids that offers clear explanations and fun experiments. ⓐⓐⓐⓐ

AEROFILES
www.aerofiles.com
Aerofiles claims to be the "most comprehensive all-American aviation historical reference and research site" on the Internet, and it's tough to disagree. This heavily researched site is geared toward hard-core enthusiasts. Sift through specs, data and photos of more than 10,000 types of U.S. aircraft. Or learn the mind-numbing details of civil aircraft registration. USAviationFirsts in the Chronology section is a good timeline of significant events. Overall, the site is content-rich but sometimes hard to navigate. ⓐⓐⓐ

FLIGHTS OF INSPIRATION
www.fi.edu/flights
The Franklin Institute Science Museum and the Science Museum of London present Flights of Inspiration, a sophisticated site offering historical glimpses into the lives of such aviation pioneers as the Wright brothers, John Alcock and Arthur Whitten Brown. The site is big on science, with an easy-to-understand section on the physics behind flight and instructions for building your own paper, balsa wood or Styrofoam airplane. Teachers should visit Teachers' Zone for lessons and activities. ⓐⓐⓐ

HISTORY OF FLIGHT
tqjunior.thinkquest.org/4027
Fly your own virtual plane! Though far from offering high-tech flight simulations, this clunky but interesting site—developed by kids for the ThinkQuest project—teaches the basics of flight: lift, drag, weight, shape, thrust and propulsion. Be careful to set the gauges correctly, or your virtual plane will crash. There is also a link to a cool customizable airplane noise simulator. See Glossary for key aviation terms. ⓐⓐⓐ

THE NINETY-NINES
www.ninety-nines.org
Founded in 1929 by 99 female pilots, The Ninety-Nines is an international organization dedicated to supporting female aviators. At this busy but decent-looking site, you can learn about the remarkable history of the organization and the women who changed aviation or read essays by female pilots. Check out the Calendar of Events for a listing of aviation conferences, races and events. Perhaps the most useful section: a listing of scholarships, grants and awards to support and help cultivate knowledge about women in aviation. ⓐⓐⓐ

TIGHAR
www.tighar.org
Bent on unraveling aviation's greatest mysteries as well as preserving historic aircraft, The International Group for Historic Aircraft Recovery investigates what really happened to such high-profile fliers as Amelia Earhart, Charles Nungesser and Francois Coli. Read theories on what happened, browse original documents and photographs, or download a video of Earhart's takeoff. You can even purchase a scale model of her plane. ⓐⓐⓐ

Biography

(originally reviewed October 1999)

BIOGRAPHY.COM
www.biography.com
This online companion to the popular television series A&E Biography is such a valuable resource, it merits another review. The different sections offer entertainment and education. A gold mine for teachers and parents is the

Classroom section, which has discussion questions and vocabulary lists pertaining to A&E's documentaries. Hollywood buffs should check This Week's Top Bios and Movie Mavericks. At the end of your visit, play Who Am I? to see what you've learned. ⓐⓐⓐⓐ

LIVES, THE BIOGRAPHY RESOURCE
amillionlives.com
Searchable by name, alphabetical listing and category, this site boasts thousands of links—each concisely described—to biographical data. Special collections include African Americans, Women, Canadians, and Holocaust Survivors and Rescuers, and feature links to oral histories, memoirs and extensive biographies. The smart design creates a new window for each link you select, which simplifies navigation. Before you leave, cast a vote for Time magazine's Person of the Century. ⓐⓐⓐⓐ

BIOGRAPHICAL DICTIONARY
www.s9.com/biography
This dictionary is a nice database of 27,000 biographies dating from ancient times to the present. The downside is that the biographies are brief. You'll also find ideas for students and teachers, such as black history lessons, by conducting a keyword search. Take the Master Biographer Challenge to test your knowledge—but watch out: It claims to be one of the "toughest on the Internet." ⓐⓐⓐ

BIOGRAPHICAL NOTES
www.marxists.org/reference/subject/philosophy/li_help.htm
Philosophy buffs and students should take note of this simple site. Created by Andy Blunden of Melbourne, Australia, its first page alphabetically lists minibiographies of great thinkers. Click More on any entry to bring up a more detailed biography and a portrait of the selected great thinker. The Portrait Gallery alphabetically lists portraits and an index of biography categories, including those of politicians, psychologists and Stalinists. ⓐⓐⓐ

HYPERHISTORY ONLINE: PEOPLE
www.hyperhistory.com/online_n2/History_n2/people.html
The concise biographies here are excellent resources, but watch out for some broken links. Famous names from history are color-coded by category—science, art, religion and politics—and displayed on timelines that range from 1000 B.C. to 1996 A.D. You can also pull up complete charts for each of the four categories. Click on a name to bring up the biography and relevant links. ⓐⓐⓐ

Columbus

(originally reviewed October 1999)

THE COLUMBUS NAVIGATION HOMEPAGE
www1.minn.net/~keithp
Created by historian and author Keith Pickering, this comprehensive site tracks the life and voyages of Christopher Columbus from his birth in 1451 to his death in 1506. In addition to detailed accounts of his various ships and crew members, this site explains at length Columbus' primary navigation style—dead reckoning. A link to the Columbus Landfall Homepage examines the debate over the explorer's first stop in the Americas. With maps, a timeline and links to biographical books, this site is a tremendous guide to the famous explorer. ⓐⓐⓐⓐ

CHRISTOPHER COLUMBUS... HIS GASTRONOMIC PERSONA
www.castellobanfi.com/features/story_contents.html
Presenting text-heavy content in a simple but pleasing design, this site takes a unique culinary angle on Columbus' historic journeys. It explains the food-preserving techniques of seafaring explorers, notes the foods they picked up at each stop and describes typical meals (plenty of fish). Since the site is created by the Castello Banfi vineyard, it is quick to mention that most courses tasted better with ample servings of wine. ⓐⓐⓐ

Columbus tributes abound on the Web.

TODAY IN HISTORY: OCTOBER 12
memory.loc.gov/ammem/today/oct12.html
On a foggy October 12 morning in 1492, sailors aboard the Pinta sighted land after 10 weeks at sea. This site tracks the creation of Columbus Day from its initial recognition in New York in 1909 to its declaration as a federal holiday in 1968. Information about the Knights of Columbus and a collection of artwork of the man that they honor are among the features of this educational offering from the Library of Congress. ⓐⓐⓐ

Explorers

(originally reviewed September 1999)

LEWIS & CLARK
www.pbs.org/lewisandclark

This beautifully designed site, a companion to the PBS film "Lewis & Clark: A Journey of the Corps of Discovery," offers a range of resources and expert historical insight on the famous journey. It provides everything from timelines, maps and journals to a list of provisions gathered for the trip. There is also information about the Native American tribes that the intrepid explorers met along the way. Hear noted historians' thoughts on the expedition, or play Into the Unknown, an interactive game that puts you in charge of the famous expedition. ⓐⓐⓐⓐ

Explore Lewis and Clark with www.pbs.org/lewisandclark.

ANTARCTIC PHILATELY
www.south-pole.com

Some of the most dramatic explorations have involved Antarctica and the quest to reach the South Pole. This site is dedicated to stamps, the postal history of the continent and these daring historic explorers. You'll learn about all the major players, including James Cook, Ernest Shackleton, Roald Amundsen and Richard Byrd. Read one survivor's account of the tragic 1946 Operation Highjump expedition. Nicely detailed biographies are supported by bibliographies, recommended books, photos, maps and a timeline. ⓐⓐⓐ

COMPTON'S ENCYCLOPEDIA ONLINE: EXPLORATION
www.comptons.com/ceo99-cgi/article?'fastweb?getdoc+viewcomptons+A+2850+19++exploration'

Traverse an historical timeline from the first known explorer, Hannu, to the high-altitude triumphs of Sir Edmund Hillary to the Galileo spacecraft. This site is a brief overview, yet it provides more than a who-did-what-when account of exploration. It examines the historical and scientific conditions that made exploration possible. The links sprinkled through the text, offer additional information on explorers and areas of exploration. ⓐⓐⓐ

EXPLORERS OF THE MILLENNIUM
tqjunior.thinkquest.org/4034

This site, designed by fifth-graders in Highland Park, Ill., is a great place for young scholars to research the world's greatest explorers. The backbone of the site is the Explorers' Hall of Fame; members were chosen by the students based on interest value and accomplishments. Brief biographies accompany the list, which includes Daniel Boone, Neil Armstrong and David Livingstone. Visitors can test their knowledge with a quiz or nominate an explorer to the Hall of Fame. ⓐⓐⓐ

THE MARINERS' MUSEUM: THE AGE OF EXPLORATION
www.mariner.org/age

Teachers searching for guides to maritime exploration should look no further than The Mariners' Museum Curriculum Guide. Students will also find this site to be a convenient resource. Just point and click to learn about Viking ships or Francis Drake. Click on Menu from the homepage and then scroll down to the excellent Activities section; it has instructions for building astrolabes, ship diagrams and a crossword puzzle. ⓐⓐⓐ

DISCOVERERS WEB
www.win.tue.nl/cs/fm/engels/discovery

Despite its text-only presentation, this site is a highly useful repository of links to dozens of exploration topics. You'll find connections to such seemingly obscure subjects as Arabian seafarers and their stories, or Polynesian voyaging traditions. The links are so extensive that the webmaster, a Netherlands-based Ph.D. student, gives visitors a What's New page to keep track of the almost daily changes made to the site. ⓐⓐ

The Holocaust

(originally reviewed October 1999)

SIMON WIESENTHAL CENTER
www.wiesenthal.com

Simon Wiesenthal, a 90-year-old Holocaust survivor, helped bring more than 1,100 Nazi war criminals to trial. This center was founded in 1977 in his name as an international organization for Holocaust remembrance. Contact a Holocaust survivor here or take a virtual tour of the renowned Museum of Tolerance. The Multimedia Learning Center features thousands of documents, photos and facts. The Making of a Skinhead offers a fascinating look at groups. ⓐⓐⓐⓐ

A TEACHER'S GUIDE TO THE HOLOCAUST
fcit.coedu.usf.edu/holocaust

A thorough breakdown of the Holocaust is presented in three major categories: Timeline, People and The Arts. Start with the site map for an outline of the 35 topics, which cover everything from the Nazi perpetrators to Jewish resistance to Holocaust museums. Links to photographs and additional information are scattered throughout the sections. The Activities section offers lesson plans for teachers, but the site's content is useful for anyone.

UNITED STATES HOLOCAUST MEMORIAL MUSEUM
www.ushmm.org

This Washington, D.C., memorial to Holocaust victims studies and documents the history of the genocide. Visit the online exhibits, which cover displaced people, pogroms, the voyage of the St. Louis and the Kovno ghetto. Accompanying the text are animations, maps and documents to help educate visitors. Personal stories and photos humanize cold, hard facts, but be prepared for some tragic photos of executed prisoners. The Learning Site in the Education section is an excellent reference for students. Overall, the solid resources and sophisticated design distinguish this site from the rest of the pack.

CYBRARY OF THE HOLOCAUST
www.remember.org

An expansive collection of photos, art, poems and essays, this site seeks to preserve memories and educate newcomers about the Holocaust. Add a memorial to the Holocaust Quilt or check out Search and Unite, an organization that—for a fee—helps locate Holocaust survivors. Moving letters and essays by survivors, liberators and rescuers are in the Witnesses section, where you can also learn about the Holocaust victims who were not Jewish. This site also features a thorough teacher's guide and a section for children of survivors.

THE HISTORY PLACE: HOLOCAUST TIMELINE
www.historyplace.com/worldwar2/holocaust/timeline.html

Using detailed accounts and more than 150 pictures, this site tells the incredible story of the Holocaust month by month, from 1933 to 1961. From Hitler's rise to the war trials that followed his reign of terror, the timeline brims with data on the many significant events during the Nazi regime. This smart site is a solid resource for facts about this historic period.

THE NIZKOR PROJECT
www.nizkor.org

Created in part to monitor and respond to falsehoods and misinformation about the Nazi regime and the Holocaust, the Nizkor Project also serves as a comprehensive guide to Holocaust camps and the Nuremberg trials. The vigilant watchdogs here use reports, documents and essays to respond to challenges by revisionists, a k a "Holocaust-deniers." Other features include transcripts of Adolf Eichmann's trial and Techniques of Holocaust Denial.

Native Americans

(originally reviewed October 1999)

INDIANZ.COM
www.indianz.com

This American Indian e-zine provides regularly updated news reports on various tribes. Other features include Indian U's student resources and The Medicine Wheel, which covers health issues faced by American Indians. Head to The Talking Circle for discussions on contemporary topics such as the proliferation of "a new breed of Indians" in America.

THE NATIVE AMERICAN HISTORY ARCHIVE
www.ilt.columbia.edu/k12/naha

Dissatisfied with the mass of unreliable online information about American Indians, the creators of this outstanding site aspired to "provide a current list of tribal resources of interest to students of Native American History." The archive is broken down into an index of tribes and a list of suggestions for teachers who want to incorporate this site into their curriculum. Visitors should click on The Navigator to browse relevant articles, maps and timelines.

WWW VIRTUAL LIBRARY: AMERICAN INDIANS
www.hanksville.org/NAresources

One of the most well-organized collections of links to American Indian resources on the Web, this fully searchable site was created primarily to provide American Indians with information and resources. Sites that are listed in the Index are prescreened and regularly checked for broken links. Visitors can investigate a plethora of American Indian online resources on history, culture, art, language, education and native nations. ⓐⓐⓐⓐ

NATIVE AMERICAN HERITAGE
www.nativeamericanheritage.com
If you suspect that you may be of American Indian ancestry, this site offers a step-by-step guide to tracing your genealogy. There are video clips of interviews with other American Indians who are researching their heritage, and you can discover how to get your Certificate of Degree of Indian Blood. Learn about essential genealogical resources such as the National Archives, the Bureau of Indian Affairs and the Dawes Rolls. ⓐⓐⓐ

SMITHSONIAN INSTITUTION: NATIONAL MUSEUM OF THE AMERICAN INDIAN
www.si.edu/nmai
Established in 1989 by Congress, the museum was created to showcase and honor the cultural achievements of American Indians. This huge site is quite overwhelming, so start at Conexus to view portions of past and present exhibitions online—click on NMAI Conexus Archive in the lower left corner for past exhibitions. The colorful photographs, slide shows, rich articles and videos draw you in, making you feel as if you were standing right in the museum gallery. ⓐⓐⓐ

THE FIRST AMERICANS
www.germantown.k12.il.us/html/intro.html
Created by a pair of elementary school teachers, this site serves as an excellent introduction for children to American Indian culture and history. Learn about the homes, food and clothing that distinguished the five major cultures—Northwest, California-Intermountain, Southwest, Plains and Woodlands. Kids can find explanations of tribal hunting habits, Indian legends and pictures of just about every aspect of Indian culture, from wigwams to war bonnets. ⓐⓐ

INDIAN RUINS OF THE SOUTHWEST
www.gorp.com/gorp/resource/archaeol/indruin.htm
This catalog offers information about ancient American Indian ruins in Colorado, Utah, Arizona and New Mexico. The listings often offer partial descriptions of the ruins themselves, as well as travel information on visiting them. Almost every single listing—from the Wupatki National Monument to the various Anasazi ruins—features links to additional Web resources. ⓐⓐ

Shipwrecks

(originally reviewed October 1999)

DISCOVERY CHANNEL ONLINE: TITANIC:RAISING A LEGEND
www.discovery.com/area/science/titanic/titanicopener.html
While this exciting site offers a history of the famed ocean liner, its primary focus is on the 1996 raising of the Titanic's hull. There are exclusive photos and video clips of the wreck. Virtual Titanic includes pre-disaster images of the ship that were recreated for a video game. Even if you missed the blockbuster movie, you can still witness the luxuriousness of first-class cabins, the grand staircase and the Turkish bath. ⓐⓐⓐⓐ

NATIONAL GEOGRAPHIC: RETURN TO MIDWAY
www.nationalgeographic.com/features/98/midway
National Geographic has done it again. This time, it offers a fabulous account of explorer Dr. Robert Ballard's quest to find ships lost during the Battle of Midway. Aside from a great layout and superb graphics, the site offers first-hand accounts from Midway survivors. Click on Dive Down to get a fresh perspective on what "deep" really means. Also, check out video clips of underwater footage taken of the USS Yorktown. Its downfall: the Maps link is impossibly slow to load, but it's worth the wait. ⓐⓐⓐⓐ

QUEEN ANNE'S REVENGE?
www.ah.dcr.state.nc.us/qar
This site documents the efforts to determine whether a shipwreck found off the North Carolina coast is the Queen Anne's Revenge, the flagship of the notorious pirate Blackbeard. A link to its education site has plenty of resources for teachers, including lesson plans. This is a

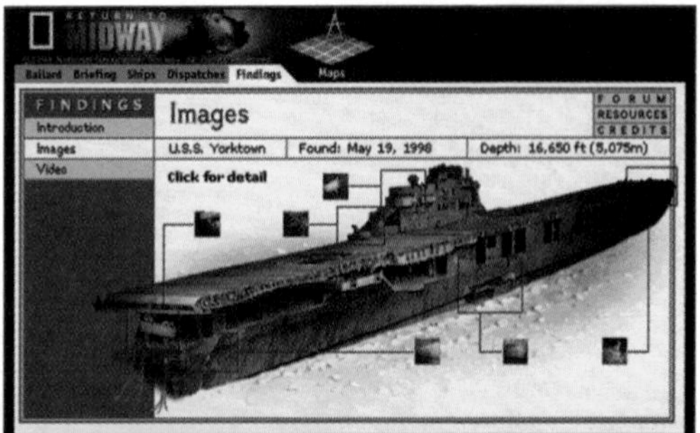

National Geographic dives down deep to get a close-up view of the Battle of Midway casualties.

must-see site for any ship enthusiast. Be sure to check out the Dive Reports, Background Histories and Artifacts & Conservation.

LA SALLE SHIPWRECK PROJECT OF THE TEXAS HISTORICAL COMMISSION
www.thc.state.tx.us/belle
In 1995, researchers found the 300-year-old shipwreck of famed explorer Robert Cavelier, Sieur (Lord) de La Salle. Now ship lovers can get up close to the Belle's chest of historical treasures. The site is low on graphics but straightforward and educational. Browse excavation photographs and read up on ship stuff, such as "French polearms" and "futtocks."

THE MARY ROSE
www.maryrose.org
More than 450 years after King Henry VIII's favorite warship was lost at sea, the Mary Rose can be found online. The University of Portsmouth and the Mary Rose Trust have put together numerous pictures of artifacts raised from the wreckage in 1982, supplementing the visuals with historical tidbits and insights. Find out what life was like for a ship surgeon in Tudor England. Take a virtual tour of the museum, and be sure to check out the 3-D interactive model.

U.S. Presidents

(originally reviewed September 1999)

THE AMERICAN PRESIDENCY
gi.grolier.com/presidents/preshome.html
Based on several encyclopedia for levels ranging from third grade to adult, this site's historical content is thorough and educational. In addition, the site offers links to current campaign sites, sound bites from the late 19th century to present and brief video clips, called Pocket Documentaries. The Flip Cards are like baseball cards for presidents, each with a portrait accompanied by trivia. The site also features complete election results from 1789 to 1996.

AMERICAN PRESIDENTS: LIFE PORTRAITS
www.americanpresidents.org
Created to accompany the "Life Portraits" TV series of 42 presidents, this welcoming C-Span site introduces you to each president with a list of life facts, both personal and political. Additional trivia and personal letters give insights into each president's distinct personality. You can also watch video clips from the series. For those looking to learn beyond the Net, there is basic information about presiden-

Grolier's The American Presidency site includes sound bites and video clips.

tial landmarks. There's also an excellent lesson-plan guide for teachers.

PRESIDENTS OF THE UNITED STATES OF AMERICA
www2.whitehouse.gov/WH/glimpse/presidents/html/presidents.html
What better place to meet the presidents than in their mutual home, the White House? After reading a greeting from President Clinton, you'll find a collection that includes a portrait of each of our 42 presidents accompanied by a biography. Links to each man's inaugural address as well as to biographies of all of the first ladies complete this collection.

TIME AND THE PRESIDENCY
www.pathfinder.com/offers/presidents
If a picture is worth a thousand words, then this virtual photography exhibit of Presidents Roosevelt through Clinton should have something to say to everyone. The extensive photo collection is complemented by selected articles from Time magazine, most of which were written within the past decade. After reading up on the presidents at the other sites, visit here to see these men in action.

THE HALL OF FORGOTTEN PRESIDENTS
www.paulsilhan.com/hallpres.htm
This brief yet worthy site with a sense of humor is devoted to "raising the public's awareness" about Presidents Arthur, Tyler and Polk. Who, you ask? These are some of the men who led our country but don't appear on currency. With quotes from each man's inaugural address, explanations of campaign slogans ("Tippecanoe and Tyler, too!") and short biographies, the fight is on to save these three from obscurity.

TRIVIA ONE
www.synnergy.com/day/prestc.htm
If you're bored by the presidential trivia at the other sites, or if you'd like to test your new presidential knowledge, check out this site's whopping 23 trivia quizzes. They cover the lives of U.S. presidents from birth to death and almost everything in between. Can you name the president who gave the shortest inaugural address? Answer: the father of our country. The site provides a link to the full text of his address, too. ⓐⓐ

Victoriana

(originally reviewed November 1999)

VICTORIANA.COM
www.victoriana.com
Travel back to the 19th century at this quaint site. Shop the Antique Marketplace or visit the Online Bookstore. The Study Center contains articles on Victorian life covering everything from corsets to cotillion favors. Don't miss Behind Closed Doors for articles about Victorian private lives. The articles from vintage issues of Harper's Bazar are a treat, as are the links to museum that celebrate the era. ⓐⓐⓐⓐ

GODEY'S LADY'S BOOK ONLINE
www.history.rochester.edu/godeys
This magazine was the reference for Victorian ladies on the subjects of fashion and homemaking. Topics such as "Dressing Baby 1850s Style" and "Bridal Fashions" are posted here, along with the graphics that originally accompanied them. Poems and stories complete this authentic Victorian experience. Unfortunately, a few sections were not working on our last trip. ⓐⓐⓐ

THE VICTORIAN GATHERING PLACE
www.thevgp.com
Join this society of ladies dedicated to Victoriana or simply enjoy their elegant site. They have posted a collection of Victorian-era recipes, ballroom dancing tips and scans of authentic dance cards—click on the Victorian Gathering Place icon to get to these features. Victorian matchmaking rules—such as redheads should marry brunettes; and thin, cold-blooded types belong with round, warm-hearted people—can be found on the homepage. There is also a set of historic, entertaining trading cards. ⓐⓐⓐ

VICTORIAN STATION
www.victorianstation.com
Enthusiasts will enjoy exploring Traditional Fashions, Architectural Treasures, Distinguished Royalty and Artists & Craftsmen at this site. The photos of Victorian homes are exquisite. And there is a section devoted to that popular symbol of Victorian times—the cameo. Historical information includes quotes from Queen Victoria's journal and a timeline. Modern concerns are also addressed: There are decorating ideas and a virtual mall. Be sure to wear your best hat to the Online Tea Room Message Board. ⓐⓐⓐ

THE VICTORIAN WEB
landow.stg.brown.edu/victorian/victov.html
Victorian history, literature and culture are the focus of academic essays here. Created by a Brown University professor, this extremely detailed site is a great resource. Ballroom etiquette, gender issues, science and technology are also found on this fairly unadorned site. Be sure to check out Charles Darwin's culturally divisive theories of evolution. ⓐⓐⓐ

LIVING VICTORIAN
www.livingvictorian.com/entrance.html
It's easy to add Victorian flair to your life with ideas from this e-zine. Decorating tips, crafts, articles on Victorian objects and customs, and antique jewelry advice are some of the features here. Create a Victorian garden or make Christmas tree ornaments. The archive of past features is very useful. ⓐⓐ

Vietnam War

(originally reviewed September 1999)

THE AMERICAN EXPERIENCE: VIETNAM ONLINE
www.pbs.org/wgbh/pages/amex/vietnam
This Net companion to WGBH Boston's 13-part, award-winning television series is stellar. Matching laser-sharp graphics with adroit, intelligent content, Vietnam Online fills you in on all of the major players and events of the most controversial U.S. war in history. The easy-to-follow timeline escorts you from one end of the saga to the other. Don't miss Reflections On A War—moving essays written by participants and witnesses on both sides of the conflict. ⓐⓐⓐⓐ

THE VIETNAM VETERANS MEMORIAL WALL
www.thewallusa.com
This respectful online version of the Vietnam Veterans Memorial is the next best option for those unable to view the actual monument in Washington. Visitors can find names on the wall using the site's search engine. Today's Casualty Listing pays tribute to those killed on this day in history with a brief account of the soldier's background. Peruse the photo gallery, or request an electronic rubbing—a simulated pencil rubbing—of a veteran's name as it appears on the wall. ⓐⓐⓐⓐ

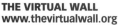

PBS' Vietnam Online's content and graphics are outstanding.

THE VIRTUAL WALL
www.thevirtualwall.org
Authorized by Congress in 1979 to build the memorial, the Vietnam Veteran's Memorial Fund has now brought the wall to the Internet. The virtual wall turns your computer screen into a simulated, black granite panel of the memorial. Click on veterans' names for bios and other information. Visit Reflections to see and hear remembrances left by loved ones. Read about how to request a free pencil rubbing or leave a rose at the wall on Father's Day. ⓐⓐⓐⓐ

HISTORY OF VIETNAM AND THE VIETNAM WAR
www.vwam.com/vets/hisintro.html
With coverage spanning the war's preliminary stages to its still-unfolding aftermath, this comprehensive, history-focused site is informative. Detailed reports on the Tet Offensive, poignant recollections from veterans and in-depth insights on military operations form the site's backbone. Note: Some of the articles and historical reports do not cite source or bibliographic information to support the facts presented. ⓐⓐⓐ

THE VIETNAM WAR INTERNET PROJECT
www.lbjlib.utexas.edu/shwv/vwiphome.html
Like many university-based projects, this site's examination of the causes and consequences of the Vietnam War is refreshingly open-minded. The Vietnam War Internet Project incorporates official documents, oral histories and personal narratives in an attempt to explore as many points of view as possible. The result is a thought-provoking Web site. Be aware that the personal narratives contain some words and images that are not for children. ⓐⓐⓐ

VIETNAM WOMEN VETERANS
www.spencergroup.net/vwv
This site offers a thorough look at the historic and vital role carried out by women during the war. Though their numbers were not large—estimates range from 1,200 to 7,000—their efforts and contributions in Vietnam were nonetheless considerable. Send in photos for the Vietnam Memories page, or use the Sister Search to track down long-lost compatriots. Listings of upcoming conferences and reunions aid those wanting to reconnect with the past and with other vets. ⓐⓐⓐ

VIETNAM VETERANS HOME PAGE
www.vietvet.org
Offering tributes to lost soldiers, information on reunions, and links to veterans associations, support groups and literature, this site is a versatile forum for vets and their loved ones. The VVHP helps people keep in touch with or locate Vietnam veterans. Its lone weakness is an underdeveloped layout. ⓐⓐ

Wild West

(originally reviewed October 1999)

THE AMERICAN WEST
www.americanwest.com
Ghost towns, American westward expansion, saloons, Western art and artifacts, cowgirls and gunslingers are a few of the topics covered here. Upcoming events are posted, including conventions and museum exhibitions. The colorful site also offers access to clip art, images from the National Archives and plenty of links—and that's only the tip of the steer's horn. ⓐⓐⓐⓐ

NEW PERSPECTIVES ON THE WEST
www.pbs.org/weta/thewest
Here is the cybercompanion to the celebrated PBS documentary by Ken Burns and Stephen Ives that aired in 1996. An interactive timeline traces the region's history, and the guide to the eight-part documentary offers photographs, commentary and links to background material. People in the West has biographies of notable

figures and an archive features memoirs, diaries and letters. Before you gallop off into the sunset, try the games and puzzlers. ⓐⓐⓐⓐ

CYBERSOUP'S THE WILD WEST
www.thewildwest.org

Not only does this site have links that cover the gun-slinging outlaws and lawmen of the old West, it has a major section on Native Americans and their culture. Various Native American legends, beliefs, artwork and notable individuals are prominent, with many tribes represented. The Cowboys section has songs, poems, trail recipes, facts of the West and cowgirls, too. Graphics are attractive and load quickly. ⓐⓐⓐ

WOMEN OF THE WEST
www.over-land.com/westpers2.html

This is a comprehensive collection of links about women's lives on the frontier. Every Wild West woman you can think of—including Calamity Jane, Laura Ingalls Wilder and Annie Oakley—is included here, along with some unfamiliar names. The links also cover broader topics, such as Black Women of the West, Cooking Along the Trail and The Lady Outlaw's Hideout. ⓐⓐⓐ

WYATT EARP HISTORICAL HOMEPAGE
www.techline.com/~nicks/earp.htm

Explore all things Earp here. You can find out about movies based on his life or study the gunfight at the OK Corral. The site offers a narrative of the showdown and illustrates it with cool animation. Excellent photos of Earp, his associates, his headstone and gun liven up the history of this famous Westerner. Significant people in his life, such as Doc Holliday and Bat Masterson, are included in Earp Associates. Don't miss the interesting section on bordellos of the 1880s. ⓐⓐⓐ

World War II

(originally reviewed December 1999)

COURT TV ONLINE: A LOOK BACK AT NUREMBERG
www.courttv.com/casefiles/nuremberg

After the end of World War II, the victorious countries indicted two dozen men, holding them accountable for the war in Europe and the deaths of millions of people. This site contains a list of the 21 Nazi defendants, a directory of trial participants, information on the tribunal's history and transcripts. It's a rich, professional site. ⓐⓐⓐⓐ

WWII: THE HOMEFRONT
library.thinkquest.org/15511

Cool graphics and an easy-to-use layout help make this site, designed by students, a great tool for teachers. In the Resources section, visit the Attic Box Lesson, a plan contributed by a grade school teacher, or Simulation, which traces the lives of five families during the 1943-1944 school year. The Museum displays many WWII artifacts. ⓐⓐⓐⓐ

WWII: The Homefront is a valuable teaching resource.

CALVIN COLLEGE: GERMAN PROPAGANDA ARCHIVE
www.calvin.edu/academic/cas/gpa

Calvin College, in Grand Rapids, Mich., has put together a fascinating site offering English translations of German propaganda documents. Among other items, the site has Nazi posters, cartoons, speeches and essays penned by Third Reich leaders such as Joseph Goebbels, Robert Ley and Adolf Hitler. If you choose to visit, be prepared for some disturbing anti-Semitic material. ⓐⓐⓐ

LEST WE FORGET: WWII
webpub.alleg.edu/student/p/paynes/war.html

This site's strength lies in its selection of historical photographs. They are divided by region—European and Pacific—and supported with timelines and essays on a range of topics, from the Nazis' use of technology to Soviet Armor Tactics to FDR's Pearl Harbor speech. Also available are examples of propaganda. Neat feature: recommended links with star ratings. ⓐⓐⓐ

THE RUTGERS ORAL HISTORY ARCHIVES OF WORLD WAR II
history.rutgers.edu/oralhistory/orlhom.htm

The history department at Rutgers University has assembled a collection of fascinating interviews with men and women who lived on the front lines. The focus of this oral history is on former students of Rutgers and New Jersey College for Women, which is now Douglass College. Worth a visit is the interesting description of the project's methodology. There are no fancy graphics at this site, but the interview transcripts are an excellent historical tool. ⓐⓐ

lifestyles

Antiques

(originally reviewed September 1999)

ANTIQUE ALLEY
www.bmark.com/aa

Connections to more than 150 shop catalogs stocked with pages of quaint items will make antiques aficionados recognize Antique Alley as a great find. Shops are listed by business name, city and product description for easy searching. If you can't find it in one of the catalogs, the Shop Guide's database of phone numbers and addresses (street and some Web) for more than 40,000 antiques stores should point you in the right direction. ⓐⓐⓐⓐ

ANTIQUES AND THE ARTS WEEKLY
www.thebee.com/aweb/aa.htm

Those in the know understand why this weekly publication is often referred to as the bible for the antiques industry. Antiques show and auction listings, along with recommendations of top galleries to visit, headline this clever, neatly designed site. The Exchange provides a place where you can ask about the value of those china dishes in grandma's attic. Also presenting reviews of books and an archive of past cover stories, Antiques and The Arts Weekly is a comprehensive guide to the antiquing field not to be missed. ⓐⓐⓐⓐ

ANTIQUE RESOURCES
www.antiqueresources.com

Complete with restoration tips and an events calendar, Antique Resources offers a reservoir of valuable information on the antiques and collectibles industry. A Virtual Mall connects you to hundreds of items for sale, while the Favorite Museums section links you to notable showcase galleries in all 50 states. Be sure to peruse this site's strong assortment of feature articles covering the intricacies of the antiquing world. The site also includes a series of articles on the art and craft of restoration. ⓐⓐⓐ

ANTIQUES BULLETIN ONLINE
www.antiquesbulletin.com

Featuring information on auctions, fairs, dealers and more, this weekly online publication covers the antiquing industry from coast to coast. Buy, sell or just browse—anything is possible for antiques connoisseurs on this comprehensive site. You can search by date for auctions or fairs, so finding a vintage market won't be a problem. Sharp in every aspect, this site also features a bookstore. ⓐⓐⓐ

ANTIQUES ORONOCO
www.antiques-oronoco.com

If you're feeling a little bit unschooled in the business of starting an antiques collection, this site can help. Novice collectors can learn a lot from browsing through this site. Pictures, information and examples of more than 25 styles of vintage collectibles—including glassware, dolls, toys and tools—help qualify Antiques Oronoco as a premier beginner's guide to the world of antiques. ⓐⓐⓐ

TIAS.COM: ANTIQUES AND COLLECTIBLES
www.tias.com

With a stable of 185 antique dealers that offer more than 210,000 vintage items for sale, TIAS (The Internet Antique Shop) is a wonderful resource for antiques collectors. Search here for everything from comic books to scientific instruments. Use the pulldown menu to select from more than 600 categories, or click on Showcase for a quick peek. Collectors can trade information with other enthusiasts on more than 50 Bulletin Board forums or browse the search engine, updated daily. ⓐⓐⓐ

ANTIQUE COLLECTORS' CLUB
www.antiquecc.com

Formed in 1966 partly in response to collectors' demands for information on what to pay for antiques, the Antique Collectors' Club publishes and distributes books for those looking to expand their knowledge of collectibles. Book synopses and order forms for hundreds of titles are available, as are back articles from the ACC-published Antique Collecting magazine. ⓐⓐ

Beauty

(originally reviewed December 1999)

BEAUTYSCENE
www.beautyscene.com

Sure, plenty of sites sell cosmetics, but how many tell you how to apply them or what the look of the moment is? Before you shop from the list of about 2,000 products, try the Product Matcher, read tips and tricks in the Beautyzine or consult the resident experts. The gift center and Beauty Glossary are also handy. Plus, beautyscene offers a 30-day, money-back guarantee and online customer service support. Bonus: Become a member for free and you don't have to pay for shipping. ⓐⓐⓐⓐ

EVE.COM
www.eve.com

Not only does this elegant site offer high-quality cosmetics with a money-back guarantee, it also has tips, Q&A, makeovers and TRY-Athletes—women of various complexions and colorings who try out the latest shades. eve.com also runs a personal consultation service. Register at the site for free, send in a color photo and any "burning beauty questions," and eve will arrange a consultation. Added bonus: If your guy is stealing your moisturizer, direct him to the men's section for shaving and skin-care supplies. ⓐⓐⓐⓐ

ORIGINS
www.origins.com

Soothing the body, mind and senses is the philosophy at Origins. This easy-to-use site is soothing just to look at. You'll find aromatherapy products designed to improve sleep or reduce stress, plus massage tools to aid tense muscles. Of course, you'll find makeup, and skin and hair care concoctions. While you're shopping, don't forget to pick up specialty items from Male Call, For the Home, Baby Care or Pet Care. ⓐⓐⓐⓐ

SEPHORA
www.sephora.com

This French retail chain recently opened its doors in the United States and online. Though its hands-on philosophy is a little difficult to incorporate on the Web, customers can browse by brand—there are more than 100—or product type. Look for upscale and hard-to-find goods here—Lorac, Christian Dior, Philosophy, Tocca and Hard Candy. Sephora offers its own less expensive line, too. Besides makeup, Sephora provides an extensive selection of Fragrances and Well-Being products. ⓐⓐⓐⓐ

AVON
www.avon.com

Although users are given the opportunity to become sales representatives, this Web site may make the Avon lady a thing of the past. Shoppers can buy products online and get beauty tips to find out which makeup shades look best on them from the Virtual Beauty Advisor. Also available, of course, are classic Avon skin-care products, such as Anew and Skin-So-Soft. Be sure to scroll down; there's a lot more material here than it looks. ⓐⓐⓐ

COSMETIC MALL
www.cosmeticmall.com

Just like any traditional mall, Cosmetic Mall has many different shops and boutiques worth exploring. Users can search by brand, such as Burt's Bees, or by category, such as Sun Care. A great feature is Ask the Experts, which allows customers to e-mail questions to the site's resident makeup experts before making a purchase. Also fun is the Custom Color Lipstick service. ⓐⓐⓐ

HARMON DISCOUNT
www.harmondiscount.com

It doesn't have much in the way of whistles and bells, but under its gruff facade, this site is loaded with some of the best cosmetics bargains on the Web. Use the pull-down menus to pick a category, say, lipsticks. You will get a list of not one or two but more than 1,000 lipsticks in a variety of brands and colors. If you know what you want, this is a good place to get a bargain on beauty supplies. ⓐⓐ

Breaking Bad Habits

(originally reviewed January 2000)

ENVIRONMENTAL NEWS NETWORK
www.enn.com

If you still don't recycle, or you still tend to toss your leaves in the garbage bin, this site offers you a chance to rise out of the environmental dark. The statistics here on garbage should inspire anyone to become more eco-friendly. And with environmental articles and reports spanning science and technology to business and industry, you'll find plenty of ways to do just that. You can join scheduled chats or visit the bookstore for additional information. ⓐⓐⓐⓐ

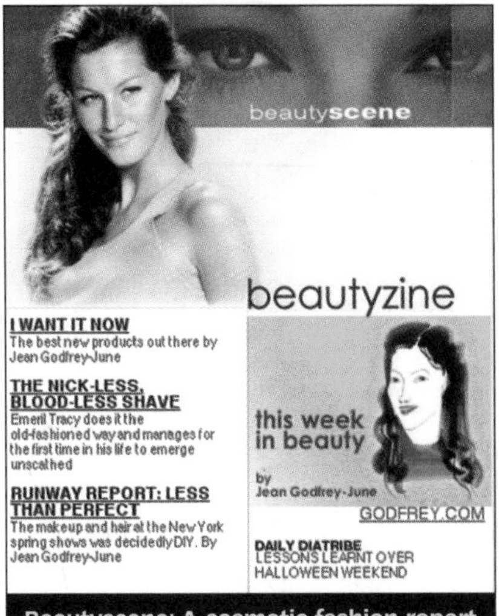

beautyscene
beautyzine
I WANT IT NOW
The best new products out there by Jean Godfrey-June
THE NICK-LESS, BLOOD-LESS SHAVE
Emeril Tracy does it the old-fashioned way and manages for the first time in his life to emerge unscathed
RUNWAY REPORT: LESS THAN PERFECT
The makeup and hair at the New York spring shows was decidedly DIY. By Jean Godfrey-June
this week in beauty
by Jean Godfrey-June
GODFREY.COM
DAILY DIATRIBE
LESSONS LEARNT OVER HALLOWEEN WEEKEND

Beautyscene: A cosmetic fashion report

ALCOHOLICS ANONYMOUS
www.alcoholics-anonymous.org
If you or a loved one wants to stop drinking, this site from the 65-year-old AA organization is a supportive and non-threatening outlet from which to seek help. The site answers common questions and includes contact information and a special section for teens. Take a brief quiz to see if AA is for you. The design here isn't sophisticated, but this is one site where substance definitely matters more than style. ⓐⓐⓐ

DRUG-FREE RESOURCE NET
www.drugfreeamerica.org
This site from the nonprofit Partnership for a Drug-Free America teaches parents how to talk to their kids about drugs and teach them to say "no." There's also advice for what to do if your child is already involved with illegal substances. ⓐⓐⓐ

GAMBLERS ANONYMOUS
www.gamblersanonymous.org
Start off with 20 Questions to find out if you or someone you know has a gambling problem. Then take a look at Q & A to find out what compulsive gambling is and how to stop. This organization offers free help to anyone who asks for it. The 12-step recovery program is outlined, as is contact information for every U.S. state and many foreign countries. ⓐⓐⓐ

GET YOUR ANGRIES OUT
members.aol.com/angriesout
If you're starting to feel like Michael Douglas' character in the movie "Falling Down," it might be time to read the anger management techniques at this site. Free articles, checklists and tip sheets target adults, children, parents, couples, teachers and therapists. Learn how to recognize angry behavior, control your reactions and calmly express your emotions. ⓐⓐⓐ

NATIONAL HIGHWAY TRAFFIC SAFETY ADMINISTRATION
www.nhtsa.dot.gov
NASCAR wannabes and others looking (or needing) to curb their reckless driving can glean information on vehicle and passenger safety here. There are specific tips for elderly, aggressive and new drivers. The reports, handbooks and articles are designed to help people play it safe behind the wheel. Before buying a new car, find out how specific models fared in crash tests. Kids can learn safety, too, from the crash test dummies in the Safety City section. ⓐⓐⓐ

THE ON-LINE BOOKS PAGE
digital.library.upenn.edu/books
With a collection of more than 10,000 free books, this online library offers a worthy alternative for those attempting to break troubling TV habits in 2000. Because of the vast selection, notable titles—including works by Mark Twain and Charles Dickens—are best found by scrolling down through subject or author listings. Beware that copyright regulations limit the number of modern titles that can be posted. Top pick: "The Adventures of Huckleberry Finn," under Banned Books. ⓐⓐⓐ

QUITSMOKINGSUPPORT.COM
www.quitsmokingsupport.com
So you've tried patches, gum, acupuncture, even hypnosis, but you still crave your precious, lethal cigarettes. For anyone who has resolved to quit smoking, the Internet, and in particular, this site, is a good place to start. With inspirational letters, health information, a teen section and, best of all, an ex-smokers list, this site could be the method that finally helps you permanently kick the habit. ⓐⓐⓐ

OVERCOMING PROCRASTINATION: A NEW LOOK
www.rebt.org/essays/procrst1.html
This very thorough site from the Albert Ellis Institute, a nonprofit educational organization, was created to help you stop putting things off. Learn what procrastination is and what causes it, and most important, how you can stop doing it. The site outlines emotional, mental and active steps that are meant to help you change your behavior. If you're a procrastinator, make time for this site; it could be the beginning of a whole new, punctual you. ⓐⓐ

Cigars

(originally reviewed November 1999)

CIGAR AFICIONADO
www.cigaraficionado.com
Most lovers of the leaf credit this magazine with single-handedly sparking the current cigar craze. So it makes sense that the publication's Web site is an online mecca for ... well, cigar aficionados; and deservedly so. All of the elements that make the print magazine a hit are here, including Cigar Ratings, reviews of cigar-friendly restaurants, profiles of cigar-smoking celebrities and a long, affectionate look at The Good Life—art, fashion, gambling, jewelry, music and sports. ⓐⓐⓐⓐ

THE CIGAR-LABEL GAZETTE
www.cigarlabelgazette.com
It's likely you've never thought of cigar labels as works of art. In fact, there has been some

exquisite artwork on cigars and cigar boxes through the years. For proof, check out the colorful images in Themes. Angels, birds, bugs, cowboys, frogs, knights and trains have all adorned cigar labels. If your interest is piqued, read the in-depth articles and find information about meetings and events for label collectors. ⓐⓐⓐ

CIGARNEXUS
www.cigarnexus.com
Executive Editor Steve Saka has put together a comprehensive, well-organized e-zine that should be a regular stop for all cigar smokers. Occupying a prominent spot is the Monthly Officious Taste Test, a blind taste test conducted by readers. Excellent articles offer advice on spotting a fake Cuban, cigar aging and even burning. Plus, there are Surveys & Contests, Celebrity Interviews and an Events Calendar. Don't forget to take a virtual tour of the National Cigar Museum. ⓐⓐⓐ

CIGAR WEEKLY
www.cigarweekly.com
Stay up-to-date with the latest cigar news and information at Cigar Weekly, which bills itself as "The Internet Cigar Magazine." One regular feature is First Look, which contains reviews of new cigars on the market. The site also has details on legislation affecting cigars and smokers, and interviews with movers and shakers in the industry. Other features include a Buyers Guide, a Bookstore, a Forums/Chat area and nicely organized Archives of past columns and articles. ⓐⓐⓐ

INTERNET CIGAR GROUP
www.cigargroup.com
Cigar smokers are people, too, so it's only natural that they have a place online to meet and greet one another. This Web site fulfills that need by offering an extensive array of resources for cigar smokers, including a Chat Room, Message Boards, FAQs and a Cigar Brand Database. The site also addresses health issues by spotlighting medical research papers on cigars and cancer. Be sure to visit the Homemade Humidor Page. ⓐⓐⓐ

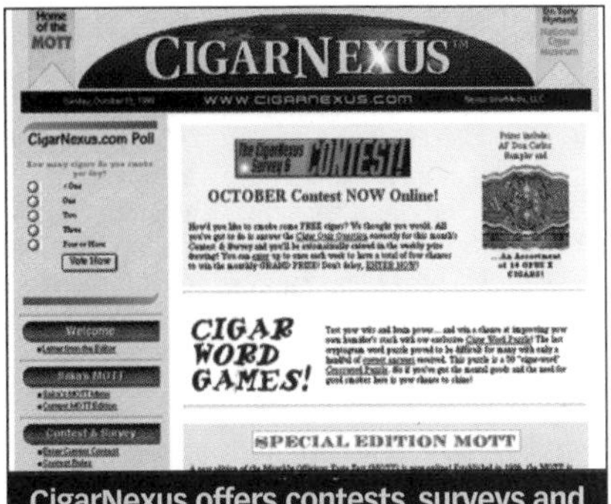

CigarNexus offers contests, surveys and cigar advice at www.cigarnexus.com.

SMOKE MAGAZINE ONLINE
www.smokemag.com
Organized much like its popular print companion, this site posts a variety of cigar-friendly features and columns, with an emphasis on celebrities, reviews and the cigar lifestyle. The Smoke Ticker highlights late-breaking cigar-related news, while the Cigar Review Database makes it easy to find information on hundreds of brands. In addition, you can shop for humidors, accessories and other products in the site's Online Shopping Guide. ⓐⓐⓐ

TOP25CIGAR
www.top25cigar.com
Before you pay a visit to your local tobacconist, pay an online visit to Top25Cigar, where the staff tests and ranks dozens of cigars each month. The blind smoke test results can help you choose wisely when you buy. Other savory features include a Brand of the Month, a Featured Cigar and a form to submit your own rating. ⓐⓐⓐ

Classic Cars

(originally reviewed October 1999)

CLASSICAR.COM
www.classicar.com
Vroom vroom. Self-promoted as the place "where car lovers click," this site features restoration services, chats, articles by classic car owners and a free e-mail newsletter. Find dates and information on classic car events, along with convenient regional listings of clubs and vintage auto museums. This is a wonderful guide to places—both virtual and real—to fulfill anyone's passion for antique vehicles. ⓐⓐⓐⓐ

HENRY FORD MUSEUM & GREENFIELD VILLAGE: ONLINE EXHIBITS
www.hfmgv.org/histories
In the traffic jam of car museum sites, this slick, informative page is a great place to tune up on automotive history. Visit the Showroom to view and read about many of the significant

vehicles of this century. That includes stuff that gear heads wouldn't normally consider, such as marketing and advertising memorabilia. Don't miss the comprehensive history guide on Henry Ford and the Ford Motor Co. In addition, the Pic of the Month archive offers plenty of legroom, with musings on all kinds of Americana. Surf this tiger!

BARX AUTOMOBILE HISTORIES & IMAGES
www.clearlight.com/~brawicz
With images and historical descriptions of classic cars from around the globe, this Canada-based site chooses quality over quantity. Well-stocked for car aficionados seeking an international bent, BaRx offers separate discussion forums about French and Polish autos in addition to the message board for general postings. Boasting strikingly lucid graphics, this site also presents an Image of the Month and carefully selected links to general auto information as well as specific models.

CAR COLLECTOR ONLINE
www.carcollector.com
Since 1967, Car Collector magazine has been serving up collector profiles, restoration tips and car value guides for classic car hobbyists. Enthusiasts know this magazine is one of the oldest and most complete classic auto resources. Its companion Web site covers the needs of everyone from serious collectors to curious newcomers. With comprehensive articles and the latest industry news, this seasoned magazine is a classic in its own right.

1965-1973 CLASSIC MUSTANG PAGE
www.vintage-mustang.com
Dedicated to the American classic of classics, this site comes fully loaded with a discussion forum, photographs and trivia. It arms you with the necessary tools to finish off your classic Ford Mustang restoration and it also offers a state-by-state directory of Mustang clubs. The design could use some polish, though, and several of the sections needed to be updated when we last visited.

Car Collector has restoration tips, news and photographs for enthusiasts.

Coffee

(originally reviewed December 1999)

EPICURE EXCHANGE
www.epicure.com
If your coffee and tea tastes are more exacting than instant Folgers crystals, try out this well-designed site. It's a virtual community for visitors around the world to share their experiences, likes and dislikes of different teas and coffees. Java Journey and Cafe Culture contain feature articles about interesting coffeehouses and the cultures within. There's also a Marketplace and a search function. If you're really into java, keep up with News and Events.

CAFFEINATED MAGAZINE
www.caffmag.com
This site makes one thing clear: Man—and woman—cannot live on gourmet coffee and fancy lattes alone. Yes, beans and brew methods are important, but the culture that surrounds coffee is also significant. Caffeinated Magazine pays special attention to that coffee culture. The combination of an organized layout and savvy writing makes this Web site a fun visit. In Cross-country, read reviews written by perky correspondents of coffee shops, diners, restaurants, hotels and cafes. There are also several witty articles and a list of songs about coffee.

GOCOFFEE.COM
www.gocoffee.com
Whether you are looking for a new coffee variety to jazz up your morning or you just want to sift through the Bargain Bin for cheap beans, this site is a great place to visit. There are short taste summaries for some of the more exotic blends, reviews, and consumer and staff picks. Site visitors can also buy Stone Creek coffee and related java accessories; shipping is free for most purchases. Not ready to commit to a 5-pound bag? Then order some free samples or subscribe to the newsletter.

GREAT COFFEE.COM
www.greatcoffee.com
This is the ultimate online retailer for coffee connoisseurs. What makes it so fun is that

while you shop, you learn about coffee blends grown and roasted around the world. If you have a hard time choosing from the hundreds of varieties, just consult the expert reviews, which rate five characteristics: aroma, acidity, body, flavor and aftertaste. There is also a wide variety of coffee-making equipment available. ⓐⓐⓐ

TOO MUCH COFFEE MAN
www.tmcm.com
It's a bird. It's a plane. No, it's everyone's favorite wired superhero—Too Much Coffee Man! Read the dozens of TMCM comics that are available on the site and appreciate the strip's seething wit. Fans can even buy TMCM merchandise. Go to Bonus Stuff for a multi-media game, a screensaver, cartoons and links. ⓐⓐⓐ

Dining Guides

(originally reviewed January 2000)

LYCOS RESTAURANT ROW
restaurantrow.lycos.com
Restaurant Row, part of Lycos' travel section, is a great resource for trip planning. No matter where you want to dine—down the block or in a city 2,000 miles away—you'll find a listing here. Diners enter a city or ZIP code and then narrow down the search by specifying type of cuisine. For large cities, choose the neighborhood option to search on a smaller scale. The site includes menus, directions, maps, online reservations, photos and reviews for many of the restaurants listed. ⓐⓐⓐⓐ

ZAGAT.COM
www.zagat.com
Zagat Survey guides, and now the Web site, are known throughout the nation for the reliability of their restaurant ratings. Based on the experiences of hundreds of diners, this site is a food lover's paradise. Sign up for a free membership to access the entire site. Select a city, and then view favorites by cuisine, décor, service or cost. After reading a review, visitors can sound off by voting on the restaurant. There are 29 U.S. metropolitan areas on the list, with more slated to be added this year. ⓐⓐⓐⓐ

ACTIVEDINER
www.activediner.com
Looking for the best brew pub in Boston or the best kosher deli in Detroit? ActiveDiner will help you find it. Although the site is a self-described "work in progress," it already offers many options for just about any style of cuisine. Pick a city from the drop-down menu, or use the map to search the United States. To zero in on smaller towns and cities, pick a major city from the menu, and you'll get a list of nearby communities. Reviews are a new feature, and many listings don't yet have them. Visitors are encouraged to add restaurants to the database or submit reviews. ⓐⓐⓐ

CUISINENET
www.cuisinenet.com
CuisineNet is a comprehensive guide to dining out in 16 major U.S. cities. The easy-to-use search engine lists restaurants by name, location, cuisine, price or amenities. The site rates food, service and ambience. CuisineNet also provides average meal prices, public transportation and parking information, and tells you what to wear (click on the restaurant name for these features). The Top Picks section is interesting; the categories include "Under $25," "Beer," and "Dinner and a Movie." Unfortunately, these lists of top food joints are from 1998, so be sure to call before making plans. This is a good resource that beats wading through the Yellow Pages. ⓐⓐⓐ

SAVVY DINER
www.savvydiner.com
Savvy Diner is a selective database for those looking for a fine dining experience in more than 20 major cities in the United States. Each restaurant recommendation includes a picture, which gives visitors a glimpse at the dining atmosphere. Peruse menus (prices included), critics' comments and maps of the restaurants' locations. If a particular restaurant appeals to you, use Savvy Diner's online form to make a reservation. This is a good site for out-of-town diners who don't want to sift through large databases. ⓐⓐⓐ

DINE.COM
www.dine.com
This is a growing guide with a nice design. While the database does a good job of listing nearly every restaurant around the country, the pickings are still a little slim for actual reviews. But Dine.com is set up for growth. Visitors can search every state by city, cuisine and, interestingly, reviewer. Because of the limited number of reviews—especially for eateries in smaller

towns—this is an excellent opportunity for would-be food critics to get in their two cents.

Get Organized

(originally reviewed January 2000)

MAGICALDESK
www.magicaldesk.com
This ingenious site offers a free, personalized "Web-based virtual desktop" that enables busy people to work from practically anywhere and still stay organized. After registering, you can take advantage of e-mail, a Web-based calendar, a personal "to do" list and an address book. The MagicalFiles Document System allows visitors to store, view and share files from any computer, anywhere. It works with Windows, UNIX and Mac platforms. The Macintosh version can be downloaded from www.imagicaldesk.com.

CLICKMARKS.COM
www.clickmarks.com
A popular Web-based bookmarks manager, Clickmarks.com offers users private access to their personal bookmark files from any computer for free. This site makes it possible to feel right at home from any geographical location, any operating system and any browser. There's even a feature that recommends sites that are similar to those you've bookmarked. Skeptical visitors can enjoy a free demo.

DIARYLAND
www.diaryland.com
Start keeping a private journal or one to share with the world. There are more than 40,000 Internet diaries at this easy-to-use and fun-to-browse site. You choose the color scheme for your pages. If you want your thoughts to remain private, assign a password to protect them. Once set up, you can post entries anywhere you have Web access—at home, on the road and even in that quaint cybercafe you find while traveling.

GET ORGANIZED NOW!
www.getorganizednow.com
Specializing in helping people organize their lives, this site might just reform pack rats everywhere. Articles address home, family, office, business and time management issues. Read about "9 Ideas for Organizing Your Child's Room" and "10 Steps to a Happy Clothes Closet." Subscribe to the free e-newsletter to receive dozens of little-known organizational tips. Past newsletters are also available on the site.

ORGANIZING SOLUTIONS
www.wco.com/~dpmiller
If you can't keep up with the trail of toys or can no longer tolerate teetering piles of mail, come here for help. Although company owner Allison Van Norman won't come to your house and organize for you (unless you live in the San Francisco area), her site has a collection of articles and links to get your life in order. Start with questions and answers about organizing in Ask Allison.

WEBCALENDAR
www.mycalendar.net
Don't forget another birthday. This free service provides an address book, "to do" list and calendar to help users keep track of deadlines, appointments, and elusive birthdays and anniversaries. Visitors can also designate co-authors and create shared calendars with friends, colleagues and clubs. Events can be added or updated from anywhere. The best part: Access it from any computer with an Internet connection.

Holiday Recipes

(originally reviewed December 1999)

CHRISTMASRECIPE.COM
www.christmasrecipe.com
It's impossible to turn to this site and not come up with more than enough ideas for a holiday feast. Cooks looking for a specific recipe should go straight to the search engine, but a more leisurely browse through the category listings is more fun—and mouth-watering. Nice extras include Recipe Roulette—click on a wreath and let the site select a recipe for you—a glossary and a selection of holiday beverage recipes. Pumpkin Nog, anyone?

EPICURIOUS FOOD: CHRISTMAS SPECTACULAR
www.epicurious.com/e_eating/e04_xmas98/spectacular.html
It's no surprise that Epicurious' Christmas section is a culinary gold mine. Feast on the recipe sections, including traditional European sweets, detailed menus and hors d'oeuvre ideas. Next, browse through the holiday brews and other liquid concoctions in Wintertime Drinks—eggnog and other favorites have recipes with and with-

out, ahem, cheer. Get solutions to cooking emergencies—such as missing ingredients and curdled cream sauce—in Holiday Kitchen 911. ⓐⓐⓐⓐ

VEGSOURCE: CHRISTMAS RECIPES
www.vegsource.com/christmas.htm
VegSource serves up three full-course vegetarian menus for the holidays, each designed to serve eight people. These menus are amazingly well balanced and will appeal even to the skeptical meat-eater. Sweet potato bread, sage and onion stuffing and Italian chocolate nut cookies are a sampling of the tasty treats here. Pick a menu for either An American Country Christmas, An English Christmas or Christmas Eve in Southern Italy. Better yet, mix and match recipes from all three tempting meals. ⓐⓐⓐ

KWANZAA RECIPES
www.freep.com/fun/food/qkwarec29.htm
Although the design is skimpy, this page from the Detroit Free Press has a handful of Kwanzaa recipes that are sure to put some meat on your bones. Scroll down the page to find recipes for black-eyed pea soup, jalapeño corn muffins, dundu oniyeri (West African fried yams) and cocoa Kwanzaa cake. Also, the page has links to articles about creative Kwanzaa traditions and the holiday's seven principles. ⓐⓐ

freep / fun / food
Catherine Blackwell lights Kwanzaa candles in her Detroit home. The Jollof Rice with Chicken in the foreground is by Phyllis Sancho, back right, a native of Liberia. (Free Press photo by J. Kyle Keener)
A creative Kwanzaa
Metro Detroiters develop their own traditions from the holiday's basic principles

Kwanzaa Recipes cooks up celebration and food ideas.

Party Planning

(originally reviewed December 1999)

EVITE
www.evite.com
This isn't just a Web site, it's a tool to help you plan and organize all kinds of events, from a child's birthday party to a large office bash. Just sign up for the free membership and tell Evite what type of event you want to arrange; it will supply cool ideas to get you going. The site provides features that let you ask your guests questions and tell them what to bring, collect RSVPs, decorate your e-mail invitations and send out digital maps to make sure everyone arrives on time. ⓐⓐⓐⓐ

PARTY 411
www.party411.com
This is party planning with a commercial slant. Dig through plenty of ideas on planning every sort of event, from Sweet 16 parties to roasts and toasts and everything in between. Get smart ideas, a list of the details you need to consider, plus weekly party Tips, Dips and Jokes. Etiquette and themes are all here, as well as professional services for hire, party books, costumes, supplies, invitations and local contacts. ⓐⓐⓐⓐ

THEPLUNGE.COM
www.theplunge.com
Make your events take flight with this indispensable tool that ties all your party details together. Get great party ideas or build a Web site that features event details and RSVP counts. Follow up after the bash with digital pictures. Short on ideas? Don't miss the Random Party Generator. While geared toward weddings, birthdays and other traditional events, thePlunge.com is also a perfect way to arrange an intimate dinner party or celebrate your favorite obscure holiday. ⓐⓐⓐⓐ

PARTYDIRECTORY.COM
www.partydirectory.com
This is a great jumping-off point for planning a party, particularly weddings. The links here provide ideas and suggestions for making every party the best, whether it's a bat mitzvah, a NewYear's fete or a 40th birthday. Of special note are regional directories of local caterers, limousines, photographers and musicians. ⓐⓐⓐ

PARTYMAKERS
www.partymakers.com
Planning a fun kid's birthday party can be a real challenge. Fortunately, this site has more than 50 great ideas for entertaining the little ones. Plan by age from 1 to 13 or theme—dinosaur party, fire engine party or luau, to name a few. There are suggestions for location, favors, decorations, food and dressing up the birthday kid. The martial arts party, for example, suggests dressing the birthday boy or girl in a "Karate Kid" outfit. Hold the party in a martial arts studio or hire an instructor to give a short lesson. Don't forget to cut the cake with a real (or fake) samurai sword. ⓐⓐⓐⓐ

SAVOIR FAIRE
www.savoirfaire.ca
This guide to "entertaining with elegance and

ease" tells you how to throw the perfect cocktail party, brunch, dinner or clambake. It's the online companion to the TV show of the same name airing on cable's HGTV. Click on Recipes & Tips for dozens of theme party ideas, photos and how-tos. From fun invitations (use old 45 records for a '50s party) to creative decorating tips (colorful Mexican blankets make great tablecloths for a Tex-Mex fiesta) the ideas and recipes here will wow your guests and put them in the party mood. ⓐⓐⓐ

EVENT PLANNER
www.event-planner.com
The design is stodgy and visually uninspiring, but there's plenty here for those arranging large-scale affairs. Event Planner offers tools to help you find photographers, caterers, locations and florists, as well as advice on what to look for when hiring professionals. There's also a very active Message Board full of tips and opportunities. ⓐⓐ

Recipes

(originally reviewed October 1999)

ALLRECIPES.COM
www.allrecipes.com
This is several sites in one: The homepage opens to 19 recipe areas, including Chickenrecipe.com, Cookierecipe.com and Thanksgiving recipe.com. The variety is a great service for specialty chefs or new cooks on a quest to learn more. Each subsite has daily recipes and Top 10 lists, plus ethnic and health-conscious options. Preparation, metric conversions and equipment tips ensure the best results for your creations. ⓐⓐⓐⓐ

TOP SECRET RECIPES
www.topsecretrecipes.com/recipes.htm
Cooks with a taste for fast-food specialties and brand-name treats can find recipes on this site to copy those famous foods. Hundreds of restaurant dishes and grocery store items have been painstakingly reproduced in TSR's kitchens since 1996, from a certain burger joint's "special sauce" to a popular chocolate chip cookie. The recipes replicate taste quite well but are not endorsed by the brands they copy, nor do they necessarily contain the exact same ingredients. ⓐⓐⓐⓐ

THE COOK'S THESAURUS
www.switcheroo.com
Have you ever run out of butter or milk in the middle of cooking? You will find the right substitutes here—applesauce, water and sour cream are a few options. No cyberchef should approach the kitchen without this indispensable food thesaurus. Cooks looking to make up for a missing ingredient, translate a recipe to a low-calorie or low-fat alternative or avoid foods due to allergies will relish this collection of sneaky substitutions. ⓐⓐⓐ

FOOD & WINE: THE RECIPE BOX
pathfinder.com/FoodWine/archive.html
Food & Wine's recipe box doesn't have fancy graphics, but its large and sometimes eccentric archive is a real treat. Since these recipes have all been published in F&W magazine, they are tested and staff-approved. Unusual choices such as banana brûleé can be found near standbys such as buffalo chicken wings. You can scan the list of recipes or type in the main ingredient that you want to use. The recipe box also contains an archive of food articles. ⓐⓐⓐ

FOOD NETWORK: RECIPES & MENUS
www.foodtv.com/recipes/re-g1/0,1729,,00.html
This searchable collection of dishes to make at home is positively sizzling. Stuff your face silly with the latest creations from all of the network's popular television programs, including the high-fat fantasies of "Two Fat Ladies," the savory meats of "Hot Off the Grill with Bobby Flay" and the practical and fast meals of "Cooking Monday to Friday." ⓐⓐⓐ

SOAR
soar.berkeley.edu/recipes
The Searchable Online Archive of Recipes isn't pretty, but when it comes to sheer quantity, it's tough to beat. More than 67,000 recipes are waiting for you here. Mercifully, they are searchable by ingredient or preparation method. Or browse various categories of cuisine, ingredients or types of food. If you can't find what you are looking for here, chances are the recipe doesn't exist. ⓐⓐⓐ

TAVOLO: RECIPES
www.tavolo.com/recipes
The cooks at this site—formerly the Digital Chef—know a thing or two about the culinary arts. The site features swift and simple menus for every day of the week, theme recipes by guest chefs and techniques to make meals sing with perfect flavor and harmony. Unlike repository sites with

recipes submitted by anyone, each dish listed has been tested in Tavolo's kitchen. The site also features kitchenware, cookbooks and gifts. ⓐⓐⓐ

Reward Yourself

(originally reviewed January 2000)

CNET GAMECENTER.COM
www.gamecenter.com
CNET's game haven gives you free downloads in every computer format and game genre—space simulations, action, adventure, sports, strategy and war. In addition to the games, you'll also find strategy guides, tips and cheats. Game News and Previews will keep you up-to-date on the industry's newest titles. There's enough here to keep you playing until you've conquered the galaxy of your choice. ⓐⓐⓐⓐ

COOKING LIGHT ONLINE
www.cookinglight.com
Get cozy in the kitchen with friends when you invite them over for a dinner party. Learn tasty tips on how to entice buddies to the stovetop. There are plenty of menu ideas and more than 2,000 recipes searchable by keyword or food category. Healthy Living has tools and articles for doing just that, while Cooking 101 (under Food) teaches you how to rattle those pots and pans. Everyone will be begging for seconds. ⓐⓐⓐⓐ

AMATEUR AROMATHERAPY
dialspace.dial.pipex.com/town/avenue/as07/menu.shtml
Ahhh, what a lovely aroma. If you have no idea how your favorite scent could possibly help you relax, fritter away a little time at this reference library. Whether you've always wondered about patchouli, or you already knew how to bond with bergamot, this site will explain the science of essential oils. But it's not just about olfactorial pleasures; you can also get a recipe for insect repellent. Latin origins, distiller tips, an oils database and a friendly webmaster make this trip to the herbalist an easy one. ⓐⓐⓐ

MYSTERYMOVIES.COM
www.mysterymovies.com
Fans, collectors, movie buffs and amateur detectives will love this digital homage to the Big Screen whodunit. Share your thoughts on the message board or pick your next flick from the Movie Guides that rate and summarize the storylines of dozens of movies. Television and movie news keep diehards in the know. And you can shop for videos on the site. ⓐⓐⓐ

TV ULTRA
www.tvultra.com
Mistress Ultra doesn't think you watch too much television, but she doesn't approve of aimless channel surfing. This site gives a smart review on the best thing to watch on the tube each night. She updates the information every day and provides links to related news coverage, if the show happens to be a documentary. We know you're resolving to read more and watch less television (wink, wink), but TV Ultra's recommendations are solid—no mindless fluff here. ⓐⓐⓐ

Get into the swing of things with the dance steps at www.zazouswing.com.

Swing Dancing

(originally reviewed September 1999)

ANY SWING GOES
www.anyswinggoes.com
Hop onto the swing bandwagon here. With a hip layout and abundant features, this site will have you scoping the latest bands and heading for the dance floor in no time. A history of swing, tips on vintage chic and ideas for adding swing to your wedding are combined with band news, a chat lounge and links to swing MP3s. Haven't had enough yet? Check out the radio show or look up band tour dates. ⓐⓐⓐⓐ

DANCESTORE.COM
www.dancestore.com
Aimed at folks who want to "dance fast and dress cool," Dancestore.com offers a fun selection of swing shoes, clothes and accessories for men and women. Clear photographs of fedoras, twirly skirts and more are supported by detailed descriptions of fabric, care instructions and sizing information. Also available are instructional videos, CDs, books and accessories such as trouser braces and cat's-eye glasses. Shipping is a flat $3 for orders sent by e-mail or fax. ⓐⓐⓐⓐ

ARCHIVES OF EARLY LINDY HOP
www.savoystyle.com

Hop historians can find abundant info and pictures here. Learn about how the Lindy Hop got started during the 1920s Harlem swing scene, or read biographies of swing legends. (For the uninitiated, Lindy Hop is the type of swing recently featured in Gap ads.) The site also features a list of movies that showcase swing dancing, great links to find swing events around the country, plus a gift shop that sells instructional videos. Shipping starts at $4.

NEOSWING
www.neoswing.com

Keep your finger on the pulse of the swing revival at this cool, upbeat site. Learn swing-speak so you can chat with cool cats or follow links to articles on swing from the Village Voice, CNN and other media sources. Read up on the latest swing news, or tap your toes to sound clips and videos from top swing bands. The Forum provides a place to discuss zoot suits and swing etiquette.

TOTAL SWING ONLINE
www.totalswing.com

You have to dig—that is, dig through—this site, where swingers and Lindy Hoppers will find history, news and band information. Click on What's New for local and international swing-related updates. The site also boasts briefs on dozens of bands. If you're in one of the states the site covers, look for listings of studios, events and workshops near you.

ZAZOU SWING
www.zazouswing.com

If you're on the nut, get your mutts on your ankles and start chinning—we're talking swing dancing, of course. The best part of this young, Baltimore-based site is the interactive Charleston lesson (requires free Flash plug-in). It's perfect for the beginner begging to find the hep groove. You'll also learn about vintage fashion and the history of this culture. Plus, you can get CD picks from those who can swing it, baby. The events listed are mid-Atlantic based, but the organizers welcome cats from afar.

Virtual Communities

(originally reviewed December 1999)

CNN INTERACTIVE COMMUNITY INDEX
community.cnn.com

Message boards are essential to a virtual community, and CNN has compiled an impressive list of them. The topics range from Nature to Entertainment, and the traffic is heavy; some categories have thousands of messages. The site builds traffic by posting engaging questions under each topic, such as "How can we truly recognize child abuse?" Since the site is from CNN, it's integrated with a video archive and news analysis.

ECIRCLES
www.ecircles.com

Those who need a better way to coordinate the annual family potluck dinner or ski trip should give this site a try. It allows users to create circles of people who share access to spaces designated just for their group, be it a family, sports team, club or high school reunion group. Groups can share photos, chat, post messages and schedule events on the group calendar—for free. Some of the audio functions require microphone and speakers.

SUPERGROUPS.COM
www.supergroups.com

Whether you're in a fraternity, on a softball league or a member of a large family, SuperGroups.com's communities—SuperFriends, SuperFamily and SuperFamilia—can help you keep in touch. Build your own free collective Web site, shop together, send messages, swap recipes and post pictures. Neat features such as community address books, SuperFridge (a clever take on the original family message board) and wish lists make this site highly useful and fun.

Create an online photo album for your far-away relatives at MyFamily.com.

MYFAMILY.COM
www.myfamily.com

In today's high-tech world, it isn't unusual for a

family to be spread across a few time zones. This easy-to-use and nicely designed site allows families to build their own free Web sites, share private chat rooms and exchange news, recipes, photos and letters. The address books and calendars will help coordinate birthdays, reunions and special events. There's even a place to upload and share your family tree. ⓐⓐⓐ

FRIENDFACTORY
www.friendfactory.com
At this British site, you can meet new folks in the main chat room (The Kitchen) "for a bit of gossip and some friendly banter." Or go to one of the specialty chat rooms, such as Money & Business, Girl Talk or Travel. For more private chats and group communication, users can create free Web sites, host discussions and send instant messages. Note: To use this site, you must download free software that is for Windows users only. ⓐⓐ

WILDABOUT.COM
www.wildabout.com
This virtual community site has the standard offerings—free e-mail, bulletin boards, news, calendars and private chat rooms for groups. The simple design makes it good for people who want a straightforward tool to communicate with friends and other groups. Teachers will want to check out the section on lesson plans. ⓐⓐ

Volunteerism

(originally reviewed January 2000)

HABITAT FOR HUMANITY INTERNATIONAL
www.habitat.org
The mission of this longstanding charitable organization is to provide affordable housing for everyone. Volunteers build houses, provide administrative support, plan projects and raise funds. Getting involved is easy: Use the Affiliate Search Engine to locate a U.S. or international chapter, and then link to its Web page. (Note: some chapters do not have Web sites; phone numbers are provided instead.) The organization also offers college and youth programs. ⓐⓐⓐⓐ

CORPORATION FOR NATIONAL SERVICE
www.cns.gov
Programs operated by this government organization tackle a variety of projects, from tutoring to foster grandparenting to disaster relief. Americorps, for people aged 18-24, provides education grants to volunteers. Senior Corps offers part-time opportunity for adults 60 and older. Learn and Serve involves kids in educational volunteer work. Applications for Americorps and contact information for the other programs are provided. ⓐⓐⓐ

VOLUNTEERMATCH
www.volunteermatch.org
Once you've decided you're ready to donate time and energy, visit this site to quickly locate volunteering opportunities in your community. Enter your ZIP code to get a list of options; each listing presents the name of the nonprofit organization, the type of assistance needed (for example, office support, Web site designer, preschool assistant) and when your services are needed. You can also search according to your interests. ⓐⓐⓐ

VOLUNTEERS OF AMERICA
www.voa.org
If you're asking, "What can I do?" Volunteers of America has some great suggestions: Drive someone to the doctor, shop for groceries, be a mentor, tutor a student. Click on Contact Us in Your Community to find the VOA affiliate nearest you. A list of Service Areas describes the organization's efforts to assist youth, families, the elderly, the incarcerated and the homeless. ⓐⓐ

Webcams

(originally reviewed October 1999)

AROUND THE WORLD IN 80 CLICKS
www.steveweb.com/80clicks
Taking as its premise a famous wager made by Phileas Fogg, the protagonist of the classic

Tune in to live views of Scotland's Loch Ness at WebcamSearch.com.

Jules Verne novel "Around the World in 80 Days," this site takes visitors through 80 Webcam views from around the world. The enthusiasm for this site is evident from the comments in the Traveler's Lounge, a respite for the weary surfer who makes it through all 80 cities. A few of the links are broken, but the wide selection of Webcams helps the site live up to its ambitious name. ⓐⓐⓐⓐ

THE ULTIMATE CAMERA PAGE
www.szym.com/cameras

This is one of the best collections of Webcam links, offering coverage of strange things from Australia to Slovakia (there are 168 cams to be exact). Because all the Webcam images from each category are crammed onto one long page, some of them are painfully slow to load. Watch a radio broadcast from San Francisco State University, check out the Chicago skyline or gaze down on a busy London street. ⓐⓐⓐⓐ

WEBCAMSEARCH.COM
www.webcamsearch.com

Search this gigantic, well-organized database of more than 11,000 Webcams by keyword, or browse the directory, which includes Pet Cams, Streaming Media and Astronomy Cams. Try to catch a glimpse of the Loch Ness Monster with the Loch Ness Live Webcam, or check out views of your favorite city. For a chuckle, Webcam Parodies offers the Peeling Paint Cam and the Duct Tape Cam, among other exciting scenes. Overall, this is a solid place to start making a list of your favorite Webcams. ⓐⓐⓐⓐ

CAMERAS FROM AROUND THE WORLD
members.theglobe.com/cameras

One of the nicest features of this Webcam collection is its clickable map of the world. The continents are peppered with red dots that represent individual Webcams, so you can choose your location. Gaze at the icy pinnacle of Mount Everest in Nepal or hop on over to the sun-drenched coast of Brazil. If you're unsure which part of the world is sleeping, there's a link that will show you satellite imagery of it. ⓐⓐⓐ

SURFLINE.COM
www.surfline.com/videocam.html

Web surfers, board surfers and surf watchers will all get a kick out of this collection. Enjoy Webcam views of famous surf sites around the world—from the pipeline in Hawaii to five major spots on the coast of Australia. Most of the images come with regularly updated surf reports detailing weather, tide information and comments. Site advisory: A few of the cams are actually links to other sites. ⓐⓐⓐ

TOMMY'S LIST OF LIVE CAM WORLDWIDE
chili.rt66.com/ozone/cam.htm

Though visitors have to wade through some clutter on this terrific site, Tommy's offers short descriptions of Webcams and links to interesting scenes. Check out the Mold Cam II, a live cam of "assorted molding leftovers from the fridge," or Panda Cam, a live image from the San Diego Zoo. Visitors should also take a peek at Sweden's notorious Fridge Cam, activated when a member of a particular Swedish family opens the refrigerator door. ⓐⓐⓐ

LEONARD'S "CAM WORLD"
www.leonardsworlds.com/camera.html

If you can be patient enough to wade through all the advertising, this selection of more than 3,000 Webcams from around the world is truly an awesome achievement. Click on Cam Hot Sites to see what Leonard's choices are for the top 1 percent of all Webcams listed on his site, and be sure to visit World Satellite Views for real-time satellite images of Earth. Be sure to visit Animal Cams. ⓐⓐ

Wine

(originally reviewed November 1999)

WINE.COM
www.wine.com

The merger of the sublime Virtual Vineyards and Wine.com produced this venture—a stellar virtual cellar. Come ready to buy; this is a top-notch retail site. Wines are divided into styles for easy browsing, and descriptions include a tasting chart, which ranks seven taste factors, such as sweetness and acidity. Don't miss Peter's Pick and Bang for the Buck. Note: Shipping laws vary by state, so select a destination before you start shopping—Wine.com will tell you whether it can ship to you. ⓐⓐⓐⓐ

WINE SPECTATOR
www.winespectator.com

If it's about wine, it's probably on this thorough and informative site. Wine Spectator treats visitors to a full glass—daily wine news, pithy feature stories, thousands of staff reviews and food and wine matching tips. Among all of the options, read the small selection of e-postcards from traveling wine writers. They write in from places such as New Zealand, New York's Finger Lakes region and Israel.

HOMEARTS FOOD: WINE NAVIGATOR
food.homearts.com/food/drinks/winen/00wnav17.htm

This handy site will help you pair wine and food, and select wines by style or price—a perfect quick reference before heading to the liquor store. Just click on the food, wine type, region or price—Wine Navigator does the rest. The site also offers a detailed glossary of terms, storage tips and a Wine of the Week.

INTO WINE
www.intowine.com

This attractive site is a concise primer on storing and enjoying wine. It contains two unusual sections: Wine and the Bible, an exploration of wine references in the holy book, and Post-A-Toast, where readers can browse famous remarks or add their own. The wine-making section seemed a bit underdeveloped on our last visit, but this site is still a good place for new wine drinkers to get their bearings.

WINEBUSINESS.COM
www.winebusiness.com

Aimed at professional wine buyers and others connected to the industry, Winebusiness.com may not be as appealing for consumers as the other sites reviewed here. But for professionals and serious collectors, Smart Wine is essential. Articles and news from Wine Business Monthly and WineBiz.com are available in full, covering marketing and supply issues, as well as retail and weather-related problems.

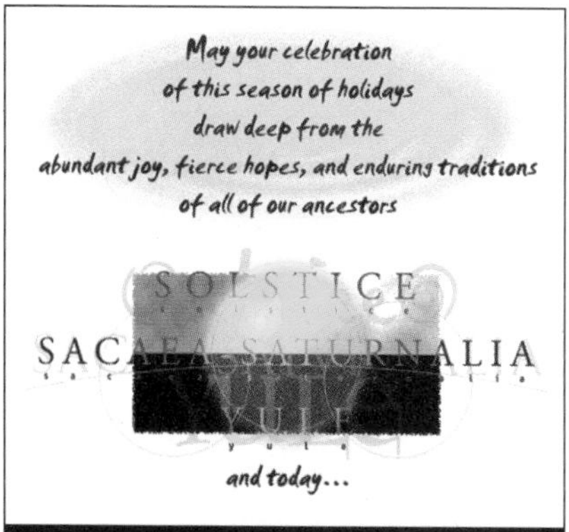
May your celebration of this season of holidays draw deep from the abundant joy, fierce hopes, and enduring traditions of all of our ancestors
SOLSTICE
YULE
and today...

Learn about winter solstice traditions from www.candlegrove.com.

Winter Solstice

(originally reviewed December 1999)

SOLSTICE
www.candlegrove.com

Mixing the practical, historical and mystical, this site is a thoughtful overview of the solstice. Commentary includes explanations of the shortest day of the year, and goes on to make note of Roman festivals, cultural traditions, Celtic celebrations and mistletoe—there's even a recipe for Twelfth Day Cake. Modern-day revelers should visit the And Today ... section for celebration ideas for the solstice and the holidays.

AN OLD-FASHIONED SOLSTICE
www.geocities.com/athens/delphi/3217/solstice.html

This cheery site examines some of the most prevalent wintertime traditions. Read through a brief history of the solstice as a pagan celebration, then use the menu at the bottom of the page to select specific traditions. Christmas trees, holly, reindeer and wassailing are among the options. And don't forget good old Santa Claus—he's covered fairly well here, from his Nordic mythology roots to alternate incarnations such as Kris Kringle and Saint Nicholas.

WINTER SOLSTICE
www.circlesanctuary.org/pholidays/WinterSolstice.html

This site focuses on the pagan roots of Christmas, with an emphasis on promoting a peaceful planet and showing love to friends and family. An interesting list of the symbolism and use of winter plants such as holly, ivy, mistletoe, oak and evergreen is provided; the ever-present mistletoe represents peace, prosperity and fertility. The section on Celebrating Winter Solstice provides ideas for the holiday, many of which mix well with traditional Christmas activities.

money & business

Business Journals

(originally reviewed October 1999)

BUSINESS 2.0
www.business2.com
Whether it's revealing that the Web's biggest moneymaker is business-to-business sales, sorting out the wireless future or divulging the secrets of an Internet business launch, Business 2.0 knows e-commerce. The site is well-designed and organized. It's a good place to find out exactly how all those e-entrepreneurs are making their millions, and maybe—just maybe—figure out how to make a few million of your own. ⓐⓐⓐⓐ

BUSINESSWEEK ONLINE
www.businessweek.com
One of the country's premier business journals does the Web thing in a major way. Browse business headlines and investor news, and discover the latest technology. Entrepreneurs can spend some quality time in Small Business for news, resources and services. Plus, locate the best business schools, get career advice and read chapters of the latest business books. With all the information to explore, make sure you still find time to work. Some areas are only available to magazine subscribers. ⓐⓐⓐⓐ

THE ECONOMIST
www.economist.com
Although it's based in Great Britain, The Economist takes an international view in its business coverage, which is reflected on its Web site. Click on Current Issue to read business news briefs from Asia, Europe and the Americas, as well as a variety of articles about world affairs. The site also includes a library and an archive. ⓐⓐⓐⓐ

Learn how e-commerce entrepreneurs make their millions at Business 2.0.

THE SMALL BUSINESS JOURNAL
www.tsbj.com
There are hundreds of concerns when you're running a small business—sales, customer service, technology, marketing, strategic planning, management and taxes. It's often tough to stay on top of them all. Come here for help. This site is easy to navigate, with clearly marked sections and discussions that are devoted to specific small-business issues. There are also a bookstore and a software store. Don't forget to sign up for the free e-mail newsletter. ⓐⓐⓐⓐ

Business Law

(originally reviewed November 1999)

IRS: TAX INFORMATION FOR BUSINESS
www.irs.ustreas.gov/prod/bus_info
The Internal Revenue Service's site for businesses is a reliable source of updated information on business tax issues. There is a helpful, printable calendar here that highlights important dates for small businesses and larger corporations, plus tax forms and information publications. The site has a pleasant interface and even offers a section explaining tax regulations in simple English. To keep up with the latest changes, read the IRS bulletins. ⓐⓐⓐⓐ

LAW.COM: BUSINESS
www.law.com/business
This sleek site offers a business-law section with excellent resources. Answers to questions on subjects ranging from bankruptcy law to arbitration and asset protection are available here. News on global business law and cases in progress keep the site timely. The combination of global-business and small-business archives ensures that there is something for everyone. ⓐⓐⓐⓐ

BUSINESS LAW
www.abanet.org/buslaw
The American Bar Association's business-law site features full-text articles from Business Law Today magazine. The site also addresses substantive new developments in business law and reports on important legal changes. For lawyers or others interested in business-law subcommittees of the ABA, there are reports about subcommittee activities. It may not be fancy, but this site has helpful tools and timely information. ⓐⓐⓐ

THE BUSINESS LAW SITE!
members.aol.com/bmethven

Run by a private law firm, this site offers a unique section on legal issues affecting electronic commerce as well as answers to basic questions about business law. The sections here are a combination of articles and links, making it a good starting point for researchers. Download legal checklists and forms, or read various states' regulations or sections of the federal legal code. ⓐⓐⓐ

COURT TV: SMALL BUSINESS LAW CENTER
www.courttv.com/legalhelp/business

As part of its Legal Help site, Court TV has compiled a small but useful page that is specifically targeted at small businesses. Unfortunately, many of the links are out of date, which can make for frustrating navigation. The Forms and Model Documents section is still functional and has good examples of contracts, company policies and forms. The Business Organization and Intellectual Property sections have short articles with helpful primers on business basics such as limited liability, sole proprietorships, copyrights and trademarks. ⓐⓐ

THE 'LECTRIC LAW LIBRARY: BUSINESS LAW
www.lectlaw.com/tbul.html

Without any fancy graphics, this site from the 'Lectric Law Library offers basic business-law information. In addition to technical sections with detailed explanations of legal subtleties, there are sections here in plain English. One offers suggestions on starting a business. Visitors can also learn about stockholders' rights and immigration law as it pertains to employers. Although the site does not aim for one-stop comprehensive coverage of business law, it does offer a helpful introduction to a complex subject. ⓐⓐ

Business to Business

(originally reviewed November 1999)

BIZBUYER.COM
www.bizbuyer.com

This vast, easy-to-use business-to-business marketplace connects thousands of buyers and sellers. Buyers go online, request price quotes anonymously and then select the best deal. Categories include computers, office equipment and financial, personnel, legal, telecommunication, print and marketing services. Buyers can request quotes for free, but sellers pay a fee to submit price quotes. The fee varies by category. ⓐⓐⓐⓐ

IBM
www.ibm.com

Hardware giant IBM isn't just for big business; it's now focusing more attention on products and services for small businesses. Besides shopping online for IBM products, users can get business advice in the Ask The Experts section and find information about setting up a virtual storefront, networking computers or developing fully integrated business communications systems. Small-business owners will also find a catalog tailored to their needs, a service center under Solutions and a small-business club, which offers free e-mail and a range of discounts for a fee. ⓐⓐⓐⓐ

IPRINT.COM
www.iprint.com

Create your own custom-printed products here, from business cards to rubber stamps to mouse pads. This self-serve, fully automated, virtual print shop connects your business printing needs with commercial printers at discount prices. Creating your product is simple: Select an item and layout, then add text, your own graphics or stock images, and color. When you're done, just indicate how many items you'd like to order, and check out. An easy-to-follow price list tells you exactly how much you will pay. The orders are placed via a secure server. Since iPrint saves your designs, reordering is a cinch. ⓐⓐⓐⓐ

OPENAIR.COM
www.openair.com

Professionals who wish to cut down on administrative tasks may wish to drop in here. OpenAir.com, formerly TimeBills, is geared to the small-business owner. It uses a Web-based system to track time and expenses, generate reports and invoices, or manage accounts receivable. The site protects against data loss by storing clients' data on its server. Click on Demo for an overview of the system and take a test drive. ⓐⓐⓐⓐ

RFPMARKET.COM
www.rfpmarket.com

RFP stands for request for proposals, and at this easy-to-use site, that's exactly what you do. Choose the products or services your business needs: professional services, construction, computers or finance, among others. Then pick one of the many subcategories and fill out a form that explains exactly what you need—your RFP. The site sends your RFP to vendors and voila!—vendors' proposals are sent to you. Pick the one you want to hire. This service is free to both vendors and buyers.

SAMEDAY.COM
www.sameday.com
Founded to "master e-commerce distribution," this newcomer to the shipping world is dedicated to helping online retailers get products into the hands of customers, fast. The site recently opened an online store that delivers the same day that an order is placed. It's only available in the Los Angeles area now, with plans to expand to other metropolitan areas including San Francisco, New York City, Chicago, Atlanta, Washington, D.C., Dallas and Seattle.

Charities

(originally reviewed December 1999)

THE BETTER BUSINESS BUREAU: PHILANTHROPIC ADVISORY SERVICE REPORTS
www.bbb.org/reports/charity.html
The Better Business Bureau rates charities based on their histories, current programs, governing bodies, fundraising practices, tax-exempt status, finances and compliance with the bureau's 23 voluntary standards for charitable solicitations. Useful, thorough reports are included for the organizations about which the bureau receives the most inquiries (not complaints). They include such high-profile groups as the American Diabetes Association, the Humane Society and Planned Parenthood.

INTERACTION
www.interaction.org
This is an up-to-the-minute resource for coordinating humanitarian aid to areas in the midst of natural and military calamities, such as earthquakes in Turkey and violence in East Timor. This coalition of more than 150 U.S.-based relief, development and refugee assistance agencies subscribes to a set of agreed-upon standards to ensure the accountability to donors, professional competence and quality of service. Read through current reports of what these agencies are doing to help victims, and find out what you can do to help.

NATIONAL CHARITIES INFORMATION BUREAU
www.give.org
The NCIB's mission is to promote "informed giving." It investigates charities' responsibilities, use of funds, annual reporting, budgeting and general accountability. To see a report on your favorite charity, check the Quick Reference Guide; codes classify all charities on the list indicating whether they meet NCIB standards. Detailed reports can be ordered for $9.95 each. Visitors can also order a Free Wise Giving Guide, read the Charity Report of the Week and take in a few Tips for Givers.

GREATERGOOD.COM
www.greatergood.com
This shopping village partners with several major retailers, including jcrew.com, OfficeMax, JCPenney and Amazon.com, to send between 5 percent and 15 percent of online purchases from the retailers to charitable organizations. Shopping is simple: Select a charity from the homepage and link to your shopping site of choice. Charities on the site's list include Special Olympics, Rails-to-Trails Conservancy, World Wildlife Fund and March of Dimes. Shoppers may also designate a charity that isn't on the list, as long as it's an IRS-registered 501(c)(3) charitable organization.

HELPING.ORG
www.helping.org
This philanthropic Web portal sponsored by America Online's AOL Foundation matches donors and volunteers with nonprofit groups. Potential donors can create personal "giving profiles" by identifying what's important to them, then search the GuideStar database of nonprofit groups for a suitable match by charity type, location or size. GuideStar reports on but does not evaluate charities.

PHILANTHROPYSEARCH
www.philanthropysearch.com
This is essentially a giant search engine of philanthropic organizations. Speed Search Find a Charity offers a quick way to find a group by category, such as Environment, Art and Culture, or Social Services. Click on

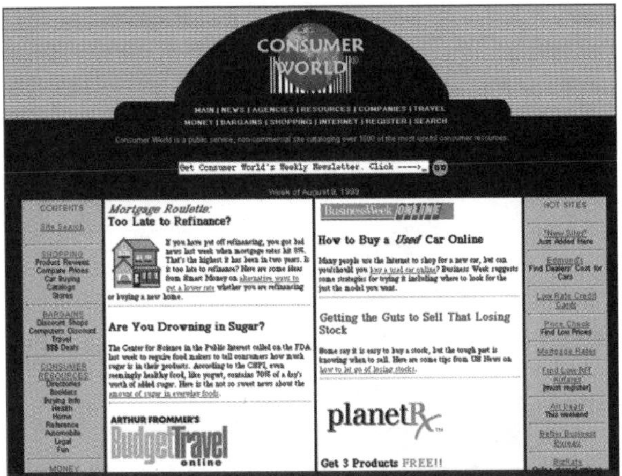

Consumer World has countless consumer-site links.

Charitable Giving under Speed Search Categories for guides and tax information. Before donating, check out individual charities through the links in this section. ⓐⓐⓐ

WEBCHARITY
www.webcharity.com
This site stages online auctions for charitable groups and runs a virtual thrift shop with left-over odds and ends. Individuals and groups donate items by filling out online forms, stating to which charity they'd like the proceeds to go. WebCharity collects from the buyers, adding a 10 percent premium to cover its operating expenses, and the sellers are responsible for shipping costs, if required. Auction items change constantly, but may include everything from Beanie Babies to butter dishes or a week's vacation at a Jamaican resort. ⓐⓐⓐ

Consumer Affairs

(originally reviewed September 1999)

THE NATIONAL CONSUMERS LEAGUE
www.natlconsumersleague.org
The NCL has been looking out for consumers since 1899. The organization's site contains pages devoted to child labor abuses, health care practices and telemarketing scams, among other things. Visit the National Fraud Information Center to learn about the Alliance Against Fraud in Telemarketing and get help staying a step ahead of scammers. The Elder Fraud Project offers good cautionary tips for seniors. And the Internet Fraud Watch provides solid advice on how to avoid being cheated online. Anyone who suspects a scam can file a report online or call the NFIC's toll-free hotline. ⓐⓐⓐⓐ

BETTER BUSINESS BUREAU
www.bbb.org
The standard recourse for Americans dissatisfied with a merchant, the Council of Better Business Bureaus has been online since 1995, helping to disseminate information on everything from saving money on auto insurance to the ins and outs of consumer credit. Check the business report database for complaints before you do business. Or, if you've been burned, the online complaint form makes it easy to report a problem about a business. ⓐⓐⓐ

BIZRATE.COM
www.bizrate.com
Leery of shopping online and want to find out with whom you're dealing before you hand over your credit card number? BizRate.com rates online merchants based on point-of-purchase evaluations from real customers. Report cards provide grades and other useful information, including customer service numbers and return policies. On the flip side, the company sells its market research information to vendors. ⓐⓐⓐ

THE CONSUMER LAW PAGE
www.consumerlawpage.com
Published by a law firm in San Jose, Calif., this site serves to promote the firm's practice, but it also provides valuable public service information on consumer issues such as dealing with defective products. There are insightful articles on various legal topics, free brochures on subjects as diverse as funerals and timeshares, and links to myriad online resources relating to consumer law. ⓐⓐⓐ

CONSUMER REPORTS ONLINE
www.consumerreports.org
Although you must subscribe to this site for total access, the online version of the ever-popular Consumer Reports magazine nevertheless offers a fair number of sample articles upfront. Fresh, insightful pieces on topics such as negotiating a car deal and shopping online intelligently may entice you to subscribe after all. If you're already getting the print magazine, you'll get a discount on this online version. ⓐⓐⓐ

FEDERAL CONSUMER INFORMATION CENTER
www.pueblo.gsa.gov
Pueblo, Colo., is home to a huge government printing press that is a self-proclaimed "one-stop shopping center" for consumer publications. Visit the Federal Consumer Information Center to view comprehensive materials on subjects as varied as air bags, safe seafood and national parks. Materials can also be ordered by mail at nominal charges. ⓐⓐⓐ

NOLO.COM LEGAL ENCYCLOPEDIA: CONSUMER
www.nolo.com/encyclopedia/ctim_ency.html
The good people at Nolo Press sell books that teach us normal folk—that is, nonlawyers—about the law: how it works, how it doesn't and what you can do if you find yourself in a jam. The site offers a good deal of solid, free consumer-oriented information. Check here for primers on everything from warranty rights to insurance issues. There is even an article on what to do "when [your] dog is a lemon." ⓐⓐⓐ

CONSUMER WORLD
www.consumerworld.org
This site is like a big warehouse full of stuff, most of which is in the form of links to consumer-related sites of every stripe. As with many such monster link lists, there is almost too much information here to understand. ⓐⓐ

INTERNET SCAMBUSTERS
www.scambusters.com
Whether you're frustrated by spamming (junk e-mails), slamming (phone companies surreptitiously switching your service) or cramming (extra hidden charges on bills), this site endeavors to help. The information is helpful and updated monthly. Learn about virus scares, the notorious "Nigerian fee scheme" and Furby scams. Sign up for free e-mail updates and keep on top of the latest hoaxes. ⓐⓐ

PUBLIC CITIZEN
www.citizen.org
Public Citizen has been a watchdog over complacent industries and powerful special-interest groups since Ralph Nader founded it in 1971. For consumer advocates and others who want to follow or take part in the organization's various campaigns, this is the online place to be. You can use the handy search engine to find information on everything from auto safety to prescription drugs. ⓐⓐ

(originally reviewed January 2000)

EPINIONS.COM
www.epinions.com
This site makes it easy to find insightful comments on a wide range of topics, including cars, electronics, shipping services and children's toys. The setup here is interesting: Epinions is made up of unedited reviews submitted by consumers who are paid a small amount of money based on the number of people who read their reviews. Membership isn't required to read reviews, but free registration is necessary to submit evaluations. Consumers can even create a Web of Trust composed of reviewers whose opinions they most value. ⓐⓐⓐⓐ

GOMEZ.COM
www.gomez.com
You'll find a wealth of helpful comparative information about e-commerce sites here. Charts full of detailed ratings help to sort out which sites offer the best value and service for products that range from books to airline tickets. Each evaluation highlights the pros and cons and shows how the site scored in several categories, such as ease of use and online resources. A nifty Compare option gives visitors a side-by-side comparison of two selected sites. ⓐⓐⓐⓐ

CONSUMERS DIGEST ONLINE
www.consumersdigest.com
The online arm of this well-known consumer magazine offers facts and figures about household goods, cars, sporting goods, fitness products and home electronics. A unique feature here is the Issues & Investigations section on government and consumer topics. Among the topics are air travel safety, funeral fraud, charities and Social Security reform. Helpful links to government and consumer association sites are another valuable feature. ⓐⓐⓐ

FEDERAL TRADE COMMISSION: CONSUMER PROTECTION
www.ftc.gov/ftc/consumer.htm
If you're hoping to become a smarter, safer consumer, this site from the Federal Trade Commission offers sensible tips on everything from buying exercise equipment to saving money on a car lease. Individual products and retailers are not reviewed here; the sensible tips cover general product and service categories, instead. ⓐⓐⓐ

FEEDBACK DIRECT
www.feedbackdirect.com
Feedback Direct's mission is to help consumers gripe productively. It's a relative newcomer that offers a business directory of customer service information and articles on consumer issues such as telemarketing and warranties. The Orange Pages help consumers compose and send letters to companies, and track responses to their queries.

Entrepreneurs

(originally reviewed November 1999)

BUSINESSWEEK ONLINE: SMALL BUSINESS
www.businessweek.com/smallbiz/index.html
BusinessWeek has assembled an easy-to-use online resource for entrepreneurs. First orient yourself with the Site Guide. Find articles on what makes a small business work, including information on employee benefits, setting salaries and how to qualify for cheap SBA loans. Download free worksheets, checklists, spreadsheets and forms. Click on Smart Answers for expert advice or visit Entrepreneur Diaries for inspiring success stories.

ENTREPRENEUR.COM
www.entrepreneur.com
If you're seeking business opportunities, visit this well-presented, content-rich site. In addition to articles and great links, you'll find a discussion forum, a useful Small Business Tools section and a section on building Web sites. The most interesting feature: The Homebased Business Opportunity 400 in HomeOfficeMag.com. It offers more than 400 ideas for starting a home-based business.

ENTREWORLD.ORG
www.entreworld.org
Founded by the Kauffman Center, long renowned for its philanthropic efforts, EntreWorld filters through the Internet's sprawling entrepreneurial information. It streamlines the best of it into this highly useful site. Organized into four main departments—Starting Your Business, Growing Your Business and Supporting Entrepreneurship—this time-saving site is also equipped with a bookstore, a glossary of business terms and a calendar of related events.

ENTREPRENEURIAL EDGE
edge.lowe.org
A remnant of the former Edge entrepreneurial magazine, this site is ideal for business owners who are seeking to join a dynamic online community. First-time users can start with the Quick Search function to scan topics that range from finance to technology. Resources include newsletters, recommended books and forums where you can interact with other entrepreneurs. Top feature: Best Business Links, articulate reviews of 400 sites to supplement research on starting a business.

STARTUPUNIVERSITY.COM
www.startupuniversity.com
Formerly iEmploy, StartUpUniversity.com now hosts online seminars for entrepreneurs. The site was still under construction at press time, but the Resources section was in full swing. There you'll find a clearinghouse of links, daily news, an archive and a bookstore. If you're after venture capital, check out the Directory section for a list of VC firms. It's a simple but handy site.

THE YOUNG ENTREPRENEURS NETWORK
www.youngandsuccessful.com
Full access to this site requires free membership, but the bevy of useful and supportive services make registration worthwhile. The site is geared toward young professionals with their own businesses. Membership includes a listing in the directory, access to discounts and a quarterly online newsletter. Well-designed and neatly organized, it's an ideal meeting place for creative young minds.

Tap into the knowledge base of fellow entrepreneurs at Entrepreneurial Edge.

Financial Calculators

(originally reviewed October 1999)

ALLSTATE: CALCULATORS AND TOOLS
www.allstate.com/tools
They say you're in good hands with Allstate, and that's the truth at this user-friendly site. The calculators are divided into three sections: auto, home, and life and estate planning. But these tools calculate much more than just monthly payments. Find out what it takes to save for a home, or whether you should buy or lease a car, for example. Each calculation comes with helpful graphs and explanations. You can also download Allstate's free family information management software to track family finances, although it's not available for Macs. ⓐⓐⓐⓐ

BANKRATE.COM: CALCULATORS
www.bankrate.com/brm/pop_calc.asp
This site offers a wide range of excellent features. Determine how much you'll be able to save for retirement, how much you can afford or what it would cost to relocate. You can also calculate which credit card offer gives you the best deal—just be sure to avoid the online ads urging you to apply for a new card as you're calculating your way out of debt. You'll also find current loan rates and how-to information in the navigation bar. ⓐⓐⓐⓐ

BLOOMBERG.COM: TOOLS
www.bloomberg.com/pfc/tools99.html
This well-known financial news service puts its expertise to good use on its Web site. The Tools section has calculators for determining mortgage payments, saving for college and figuring out the value of your 401(k). There's also a helpful glossary of financial terms. While you're at it, use the site's links to keep tabs on the stock market and current interest rates. ⓐⓐⓐ

DINKYTOWN.NET: JAVA FINANCIAL CALCULATORS
www.dinkytown.net
Despite the name, there's nothing dinky about this clear-cut site. These calculators help you estimate taxes, calculate IRA earnings, balance your checkbook and analyze your home budget. Colorful charts are generated with each calculation. As the name suggests, you need a Java-enabled browser. Pages can be a little slow to load. ⓐⓐⓐ

MORTGAGE AND FINANCIAL CALCULATORS
www.homes4usa.com/tools.html
This no-frills site can take some of the mystery out of buying a home or saving for retirement. There are standard calculators to figure out loan and mortgage payments. These will tell you how much house you can buy and then how prepaying a chunk of your loan will affect your payments. There's even a special calculator to figure out how much to save to send the little ones to college. ⓐⓐⓐ

Home Offices

(originally reviewed November 1999)

ENTREPRENEUR'S HOMEOFFICEMAG.COM
www.homeofficemag.com
There's so much available at this site, you can't afford to do business without it. Garner the advice of HomeOfficeMag.com's savvy columnists. On our last visit, we discovered inexpensive networking options, insights on logos and branding, and tips on staying organized when you're short on time and space. E-commerce how-tos, a free newsletter and free Web tools are also great assets. ⓐⓐⓐⓐ

IVILLAGE: WORK FROM HOME
www.ivillage.com/work
Women who work from home can tap into this supportive community of professionals who make their living in bunny slippers. Get expert advice, tips, tricks and Web-based tools to keep your business organized. Post questions or responses on the Message Boards, get help writing a business plan, and use the Personal Mission Statement Builder to get going in the right direction. Women thinking about giving at-home careers a go will also find the assistance and incentive they need. ⓐⓐⓐⓐ

NOLO.COM LEGAL ENCYCLOPEDIA: SMALL BUSINESS
www.nolo.com/encyclopedia/sb_ency.html
Thinking of launching a home business or non-profit company? Has your small business grown

enough that you need to hire other employees? Nolo, an online legal encyclopedia, helps you learn the laws about owning, operating and optimizing a home office. You can also learn about tax issues. Plow through piles of articles packed with helpful advice, or visit the Law Store for useful books and resource guides. ⓐⓐⓐⓐ

FREE AGENT NATION
www.freeagentnation.com
Publisher Daniel Pink is obsessed with the growing trend of people working for themselves. He calls his Web site "the information hub for people working on their own." His analysis, advice and experience are critical for anyone who is self-employed or considering a transition to an independent job. Highlights include networking opportunities and answers to logistical questions, such as getting health insurance, using contracts and filing taxes. There's also a large archive of articles that are useful for people who work from home. ⓐⓐⓐ

JUNE LANGHOFF'S TELECOMMUTING RESOURCE CENTER
www.langhoff.com
Don't let the odd graphics fool you. When it comes to giving good advice on working from home, Langhoff doesn't goof around. Looking for work that will allow you to telecommute? Planning a move but want to keep your current job? Or do you just want to see if running a home office is right for you? This is a great place to get the answers to these questions. ⓐⓐⓐ

June Langhoff has serious advice for those who work from home.

Improve Career

(originally reviewed January 2000)

CAREER PATHS ONLINE
www.careerpathsonline.com
If you're a Generation-Xer seeking direction for your future, then this Canadian site is for you. The interactive 10 Step Career Planning Guide is a great resource, for discovering your talents and "sculpting" a fulfilling career. Another highlight is the Career Paths Time Machine. It outlines "defining features" of the 1940s through the 1990s to illustrate how the work world has changed over time. Don't miss the valuable information in Career Articles. ⓐⓐⓐⓐ

JOB-INTERVIEW.NET
www.job-interview.net
If interviewing for a job makes you nervous, visit this site and learn to say buh-bye to those fears. Job-interview.net goes into detail about every aspect of an interview—from what to wear to what is the best time of day for an interview. The Mock Job Interviews are also helpful, containing dozens of sample questions. There are strategies for answering questions, as well as a section of illegal interview questions of which you should be aware. ⓐⓐⓐⓐ

WETFEET.COM
www.wetfeet.com
Attention job seekers: This site is a must-see. Research dozens of industries and hundreds of companies. You'll get free overviews and facts, plus job profiles from people in your chosen field. Learn what a typical day is like, what skills or education you need, and the job's perks and headaches. The site also sells Insider Guides, but the quality of the free information is so valuable, you may not need anything else. There's also advice on networking, interviewing and resumes. If you're relocating, don't overlook the valuable profiles of major U.S. cities. ⓐⓐⓐⓐ

CAREERLAB
www.careerlab.com
The best part of this site is the Cover Letter Library. In addition to sample cover letters, it offers invaluable advice on everything from how best to express your skills and strengths, to saying "thank you" with class. Be sure to read articles by the Career Advisor under For Your Career on everything from job loss to resumes and networking to career management and focus. CareerLab also sells books and assessment tests. ⓐⓐⓐ

EXPERIENCE.COM
www.experience.com
Before heading off to an interview, you should learn something about the company with which

you're interviewing. Trouble is, aside from simply calling around or looking up statistics at the library—if they even exist—it's hard to find good information. This site solves that problem by providing "insider reports" on more than 350 companies in 25 industries. If it's a new, competitive industry into which you're trying to break, check here for the inside scoop on how to do so. ⓐⓐⓐ

FAMILYFRIENDLY.COM
www.familyfriendly.com
This helpful site is geared toward the family man or woman who wants to get some serious advice on looking for a new job or career. Input your skills (marketing or budgeting, for example) and what type of person you are (innovative or creative). The site then generates a list of jobs that should suit you. To learn skills for a new job, visit The Skill Builder. There is also targeted information for women as well as information on companies with family-friendly programs. ⓐⓐ

Marketing

(originally reviewed September 1999)

ADVERTISING AGE
www.adage.com
The online presence of this venerable magazine features a crisp design, exclusive industry data, a guide to marketing conferences and events, and Account Action—a table of accounts in play, won and lost. Scan the latest headlines about advertising-related news or read Bob Garfield's funny and penetrating weekly analysis of advertising trends and popular spots. Of special interest: the Advertising Century, an exploration of how advertising has shaped U.S. commerce in the last 100 years. ⓐⓐⓐⓐ

Advertising Age offers exclusive data and sharp analyses.

AMERICAN MARKETING ASSOCIATION
www.ama.org
Visitors to this site can browse full-text articles, abstracts, editorials and reviews from the American Marketing Association's eight major publications. For example, articles include "Surfing for Seniors" in Marketing News and "Perceptions of Price Unfairness" in the Journal of Marketing Research. Look in the resources area to find links to special-interest and marketing research groups, or search the events calendar for upcoming marketing conferences. The AMA also offers special member services for an annual fee. ⓐⓐⓐ

THE MARKETING RESOURCE CENTER
www.marketingsource.com
Designed to assist businesses with traditional and Internet marketing efforts, this site boasts an archive of more than 250 marketing-related articles on home-based businesses, Internet commerce, time management and traditional advertising. There's also a special section devoted to Internet marketing. Plus, visitors can participate in discussions in the Marketing Forum, register to receive a free biweekly newsletter or draw inspiration from the Quote of the Day. ⓐⓐⓐ

THE STANDARD
www.thestandard.net
Here is a stunning and comprehensive resource for the latest Internet and e-commerce news. The articles are excellent, featuring news, analysis and reviews about corporate mergers, the "free" computers trend and big money that's being dumped into online advertising. The site also offers Metrics, a wide array of downloadable research, data, statistics and analyses. ⓐⓐⓐ

AMERICAN DEMOGRAPHICS
www.demographics.com
If you need detailed information about the leading trade shows or are interested in the demographics of various segments of the U.S. population, look here. There is a wealth of useful information in the archive of American Demographics magazine; it includes past issues back to 1995 that cover such subjects as product tie-ins and marketing to single mothers. ⓐⓐ

Money

(originally reviewed December 1999)

BLOOMBERG.COM: MONEY
www.bloomberg.com/pfc
Designed for those who are proactive with their finances, this site is a good resource for devel-

oping big-picture money strategies. From the Loan Advisor to the Market Monitor, Bloomberg.com is loaded with articles and free services that are geared toward making the most of your assets. Whether refinancing a mortgage or reading the latest news on mutual funds, users can expect to find highly involved insight on a wide range of money matters. ⓐⓐⓐⓐ

FAMILY MONEY
www.familymoney.com

When it comes to keeping your personal finances in check, running a family can be a pretty complicated undertaking. This magazine from Better Homes & Gardens has articles and advice about household budgeting, kids' saving and spending, and college planning. It aims to simplify the often arduous process of improving—or at least stabilizing—a family's financial status. Savvy tips for tax planning, investing and saving make this site an all-inclusive resource for streamlining your family's economic operation. ⓐⓐⓐⓐ

MONEYMINDED
www.moneyminded.com

Dedicated to advancing women's financial goals, this sharp site that is part of the Women.com network offers prudent advice on baby economics, lending money to family and friends, retirement planning and the inevitable bevy of financial issues that crop up in between. Expansive but clearly organized, this site's strength is its ability to convey comprehensive financial information in plain English. Professional, complete and progressive, MoneyMinded is a tremendous asset for busy women who are looking for savvy, quick-hitting economic information. ⓐⓐⓐⓐ

SMARTMONEY.COM
www.smartmoney.com

With hourly stock updates, daily market analysis and breaking financial news coverage, the resources at this site will be especially useful for people who are looking to keep pace with the high-speed world of finance. There are money pointers on topics that range from mortgages to international investing, while the broker ratings can help users decide which companies can make their money grow. Also offering portfolio tracking, planning advice and a free newsletter, SmartMoney.com is a valuable asset for any investor. ⓐⓐⓐⓐ

MONEY MOVES
www.pbs.org/moneymoves

Hosted by comedian Jack Gallagher, this online version of the PBS television series "Money Moves" offers light but informative insight on personal finance. Broken down by episode under Hot Topics, the articles include ideas for cheap travel, investment clubs, building nest eggs and creative methods of reducing debt. For a brief but interesting history of paper currency, check out the Money FAQs section. Those wrapped up in a financial pickle can find recommended resources to help get out of it. ⓐⓐⓐ

STRONGKIDS.COM
www.strongkids.com

So Junior wants a crack at the market, huh? With basic but sound financial tips, this site from Strong Capital Management is a good starting point for kids who are interested in putting their money to work. Options on different ways to save and examples of practical goal-setting serve as valuable primers for future experience. Priceless feature: A dictionary of economic terms offers future investors a crash course in valuable verbiage. ⓐⓐⓐ

THE BUCKEY BUZZ.COM
www.buckeybuzz.com

Created and run by six veteran financial journalists, this business e-zine provides fiscal information for a diverse clientele. There are columns for newcomers to the world of money management, while more experienced financial players can get regularly updated stock quotes, analyze future stocks or scour articles for portfolio-building advice. Bonus: The Daily Money Tip and Daily Travel Tip lend advice that is useful for saving dough in unexpected places. ⓐⓐ

Organize Finances

(originally reviewed January 2000)

BUCKINVESTOR.COM
www.buckinvestor.com

Emphasizing long-term investment as a means to grow your wealth, BuckInvestor.com puts a variety of articles, tools and resources at your fingertips. Start by reading the Investment Basics. Then check out the articles on retirement planning, credit and insurance in the

Personal Finance section. Find out how to form an investment club, invest online or sign up for a free newsletter.

INVESTORAMA.COM
www.investorama.com
Financial gurus agree that savvy investing is the smartest way to build a nest egg for the future. But where do you turn if you're new to the world of stocks, bonds and mutual funds? Our answer is Investorama.com. Start with the Financial Guides for articles and strategies on many investing topics. Each topic also features profiles of real-life investors, archives, message boards, recommended books and an ask the expert section. For links to thousands of recommended Web sites, click on the directory under the Quick Index on the homepage.

THEWHIZ.COM
www.thewhiz.com
If you're not a whiz when it comes to personal finances, theWhiz.com can help you become one. Articles on credit, debt, insurance, taxes, banking, investing and "the cost of life" are complemented with information on handling money issues at work, home and play. Particularly helpful are the WHZ-101 articles, which deal with personal finance basics. If you have a financial question, ask the Dollar Diva.

FINANCENTER.COM
www.financenter.com
So, you want to be a millionaire. Well, forget the TV game shows and the lottery and head to this simple yet helpful site. It offers an online tool called ClickCalcs that helps you to determine such things as how much money to save in order to be a millionaire when you retire. In all, there are more than 100 different financial calculators for everything from autos and homes to credit cards and budgeting.

ZDTV: THE MONEY MACHINE
www.zdnet.com/zdtv/moneymachine
Both a Web site and a TV show, The Money Machine features stories and tips that explain how to "make, save and manage money with your computer." The site contains comprehensive details on investing and personal finance, plus money tools and financial calculators. Post questions to host Carmine Gallo, read columns and articles, and watch video clips from the show. Penny-pincher tip: Check out Deals of the Day.

Shipping

(originally reviewed October 1999)

FEDEX
www.fedex.com
This is what a business site should be—great-looking, filled with useful information and a cinch to use. Get all of the info on FedEx's various domestic and international shipping plans and rates, or use FedEx's interNetShip to prepare your shipments online. Fill out the shipping form, pay with your credit card or FedEx account, print out the label, and you're ready to drop off your package at the nearest FedEx location. The site also tracks packages.

UPS
www.ups.com
UPS offers the most advanced services of any of the online shipping options. Registered users of My UPS.com, which offers customized services, can whiz through the whole shipping process online without making a single phone call, from labeling the package to tracking it to its delivery point. My UPS.com has a personalized address book, so you don't have to re-enter frequent destinations. Even the pickup schedule and drop-off locator are automated with a simple, intuitive form.

UNITED STATES POSTAL SERVICE
www.usps.gov
The official site of the USPS is efficient and information-rich, offering a spiffy postage rate calculator, Express Mail tracking, ZIP-code look-up and change-of-address forms. Customers can even order postage stamps online. Add to that list comprehensive background on the USPS and a fascinating exhibit of historical letters, and you get the whole picture. Forget about those long lines at the post office.

Women in Business

(originally reviewed October 1999)

ADVANCING WOMEN
www.advancingwomen.com
Tackle all of your career and business-related concerns at this essential site. Original features that address topics from raising funds to balancing career and home life are packed with information and links to other useful sites. There is so much at Advancing Women that you may never see it all, but trying sure is educational. Invest some time in Market Mavens—and don't miss Web Women. ⓐⓐⓐⓐ

ONLINE WOMEN'S BUSINESS CENTER
www.onlinewbc.org
Many business sites include a directory of useful links. The OWBC has that in spades, but it also offers up something different: a step-by-step guide to starting a business—from leasing your first office space to managing a board of directors. It follows up by providing excellent tutorials on financial statements, managing employees, and growing and expanding your business. This thorough handbook is an invaluable resource for businesswomen at almost any level, but it's particularly useful for those new to entrepreneurship. ⓐⓐⓐⓐ

SMALL BUSINESS AT WOMEN.COM
www.women.com/smallbiz
This is the biggie of women's sites. Women.com, formerly Women's Wire, was one of the first to cater to female Web surfers. Working women will find a valuable source of information in this deep file of business features that runs the gamut from writing business plans to the ins and outs of various career choices to negotiation strategies. An online financial calculator can help you determine the startup costs and monthly expenses of a new business. Ask Biz Shrink a question before you leave. ⓐⓐⓐⓐ

WORKINGWOMAN.COM
www.workingwoman.com
This recently revamped site combines the resources of several women's publications and organizations, including Working Woman, Working Mother, the National Association for Female Executives and the Business Women's Network. The articles are always savvy and eminently readable, whether they're hard-hitting market analyses, state-by-state child care reports or fun features. We only wish that the site included an archive of back issues. ⓐⓐⓐⓐ

WOMENCONNECT.COM
www.womenconnect.com
The site is updated daily and has a stronger focus on business news than most of the other sites reviewed here. Don't overlook its many other great features. You'll find targeted news, feature articles and a searchable two-month news archive. Perhaps the most impressive feature is the collection of advice on starting and running a business and on career management—truly a deep well of strategy suggestions for any woman looking to sharpen her business savvy. ⓐⓐⓐ

WOMEN IN BUSINESS CYBERSPACE FIELD OF DREAMS
www.fodreams.com
A heck of a mouthful, that name, but fortunately, the site is meaty enough to merit all the syllables. Feature articles that address various topics of concern to working women join a thorough directory of business-oriented sites. Find resources on finance, proposals, mentors and advertising. List your business on the related Web ring for free, or check out the fee-based site-hosting services. The design may look plain and homespun, but this site is solid. ⓐⓐⓐ

WOWFACTOR: WOMEN'S BUSINESS SOLUTIONS
www.wowfactor.com
A wonderfully thorough and concise overview of planning and launching an e-commerce business awaits you here—especially if you use this company to host your site. To be frank, however, that's the best part of this site. WOWFactor touts its interactive directory of more than a million women-owned businesses, but it doesn't explain how it promotes members. It's free to list or search for a business, but aside from the TradeSecrets moderated discussion group and the PowWow listserv, content is a bit thin. ⓐⓐ

reference

Almanacs

(originally reviewed January 2000)

INFOPLEASE.COM KIDS' ALMANAC
kids.infoplease.com
Serious and fun facts are all just a mouse click away on this eye-catching site. The site search engine is easy for kids to use (there's a help area to guide newbies through searches), and the content is divided into familiar categories, such as sports, world, people and science. Neat features include charts of popular kids' names and Fun Facts. ⓐⓐⓐⓐ

THE OLD FARMER'S ALMANAC
www.almanac.com
The online version of this classic has all of the same useful information as the print version, but with one major advantage: It is updated daily, not yearly. The homepage offers daily and weekly weather reports, as well as monthly information for up to two months. Read the long-range forecast for the year, weather history, seasonal tips and short daily Radio Reports. For information on cooking, gardening, celestial happenings, tide schedules and puzzles, use the pull-down menu at the top of the page. ⓐⓐⓐⓐ

THE POLITICAL REFERENCE ALMANAC
www.polisci.com/almanac/almanac.htm
This site is an excellent place to go for answers to questions about American government and political history. Plus, there's a fair amount of international information. The Calendar, World, Economics and History sections document events, elections, political systems and backgrounds for the United States and other countries. The other sections here focus solely on U.S. government, providing good overviews of the executive, legislative and judicial branches, political parties, state government, and important historical documents. ⓐⓐⓐⓐ

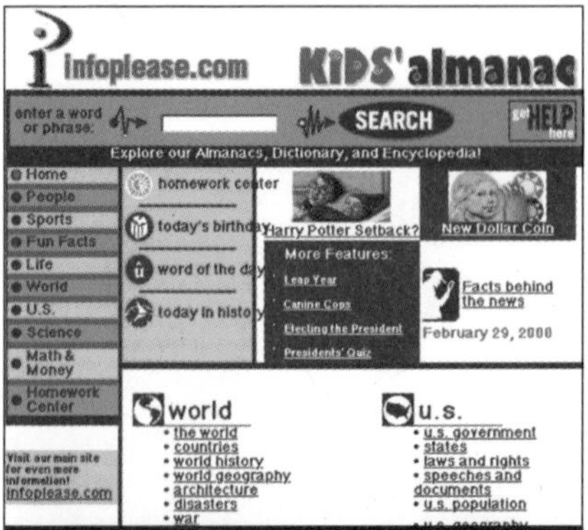

When Mom and Dad don't have the answers, kids can turn to the Infoplease.com Kids' Almanac.

STARDATE ONLINE: SKY ALMANAC
stardate.utexas.edu/nightsky/almanac/s_current_alm.html
Beginner stargazers would do well to visit this simple monthly primer for celestial events. Start with the homepage, which gives moon phases, planet positions and special events for the month. Weekly Tips provides more detail, and Planets provides general information about sighting Earth's celestial siblings. There are also listings of meteor showers. Don't forget to check into Get Started for helpful hints about watching the night sky. ⓐⓐⓐ

DAILY ALMANACS
www.dailyalmanacs.com
The design of this almanac may seem a little unconventional, but the information here is extensive and helpful. Click on any date on the interactive calendar, and an incredibly comprehensive list of births, deaths, events and holidays for that given day will pop up. Impatient visitors can click on the Today link at the top of the page to avoid scrolling through the entire calendar. ⓐⓐ

Data & Statistics

(originally reviewed September 1999)

EDGAR DATABASE
www.sec.gov/edgarhp.htm
Use this site's thorough search engine to sift through the financial data housed at the definitive source for Securities and Exchange Commission filings. Because EDGAR is a database of public U.S. companies, it's not as comprehensive as, say, Hoover's (the ultimate directory for corporate information). But for corporate info straight from the horse's mouth, EDGAR gives quick, easy access to filings dating back to 1994. ⓐⓐⓐⓐ

FEDSTATS
www.fedstats.gov
Statistics from more than 70 federal agencies are available from this government site. You'll get easy access to labor, census, transportation, immigration and economic statistics, as well as data from the Centers for Disease Control and Prevention, the Federal Bureau of Prisons, the Small Business Administration, NASA, the Environmental Protection Agency and more.

Dealing with the government should always be this easy. ⓐⓐⓐⓐ

INFONATION
www.un.org/Pubs/CyberSchoolBus/infonation/e_infonation.htm

This neat little database organizes current statistics from the United Nations on 185 countries. The subjects covered are basic—average temperatures, population, employment and the like—but the site is irresistibly easy to use. Simply choose a country, and then click for a list of available statistics from that country. Pick the stats you want to see, then click for an organized table of the data. ⓐⓐⓐⓐ

INFOPLEASE.COM
www.infoplease.com

Professing to have "all the knowledge you need," this site offers data and statistics on a range of topics. It covers the expected—elections, sports, world facts, business, science, entertainment, education—and the unexpected, such as top baby names from 1900 to 1998 and a table of the deadliest volcanic eruptions. But don't look for in-depth information here; the coverage is broad but shallow. ⓐⓐⓐ

STATISTICAL RESOURCES ON THE WEB
www.lib.umich.edu/libhome/Documents.center/stats.html

So what kinds of statistics are you looking for—lists of casualties from U.S. wars? Idaho's energy consumption? Results of the latest Roper Poll? Whatever kind of data you need, there's probably a link to it, reviewed and categorized, at this site from the University of Michigan's Documents Center. It's best to browse rather than search through the wealth of links because the site's search engine can be imprecise and spotty at times. ⓐⓐ

Expert Advice

(originally reviewed January 2000)

ALLEXPERTS.COM
www.allexperts.com

Billed as the first large-scale expert site on the Internet, Allexperts.com has thousands of volunteers who dole out advice on more than 1,500 topics, including computers, automotive repair, movie stars, travel and small business. The service here is free, a benefit that counterbalances its somewhat dull design. If you want to become a volunteer, pick a subject and sign up on a trial basis. Students will find the site to be a handy homework helper, too. ⓐⓐⓐⓐ

EHOW
www.ehow.com

Although visitors can't e-mail the experts here, this is the place to go for solid answers to almost any question—at no charge. Each tutorial is written by a different person. To check the writer's credentials, click on his or her name. You'll get a brief bio, areas of expertise and a list of the person's other contributions to the site. Topics here are truly wide-ranging; we found everything from "how to ask for maternity leave" to "how to brake properly on a motorcycle." Check the Top 10 eHows for some of the more popular tutorials. ⓐⓐⓐⓐ

EXPERTCENTRAL.COM
www.expertcentral.com

With a pool of more than 5,600 experts in dozens of categories, ExpertCentral.com is a great resource. Hobbies & Collectibles, for example, includes experts on topics from antiques to visual arts. The site recruits top experts whenever possible; several doctors from the Tufts School of Veterinary Medicine can be found under Pets & Animals. Post a question, and an expert will send you a bid that you can accept, decline or negotiate. Although the experts here have the option of charging for their answers, they may answer easy questions for free. ⓐⓐⓐⓐ

EXP
www.exp.com

Formerly Advoco.com, this site has a polished look and feel. The nice thing about EXP is that the experts publish their rates up front. If you're a hopeless romantic, check out the section on finding a soul mate, or ask "cyberflirt" expert Susan Rabin a question about online romance. Warning: If you're on a piggybank budget, some of the fees might be steep. Rabin, for instance, charges $50 for the first answer. ⓐⓐⓐ

EXPERTCITY.COM
www.expertcity.com

Just type in your computer-related question at

this site and wait for a few seconds. If you visit during scheduled business hours, an expert will soon arrive to deliver a bid for his or her services. If the fee is acceptable, the fun begins. Download a free screen-sharing application and talk to the expert in real time. The site only supports communication with Windows-based computers, but Mac and Unix versions of the chat software are said to be in the works.

ASKME.COM
www.askme.com
This free site has the cozy, conversational feel of a chat room, but the Q&A structure keeps everyone on track. Pick a topic from among the 14 categories, and then pick your expert. Profiles and ratings are listed for each expert, although not every expert has been rated. It's not unusual for visitors to submit their query to more than one specialist; part of the fun is browsing previous questions to compare the experts' answers. After the expert responds, rate his or her answer. The ratings give the whole system a more personal feel.

INFOMARKETS.COM
www.infomarco.com
This "place where people with questions find people with answers" offers 34 categories to choose from, from C++ programming to fitness to traveling in Australia. You pay nothing to ask a question, but pay once you accept the expert's answer. The site's Question of the Day section highlights interesting questions and answers. The site also deserves kudos for its clear and helpful FAQ section and its easy-to-navigate design.

Inner Workings

(originally reviewed September 1999)

HOW STUFF WORKS
www.howstuffworks.com
The aptly named site creator, Marshall Brain, endeavors to help people understand the world around them with this outstanding site. Each week, Brain publishes a new article explaining the inner workings of everything from rocket engines to root canals. These in-depth articles are beautifully illustrated with clear diagrams and provide a list of relevant links for further reading. To top it off, every weekday, Brain answers a reader's question of the day.

HOW THINGS WORK
rabi.phys.virginia.edu/HTW/
Hosted by physics professor Louis Bloomfield, this straightforward site consists primarily of a running archive of hundreds of questions from visitors about the "physics of everyday life." Bloomfield's approach to physics is to start with objects and situations and explain in layman's terms how things work, rather than focusing on mathematics and abstract concepts, which makes the site a great resource for students.

Ask Dr. Universe answers kids' toughest questions.

THE MAD SCIENTIST NETWORK
www.madsci.org
A worldwide network of hundreds of enthusiastic scientists, teachers and students have volunteered to answer your science questions at this visually stimulating site. Browse categories of questions, where students ask about perpetual motion machines and why curves on roads are banked. Check out Mad Labs for fun experiments you can do at home and a tour of the human body. If you still have questions, explore the MadSci Library for links to more resources.

ASK DR. UNIVERSE
www.wsu.edu/druniverse
Dr. Universe is "the world's most curious cat" and, fortunately for curious kids, she has connections. She takes their toughest questions, such as "Why does electricity shock?" and "How do mirrors work?" and gets the answers from her friends, the researchers at Washington State University. The information is then presented in a fun and easy-to-navigate format.

ENGINEERING CURRICULUM IDEAS
ldaps.ivv.nasa.gov/Curriculum
Sometimes figuring out how things work requires a little hands-on experience. Using LEGOs and other appealing materials, this site uses projects to show how gears, basic kitchen objects, wind tunnels and gliders, among other things, work. Project instructions are accompanied by photographs and diagrams. The site also features physics experiments that

demonstrate the concepts of force, velocity and energy. ⓐⓐ

Maps & Atlases

(originally reviewed November 1999)

LIBRARY OF CONGRESS: MAP COLLECTIONS 1544-1999
lcweb2.loc.gov/ammem/gmdhtml
Military maps. Environmental maps. Maps that "record the evolution" of American cities. This Library of Congress site is rich in content and easy to use, offering more than 4.5 million old and new maps. Want something as obscure as a bird's-eye view of Marshalltown, Iowa, from 1868? It's here. Search by keyword or browse the sections. Once you find the map you need, you can zoom in or out, adjust window size and then download it for later viewing. ⓐⓐⓐⓐ

ATLAPEDIA ONLINE
www.atlapedia.com
Select either the political or the physical world map index at Atlapedia (combination atlas and encyclopedia) before choosing a country. Once you've narrowed the field, you can zoom in on your area of interest. The maps are in full color but are a little coarse. However, the strength of this site is its exhaustive warehouse of accompanying statistical data. Locate Sarajevo or find out the average life expectancy in Canada. A little plain but simple to use, Atlapedia is immensely useful, especially for students. ⓐⓐⓐ

CARTOGRAPHIC IMAGES
http://www.henry-davis.com/MAPS/carto.html
Students, researchers and history buffs will want to visit this site. The collection consists of ancient, early medieval, late medieval and Renaissance maps. For example, there's a Mesopotamian city plan from 1500 B.C. The serious map lover can enjoy some 2,240 low-resolution JPEG images that are accompanied by monographs and bibliographies. There are also numerous links and a time chart of ancient cartography. Don't expect many bells or whistles, but there are plenty of facts. ⓐⓐⓐ

NATIONAL ATLAS OF THE UNITED STATES
www.nationalatlas.gov
This U.S. Geological Survey site presents all kinds of information that has been collected by the federal government in atlas form—from butterfly habitats to locations of abandoned mines. With the right software—you'll need to download the Shockwave plug-in—you can click your way through animated, interactive maps or create and download custom map layers for free. Note: The site is packed with data but is a bit crowded and confusing to navigate. ⓐⓐⓐ

GREEN MAP SYSTEM
www.greenmap.com/home/home.html
The Green Map System won't get you from point A to point B. It will help you locate eco-friendly information and businesses, from museums to grocers to renewable resources. Made by city-dwellers—urban planners, architects, graduate students—from all over the world, these "green" community maps trace human impact on cities from San Francisco to Utrecht, Holland. Visit Kids' Neighborhood for maps built by youngsters. The selection is limited but growing fast. ⓐⓐ

Online Libraries

(originally reviewed October 1999)

THE LIBRARY OF CONGRESS
www.loc.gov
Though visitors can search the Library of Congress site as they would any other library, only a portion of its 17 million books and 95 million images, audio recordings, maps and other items are accessible online. What is available, from the Gettysburg Address to a Frank Lloyd Wright exhibition, makes for a mind-boggling resource. Visitors can take advantage of THOMAS, a congressional database, or American Memory, an ongoing initiative to digitize the library's historical Americana holdings. The Electronic Texts and Publishing Resources page offers links to libraries with electronic books. ⓐⓐⓐⓐ

LIBRARYSPOT
www.libraryspot.com
This compact, efficient site offers a plethora of links but only to the best library and reference sites. Research everything under the sun, from music and maps to genealogy and grant writing. Visitors can read the latest topics in the

Reading Room, a collection of online journals, newspapers, magazines and books. Finally, the site provides links to a variety of excellent legal, medical and general online libraries as well.

U.S. NATIONAL LIBRARY OF MEDICINE
www.nlm.nih.gov
The medical counterpart to the Library of Congress allows visitors to search a full dictionary of health topics, download books and journals, or access a database of references from 11 million articles. There are also special sections on HIV/AIDS and the history of medicine. If the NLM doesn't have the information you want, the library offers links to hospitals, doctors and general health care information.

AMERICAN VERSE PROJECT
www.hti.umich.edu/english/amverse
The American Verse Project at the University of Michigan is growing an electronic archive of 19th-century American poetry, although a few 18th- and early 20th-century texts are included. The site encourages scholarly research with its accuracy and sophisticated search options. First-time visitors should check out the notable selection of Emily Dickinson poems or the complete poems of Edgar Allen Poe.

BIBLIOMANIA
www.bibliomania.com
A site of special interest to students and writers, Bibliomania offers a selection of electronic texts, searchable by engine or category. Visitors will find Freud's "The Interpretation of Dreams," poetry and 60 classic novels, including Joseph Conrad's "Heart of Darkness." Browse Culpeper's "The Complete Herbal," a guide to herbal remedies written in 1654, or Brewer's "Dictionary of Phrase and Fable," a fascinating compendium of common English colloquial expressions and their origins.

THE INTERNET PUBLIC LIBRARY
www.ipl.org
The first public library of the Internet, IPL is one of the Web's largest searchable collections of links for those who want to know more about subjects ranging from oceanography to accounting. In the Youth Division, children can get help with basic math or read about dinosaurs. Teens can browse links devoted specifically to them, including a guide to research papers. There are also links to magazines and newspapers.

UNIVERSITY OF VIRGINIA LIBRARY: ELECTRONIC TEXT CENTER
etext.lib.virginia.edu
One of the largest electronic text archives, this site contains holdings in 14 languages. Although commercial texts, such as the Oxford English Dictionary, are available only to UVA users, the general public can legally access everything else ("Aesop's Fables" and the Koran, for example). There are sections on the Civil War, Shakespeare, Women Writers and more. In the Young Readers section, children can read illustrated versions of classics, such as Lewis Carroll's "Alice's Adventures in Wonderland."

Time and Calendars

(originally reviewed November 1999)

CLICKABLE CALENDARS
www.clickablecalendars.com
Most people have had a "fact-a-day" or similar calendar sitting on their desk at some point. This clever site takes that concept off the desk and puts it online. The calendars here offer history tidbits, sound effects and monthly quizzes. Sample question: What did Thomas Crapper invent on Feb. 2, 1837? The flush toilet.

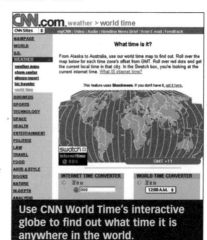

Use CNN World Time's interactive globe to find out what time it is anywhere in the world.

CNN WORLD TIME
www.cnn.com/weather/worldtime
This nifty site is anchored by an interactive globe displaying all of the time zones. As you move your cursor over the globe, each zone lights up. A display at the bottom of the globe tells you how many hours each zone is behind or ahead of Greenwich Mean Time. To find a local time, hold the cursor over the red dots that represent cities. The time converter is a handy tool.

THE WORLDWIDE HOLIDAY & FESTIVAL SITE
www.holidayfestival.com
If you've ever traveled internationally on business or vacation and discovered that you've arrived during a holiday, then you know how inconvenient it can be to meet customers, get a taxi or find an open restaurant. Before your next trip, check this site's list of world holidays and celebrations. Pick a country for a list of holidays, or go to This Month for a calendar that shows which countries are celebrating holidays each day. There are also religious holiday calendars, including those for Christianity, Islam, Judaism and Sikh. ⓐⓐⓐⓐ

CALENDAR ZONE
www.calendarzone.com
The extensive lists of links at this site lead you to hundreds of calendars organized by subject, including religious, historic, Y2K and geographic. The Women section offers due date and pregnancy calendars, while the Daily section has a "Jeopardy!" trivia calendar. Check out the Miscellaneous section for some unusual finds, including a Swedish calendar that celebrates a first name each day. With so many calendars, every day can seem special. ⓐⓐⓐ

WORLDTIME
www.worldtime.com
With local sunrise and sunset times and a day/night feature that shades a global map, this site is a good resource for travelers. Click on an area of the map; the day/night shade will shift accordingly. Latitude and longitude are shown, along with the date and Greenwich Mean Time. You can also select a country for the current time and holiday information. ⓐⓐⓐ

Quotations

(originally reviewed September 1999)

QUOTELAND.COM
www.quoteland.com
"Drop your trousers here for best results" is one of the funny foreign mistranslations found at this land of quotes—it was spotted outside a Bangkok dry cleaner. The highlight of this site is Humorous Quotes, where you'll find memorable movie, television and song lines, celebrity insults and stupid things said by famous people. Don't overlook the numerous literary quotes and also those about love, life and adversity, among other things. Use the search engine or discussion groups to track down the elusive ones. ⓐⓐⓐⓐ

QUOTEZ
www.quotations.co.uk
If it's been said, it must be here. This British site boasts 13,500 quotes that are organized by more than 500 subjects and more than 2,000 authors. Use the search engine, but if you are positively stumped, you can send your query to the site's creator, Mark Fryer, and he'll try and help out. Stupid quotes, newspaper gaffes and amusing safety tips round out a top-notch site. ⓐⓐⓐⓐ

BARTLETT'S FAMILIAR QUOTATIONS
www.bartleby.com/99/
The authority on literary quotations is now available online. John Bartlett's collection of notable quotables can enhance any research paper or article. The wise words of philosophers, writers and statesmen are organized alphabetically for quick reference (look under Alphabetical Index of All Authors). Or you can search by keywords. Next time you're at a loss for words, let Voltaire, Chaucer or Lincoln say it for you, eloquently. ⓐⓐⓐ

THE QUOTATIONS PAGE
www.starlingtech.com/quotes
Check back regularly for Quotes of the Day and Motivational Quotes of the Day at this attractive and easy-to-use site. Search the archives for specific quotations, or pull up random ones from a variety of collections including Quotations by Women, 20th Century Quotations and the ever-popular Deep Thoughts by Jack Handey. The site also features a nice selection of links. ⓐⓐⓐ

SEINFELD QUOTES
netnow.micron.net/~philco/seinfeld/seinfeld.htm
If you're a "Seinfeld" fan, these are the lines you've repeated again and again. The numerous quotes are cleverly organized by episode, such as The Stall ("I can't spare a square.") and The Dinner Party ("Oh look Elaine, the black and white cookie. I love the black and white. Two races of flavor living side by side in harmony. It's a wonderful thing, isn't it?"). Like Jerry, this site is straightforward, tidy and unpretentious. ⓐⓐⓐ

CREATIVE QUOTATIONS
www.bemorecreative.com/home-cq.htm

This site features quotations by famous people speaking about five specific "components of creativity": foraging, reflecting, adopting, nurturing and knuckling down. Find the famous people and their quotes listed on a calendar, under their birthday. Click on a person's name and read the quotes. This site is useful for birthdays, anniversaries or graduations: Send an e-mail or a card to someone with inspiring quotes from a notable person born on his or her special day. ⓐⓐ

THE NUBIAN MESSAGE ONLINE: AFRIKAN AMERICAN QUOTES PAGE
sma.ncsu.edu/Nubian/Quotes/indexFrames.html

"You may shoot me with your words. You may cut me with your eyes. You may kill me with your hatefulness. But still, like air, I'll rise." You'll find these words of Maya Angelou, along with those of W. E. B. DuBois, Oprah Winfrey, Jesse Jackson, Duke Ellington and many others at this basic but functional site, which is part of an e-zine. Although these quotes by great thinkers, leaders and entertainers are geared toward blacks, everyone can benefit from these messages of hope, strength and equality. ⓐⓐ

THE WEEKLY MOVIE QUOTE TEST
www.quotetest.com

Name the movie this quote is from: "I hate you! I wish I was never artificially created in a lab!" It's "Austin Powers," baby! Test your movie knowledge with the site's fun weekly quiz. You can also search for movie quotes by key words or by movie title, though the selection is limited. May the force be with you. ⓐⓐ

science & technology

Dinosaurs

(originally reviewed October 1999)

DINOSAUR EGGS @ NATIONALGEOGRAPHIC.COM
www.nationalgeographic.com/dinoeggs
This sharp site is based on a 1996 National Geographic article, "The Great Dinosaur Egg Hunt." It leads visitors through an exciting dinosaur egg hunt, features a cool CT scan of an egg and reveals the latest discoveries of fossil excavators. This easy-to-navigate site also features the Dinosaur Eggs Museum, which examines the interfamily dynamics of these reptiles and displays models of hatchlings.

THE DINOSAURIA
www.ucmp.berkeley.edu/diapsids/dinosaur.html
The Dinosauria clarifies common dinosaur misconceptions. For instance, not all large prehistoric creatures were dinosaurs. Nicely classified into four manageable sections, this site examines everything from how dinosaurs walked to what they ate. Cruise through special exhibits such as Dinobuzz, which features the biology of these beasts and cool photos.

DISCOVERY CHANNEL ONLINE: FOSSIL ZONE
www.discovery.com/exp/fossilzone/fossilzone.html
Brimming with resources such as the Polar Dinosaurs Expedition Slideshow and discussion forums with paleontologists, the Fossil Zone is visually and intellectually dazzling—typical of Discovery Channel production. Read up on the latest excavations and discoveries, dig out upcoming fossil events or learn how to take part in fossil exploration. Stocked with amazing photographs, this first-class site includes a listing of dinosaur-related television programs and interactive games for kids.

DINOSAUR ILLUSTRATIONS
web.syr.edu/~dbgoldma/pictures.html
This site displays thumbnail sketches of hundreds of prehistoric images with author names and links to their host Web sites. The alphabetical list of images makes this page an efficient timesaver for finding a specific type of dinosaur. There is also a small selection of panoramas and a way to send dinosaur postcards.

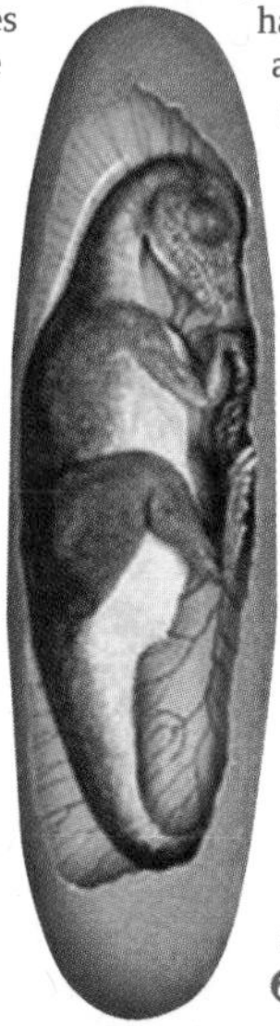

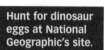

Hunt for dinosaur eggs at National Geographic's site.

Earthquakes

(originally reviewed October 1999)

EARTHQUAKE INFORMATION FROM THE USGS
quake.usgs.gov
There's plenty of great data for those interested in earthquakes, including lists and interactive maps of the most recent quakes to rock the globe. Prepare yourself with the guide to hazards and precautions and get quick answers about quakes from the glossary and the list of frequently asked questions. Read cutting-edge scientific studies and information about seismology and geophysics.

EARTHQUAKE ENGINEERING RESEARCH INSTITUTE
www.eeri.org
EERI is primarily a nonprofit research organization for scientists, engineers and architects, but laypeople will also be interested in the recent advances in building and bridge construction that are discussed here. The organization provides detailed earthquake data, which it uses to design safer, more stable communities. Visit often for timely news, photos of quake damage under Web Exclusives, seismic legislation, membership and meeting information.

EQE EARTHQUAKE HOME PREPAREDNESS GUIDE
www.eqe.com/publications/homeprep
Are you prepared? Though not a graphic design triumph, there is truly useful information here for anyone who lives in an earthquake zone. Find survival tips, suggestions for making your home as safe as possible and information about earthquake insurance. Learn how to survey your home's construction—the site claims there is a 70 percent chance you'll be at home when the next quake hits—and find out what steps you should take after an earthquake.

THE GREAT 1906 EARTHQUAKE AND FIRE
www.sfmuseum.org/1906/06.html
In 1906, one of the most violent quakes in U.S. history killed more than 700 people, demolished 28,000 buildings and destroyed much of San Francisco. This interesting site from the Museum of the City of San Francisco has an

excellent collection of information and documents related to that monstrous earthquake. You can see dozens of stunning photographs, read chilling accounts by survivors and view actual newspaper clips. The site also features an interesting timeline of events. @@@

SAVAGE EARTH: THE RESTLESS PLANET: EARTHQUAKES
www.wnet.org/savageearth/earthquakes
You'll find a well-written, well-researched collection of articles here from the giant brains at PBS. It's a straightforward, quick overview of how earthquakes occur, famous planet-quaking events and what earthquakes teach us about Earth. It is also a good introduction to plate tectonics, seismology, quake preparation and scientific research on quake prediction. Explanatory animation and cool photographs bring this site to life. There's not abundant data here, but what is available is top-quality. @@@

GLOBAL EARTHQUAKE RESPONSE CENTER
www.earthquake.com
When the big one strikes, will your home or office be ready to stand strong? This site offers solutions to all of your earth-shattering problems. Shop the online catalog for every type of brace, bracket and tether to keep your stuff in place when the ground starts to shake. Secure heavy furniture or computer equipment to the wall—and hope that the wall will still be standing after a quake. You can also tune in here for the latest earthquake news. @@

Freeware and Shareware

(originally reviewed December 1999)

DAVECENTRAL SHAREWARE ARCHIVE
www.davecentral.com
System utilities, browser utilities, database managers and cache managers are just a few of the things you'll find here. It doesn't matter if you're running Windows or Linux; there are offerings for both. Don't forget to check the archive. There is also a link to Dave's parent company, Andover.Net, where you'll find things such as an Internet Traffic Report and FreeCode, a free programming source code archive. @@@@

FREE STUFF LINKS
www.free-stuff-links.com
This snazzy, well-designed site is a great place to find links to free games, e-mail services, fonts, screensavers, Web graphics and freeware. Sign up in Miscellaneous for daily gossip e-mail. The offerings are truly diverse, and you can get weekly notices of new additions. Don't miss the links to MP3s and the Webmaster Resources. @@@@

THE MAC OS ZONE
www.macoszone.com
This nonprofit site provides freeware for the Mac community. Among the software choices are launcher utilities, antivirus programs, multiparty Internet conferencing tools, fonts, icon sets and games. The site's reviews will be great help in deciding which programs are worth downloading. @@@@

THE SOFTWARE SHAK
www.softwareshak.com
Although this site could benefit from a search engine, the shareware it offers can help you do pretty much anything. If you're into animations or multimedia interaction, there are tools for creating dynamic Web pages. If it's security that you need, check out the free software in Network Tools. The remote spying tools in Desktop Tools will allow you to secretly monitor what's happening on your computer when you're not there. There's also stuff for UNIX, DOS and Macs, too. @@@@

FREEHOUND FREEWARE-N-STUFF
www.freehound.com
As its tagline implies—"sniffin' the Web for freebies!"—Freehound covers a lot of ground, linking visitors to some of the best freeware out there. You will find audio and graphics tools, desktop utilities and screensavers. Look for deals that help you earn or save money while you surf. @@@

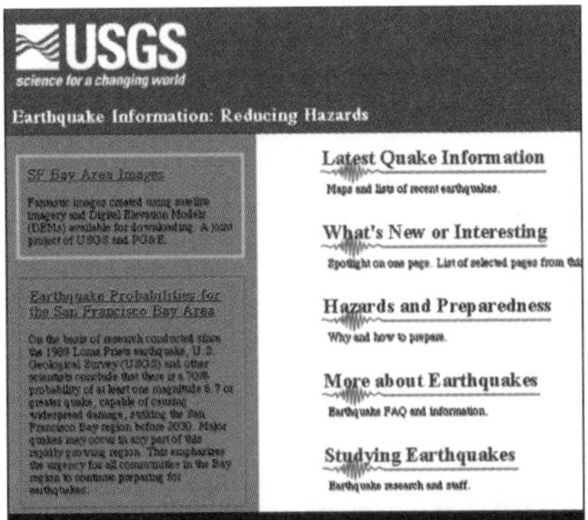

Prepare for an earthquake with Earthquake Information from the USGS.

HTML Guides

(originally reviewed October 1999)

THE BARE BONES GUIDE TO HTML
www.werbach.com/barebones
Though the title (not affiliated with Bare Bones software) suggests quick-hit instructions, the content is anything but skimpy. Readers can find information on various HTML symbols and compatibility requirements for the code, as well as specifications on positioning, links, graphics and sounds. One of the greatest assets of this site, aside from its easy navigability, is that the instructions are translated into 21 languages—everything from Chinese to Estonian, French, or Swedish. Cost to download? Free.

TIPS, TRICKS, HOW-TO, AND BEYOND
www.tips-tricks.com
This easy-to-navigate site has a simple mission: to help anyone design a better Web page. This site has useful tips for everyone from Web site novices to skilled webmasters. There is a section on how to build tables and frames, with the actual HTML code displayed and step-by-step instructions. Start with basic HTML code, then advance to graphics. There is a discussion board to post your questions.

A GUIDE TO HTML AND CGI SCRIPTS
snowwhite.it.brighton.ac.uk/~mas/mas/courses/html/html.html
Because HTML format isn't simple, neither is this site. But the highly organized and gradually escalating levels of information make digesting the material achievable. Learn by doing with the interactive exercises in Try It and with the sample programs that accompany each instruction section. Clear charts and spacious graphs help clarify the seemingly endless array of information in this very advanced HTML guide.

HTML novices and experts can learn from www.nashville.net/~carl/htmlguide.

HOW DO THEY DO THAT WITH HTML?
www.nashville.net/~carl/htmlguide
With straightforward advice on Web page content, aesthetics and design, this site translates HTML-speak from confusing rubbish into a comprehensible language. Beginners and experts alike will benefit from this thorough compilation of tips, from backgrounds and colors to tables and frames. Creatively designed and loaded with helpful examples, this site also includes chat and a message board.

HTML MADE REALLY EASY
www.jmarshall.com/easy/html
This no-frills site is in an easy-to-read, if somewhat unexciting, form. It breaks down HTML into its basic components—starting with a definition of HTML—and explains how to write tags and create pages. The tutorials are a useful feature and allow you to practice what you're learning. The text of the site is also available in Spanish.

2K COMMUNICATIONS: GUIDE TO PUBLISHING HTML
www.2kweb.net/html-tutorial
This Tennessee-based Internet service provider primarily offers Internet access and Web hosting services. However, its Web site boasts a fairly comprehensive HTML guide that is better suited to budding Web builders than seasoned pros. The personable graphics and basic layout allow you to concentrate on the task at hand—learning a new visual language.

Macintosh Help

(originally reviewed November 1999)

ABOUT.COM: FOCUS ON MAC SUPPORT
macsupport.about.com/compute/macsupport/
Even Mac veterans can learn a thing or two from Dave Merten and Shari Schroeder, who oversee this comprehensive Mac support page. If you're looking for Mac OS, ColorSync or Sherlock support, it's here, as is help for your modem, printer or a specific Mac model. Using Adobe Acrobat you can also view a variety of Apple support manuals. Other resources include iMac updates, a specs database and memory installation guides.

APPLECARE TECH INFO LIBRARY
til.info.apple.com
Sometimes when you're having computer problems, it's best to seek help right from the source.

For Macintosh users, that means going to the AppleCare Tech Info Library, or TIL. Here resides the collected Mac wisdom of untold generations—well, 10 or 15 years, at least. Updated daily, the TIL contains more than 14,000 articles, with information on products, technical specifications and troubleshooting. Search for specific topics using Apple's search engine, or browse through the various product areas to see what is new and useful. ⓐⓐⓐⓐ

MACFIXIT
www.macfixit.com
Got bombs? If so, MacFixIt can help you diffuse them. With all of the resources here, it's likely you will find a solution for your Mac problem. Start by checking Reports for a long list of trouble-shooting guides for Mac hardware and software. The Download Library posts dozens of related freeware and shareware utilities. Or browse Forums, which includes thousands of questions and answers covering all aspects of the Macintosh. Don't know where to begin? Use the custom search engine. ⓐⓐⓐ

MYHELPDESK.COM: APPLE MACINTOSH OPERATING SYSTEM HELP DIRECTORY
www.myhelpdesk.com/tabs/directorytab.asp?productid=58
This Web site offers free, comprehensive tech support, no matter what kind of software or hardware you use. It tells you how to get support via e-mail, phone or fax, and it provides links to vendor support sites and authorized service centers. MyHelpdesk.com also offers forums and message boards. Head to the above URL for Mac-specific tech support, or check the homepage (*www.myhelpdesk.com*) for help with other software or hardware problems. ⓐⓐⓐ

THE ULTIMATE MACINTOSH
www.flashpaper.com/umac
When a site boasts that it's "the biggest, ugliest, and most useful Macintosh page on the Web," it certainly gets your attention. More important, it had better fulfill its promise. After spending a few minutes exploring The Ultimate Macintosh, you'll probably come to a number of conclusions: This site is big, it's useful, and it's sort of ugly. But what is most apparent is the sheer volume of information that's available to Macintosh users. Bookmark this treasure, and visit often. Be sure to check Daily Diffs to see what's new at this extensive site. ⓐⓐⓐ

ALLEXPERTS.COM: MACINTOSH
www.allexperts.com/getExpert.asp?category=1063
Sure, there are plenty of Mac troubleshooting guides, reports, archives, how-tos, FAQs and other support resources on the Web. But sometimes, you need human help. AllExperts.com is a free service with more than a dozen volunteer Mac experts—a fraction of the more than 4,000 volunteer experts on the main site. E-mail one of them an explanation of your Mac problem; the volunteer will reply promptly with a detailed solution. ⓐⓐ

VERSIONTRACKER.COM
www.versiontracker.com
Many Macintosh problems are caused by software conflicts. Therefore, sometimes the best solution is to upgrade your software. But how do you know if a newer version is available? Check this site. New software updates are posted every day, including those for commercial, shareware and freeware programs. If you see an update you want, just click on the version number, and you will be whisked away to the appropriate download page. ⓐⓐ

Marine Biology

(originally reviewed October 1999)

REEFS OF THE GULF
gulftour.tamu.edu
Jump in your own virtual submarine and cruise through scientists' journals and photos at this colorful site that explores the Gulf of Mexico. You'll get a close-up look at the NR-1, the world's smallest nuclear submarine, as you follow its undersea adventures. Explore the world of the loggerhead sea turtles, learn about gas and oil seepages on the sea floor, and journey to the site of the USS Monitor, a sunken Civil War ship. ⓐⓐⓐⓐ

FINS: FISH INFORMATION SERVICE
www.actwin.com/fish
Brush up on your fish facts at FINS, where aquarists can learn how to keep freshwater and marine reef aquariums. Before stocking your new tank, check the Index, which lists hundreds of species and accompanying photos. Use the diagnostic chart to find out what's wrong with your sick fish. Find out about filters, skimmers and other essential equipment in the Reefkeepers FAQ section. Plus, you can watch

movies of aquariums or link to public aquarium sites. ⓐⓐⓐ

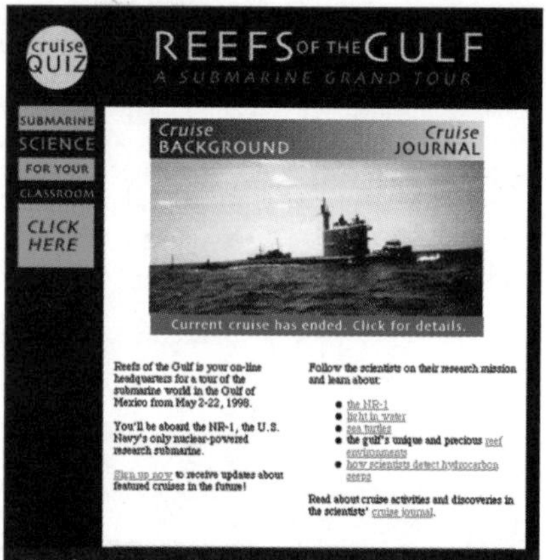

Explore the depths of the Gulf of Mexico at Reefs of the Gulf site.

MARINE BIOLOGICAL LABORATORY
www.mbl.edu
Located in Woods Hole, Mass., this institution has been an educational leader and scientists' mecca for more than 100 years. At the laboratory's easy-to-use Web site, you can check out its wide variety of resources, including a collection of more than 2,700 fish slides and special collections. ⓐⓐⓐ

OCEANLINK
oceanlink.island.net
Families will find plenty to explore at this fun site. Young scientists can read through the AquaFacts for information about beluga whales, sea otters and sharks, or visit Ask a Scientist for answers to questions about eels or sand dollars. Visitors can also read articles from the OceanNews online newsletter, explore the profession of marine biology in CareerInfo or learn fascinating facts about marine animals in Records. Did you know that the largest squid on record weighed about 4,000 pounds? ⓐⓐⓐ

MARINE BIOLOGY LEARNING CENTER
www.marinebiology.org
Ichthyology may be a fishy business, but if you're a fan, this site offers a crash course in sharks, rays, bony fish and coral reef fish. Learn about dolphins—those darlings of the sea—and brush up on your general knowledge of oceanography and coral reefs. If you really want to make waves, click on over to Odyssey Expeditions to book your own aquatic adventure on the high seas. ⓐⓐ

Meteorology

(originally reviewed October 1999)

INTELLICAST: WEATHER FOR ACTIVE LIVES
www.intellicast.com
If you wait five minutes, the weather will probably change, but at least now you can find out why it's changing. Get a look at weather patterns and storm fronts, thanks to satellite photographs. Dr. Dewpoint offers meteorology lessons and weather Q&As. But what's truly great here is the ability to check your local weather anytime—no waiting for the television or radio forecast. Before you know it, you might even be making your own forecasts. ⓐⓐⓐⓐ

NATIONAL CLIMATIC DATA CENTER
www.ncdc.noaa.gov
For true weather fanatics, this colorful site is practically a gift from the heavens. The NCDC compiles data on weather events from the past century. You'll find reports on temperature extremes, tornadoes and billion-dollar weather disasters. Amateur meteorologists will also love the maps and radar images. ⓐⓐⓐ

UNITED STATES WEATHER PAGES
www.uswx.com/us/wx
From the U.S. map on this site's front page you can check current temperatures, dew points, air pressure and 24-hour maximum and minimum temperatures nationwide—all with a click of the mouse. Severe weather alerts are posted by state, making it easy to check your area. The site also includes a glossary of meteorological terms, an almanac of local weather information by ZIP code and an event planner to find out what the forecast is likely to be next weekend, next year or in 2003. ⓐⓐⓐ

BAD METEOROLOGY
www.ems.psu.edu/~fraser/BadMeteorology.html
Geared toward teachers, parents and anyone interested in true meteorology, this site clears up some misconceptions. For instance, raindrops are not teardrop-shaped; small raindrops are spherical, and larger ones are shaped like hamburger buns. Why? Alistair B. Fraser of Pennsylvania State University's Meteorology Department explains it all and sets the record straight. ⓐⓐ

Pollution

(originally reviewed October 1999)

ENVIRONMENTAL DEFENSE
www.edf.org
This nonprofit group is concerned with all types of pollution, from agricultural run-off to

pesticides. Scroll down the page for interactive quizzes, news releases and reports on environmental projects. You'll also find out how you can help; there are tips on "green" electricity, recycling and vehicle use. Earth to Kids features games, art, poems and teacher resources. ⓐⓐⓐⓐ

ENVIRONMENTAL PROTECTION AGENCY
www.epa.gov
Everything you ever wanted to know about protecting the environment is here. You'll find an extensive database of environmental facts and current information on EPA programs, resources, events, news and laws. Use the ZIP-code search to find trouble spots, environmental profiles and watershed conditions in your area. There are excellent sections for students and teachers, and the site is available in Spanish. ⓐⓐⓐⓐ

GROUND-WATER REMEDIATION TECHNOLOGIES ANALYSIS CENTER
www.gwrtac.org
This is a virtual treasure-trove of technical documents and study databases about ground-water remediation technologies. A glossary of hydrogeologic terms in the Remediation Technologies section can help the less hydro-savvy find their way through the documents. Notices about conferences on ground water and related subjects are provided, as is a toll-free number to report ground-water contamination. ⓐⓐⓐ

CENTER FOR SUSTAINABLE SYSTEMS
www.umich.edu/~nppcpub
This site run by the University of Michigan is designed with students, faculty and professionals in mind, but it's useful to anyone who needs research materials. The nicely organized CSS Resources section is a good first stop. Free information on topics that include corporate environmental strategy, agriculture and coastal zone management is available as downloadable PDF (portable document format) files; for a fee you can get printed copies mailed to you. There's also detailed information on its projects and a long list of environmental links. ⓐⓐⓐ

NEW IDEAS IN POLLUTION REGULATION
www.worldbank.org/nipr
Industrial pollution in developing countries is a major environmental concern. This site addresses the issue with an eye toward corporations' responsibilities and behavioral motivations. Cost-effective solutions, public policy models and country briefings are among the offerings here. You won't find quick statistics, but it is an excellent resource for information on industrial pollution. ⓐⓐⓐ

NOISE POLLUTION CLEARINGHOUSE
www.nonoise.org
There are no bells and whistles at this site—no wonder, since its motto is "good neighbors keep their noise to themselves." Traffic, jet skis, construction, airplanes, gardening equipment and boomboxes are some of the noisemakers addressed here. Information on what is being done in government, classrooms and national parks is provided, as is a library for more in-depth research. Visitors with noise problems can check out Quietnet, a listing of noise groups and organizations dedicated to making the world quieter. ⓐⓐⓐ

U.S. DEPARTMENT OF ENERGY: ENVIRONMENTAL MANAGEMENT
www.em.doe.gov
This slightly stiff but earnest site offers information on waste management, nuclear material stabilization and environmental restoration. The table of contents has information on topics as diverse as Accelerating Cleanup and Six Phase Soil Heating. The site also offers links to current and past editions of the EnviroWatch newsletter, which tackles mercury treatment, radioactive waste and environmental regulations. ⓐⓐⓐ

Science Museums

(originally reviewed November 1999)

AMERICAN MUSEUM OF NATURAL HISTORY
www.amnh.org
This is a top-notch example of what a virtual science museum should be. Not only does the AMNH site offer an interactive tour of the Planet Earth exhibit (in the Rose Center; follow easy instructions to load the required free software), it is packed with educational activities, photographs and video clips on a range of topics. Browse Natural History magazine, or check in on the current exhibits. ⓐⓐⓐⓐ

BOSTON'S MUSEUM OF SCIENCE
www.mos.org
This colorful and clean site is a joy to explore. Online exhibits include photos, activities and essays from scientists. During our last

visit, we explored the Messages exhibit, which investigates the many ways people and animals communicate. It even contains a Bee Cam—a Webcam focused on the museum's beehive. Other exhibits include Everest, demonstrations of scanning electron microscopes and an interactive display on the art and inventions of the multitalented Leonardo da Vinci.

THE EXPLORATORIUM
www.exploratorium.edu

At this thrilling science museum, there's more than meets the eye. Online exhibits play with optical illusions and mental tricks, measure reaction time and examine sounds. Inquisitive visitors can also watch videos of solar eclipses, deconstruct the swing of a baseball bat, listen to the rainforest and take a look at a sheep's brain. Still curious? Try the featured activity or poke around the digital library.

MUSEUM OF SCIENCE AND INDUSTRY
www.msichicago.org

Elegant design and great photographs are the highlights of this Chicago museum's online home. Enter the Exhibits area to find the online displays. Descend into a coal mine, or tour a WWII-era German U-boat via QuickTime videos. Learn about streamlined design and the legendary Pioneer Zephyr train, or explore a miniature fairy castle filled with gems and original artistic works. Descriptions and photos of more than a dozen permanent exhibits are also available.

QUESTACON
www.questacon.edu.au

This Australian science and technology museum is full of educational and entertaining features. Visit the Fun Zone for star charts, dinosaur games, do-at-home activities and 3-D World. Or take a virtual tour to learn about spiders, force and illusion. This visually stimulating site even has resources for teachers. On the downside, you'll need several plug-ins to view many of the online exhibits.

THE FRANKLIN INSTITUTE SCIENCE MUSEUM
sln.fi.edu

A handful of good online exhibits makes this museum's site worth a visit. Browse Franklin's Forecast to learn about weather events and radar or create a home weather station. For smaller exhibits on forest fires, spiders, robotics and light, among other things, check under The Spotlights. The inQuiry Attic explores important scientific instruments, while inQuiry Almanack features classroom activities.

Screensavers

(originally reviewed November 1999)

FREE-SAVERS.COM
www.free-savers.com

This may not be "your #1 choice for best screen savers" as the site touts, but it's pretty darn good. Each screensaver is described briefly, with careful details about how to properly download the files. There are several categories from which to choose, including 3D, Photographic and Cartoon. If you don't find the screensaver you're looking for here, there are links to other sites that may have what you want.

SOFTSEEK: SCREEN SAVERS
www.softseek.com/desktop_enhancements/screen_savers

Consider this a portal for screensavers. There are hundreds of links on this page to sites that have some of the trendiest ways to save your screen. Find screensavers based on current movies and wacky images such as the surrealistic spinning Fotocube. There's also an MP3 screensaver that lets users customize images as well as music.

THE UNLEASHED
www.theunleashed.com

Name the screensaver you want, and this fun site probably has it. There are thousands of easy-to-download screensavers and desktop patterns. Choose from People, Animal, Cartoon, Holiday, Art, Sci-Fi, Sport and Nature, to name but a few categories. New savers are added each day, so be sure to check back often. To use the files, you'll have to first decompress them with WinZip 7.0, which you can download for free from the site.

CINEMA DESKTOP THEMES
cinemadesktopthemes.com
If movie stars and Hollywood glitter are your thing, then roll your mouse to this site. The latest movie, television and celebrity desktop themes, wallpaper and screensavers are highlighted here. For newbies to the download scene, read FAQ to discover what all the lingo means. For example, learn the difference between a theme and wallpaper. Everything here is free, and there are clear details about how long files take to download and install. ⓐⓐⓐ

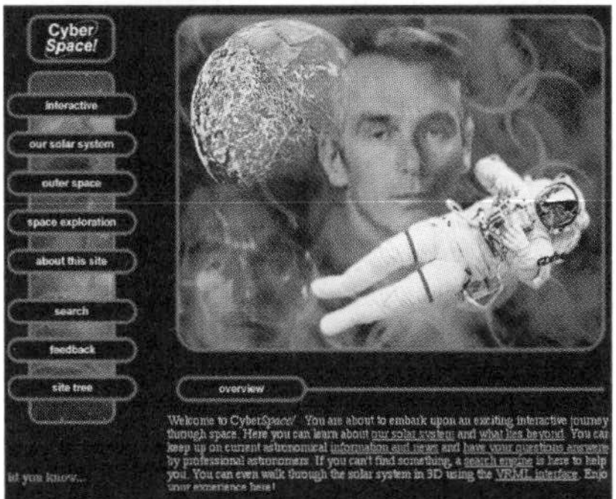

CyberSpace! is an out-of-this-world site created by students in Tucson, Ariz.

SCREEN SAVERS BONANZA
www.bonanzas.com/ssavers
OK, so it's not the best looking site, nor does it have the largest selection. What places this site above others is that the screensavers are organized by operating system—and there's a section for Macs (after all, Mac users should be able to have some fun, too). Thorough specifications for each screensaver are also provided, including file size, a brief description, a rating from "good" to "highly recommended" and even contact information to reach the screensavers' authors. ⓐⓐⓐ

SNAP-SHOT WALLPAPER
www.snap-shot.com
This site is the proverbial wallflower that belongs in the middle of the dance floor. Despite its home-brewed design, Snap-Shot Wallpaper is actually a downloading powerhouse. What makes it strong—aside from the thousands of free images—is a free software program called Webshots Desktop for Windows 95/98/NT/2000. It helps optimize your desktop and screensaver capabilities. Don't miss it. ⓐⓐⓐ

Space

(originally reviewed January 2000)

CYBERSPACE!
library.thinkquest.org/12659
Just one of the many great sites created by students for the national Web-building project ThinkQuest, CyberSpace! skillfully tackles the universe. Ponder the mysteries of our solar system and outer space with the students. Intelligible, nontechnical text explains phenomena such as gravity and the life cycle of a star. Great graphics and photos accompany each page, and there's a clever VRML (virtual reality modeling language) representation of the universe that lets you explore a 3-D solar system. ⓐⓐⓐⓐ

SPACE.COM
www.space.com
This intriguing project about space combines news and entertainment. News junkies and space buffs alike could get lost in this site for days. Lavish illustrations and brilliant photos liven up a place most of us think of as cold and dark. Entertainment contains reviews of TV shows, movies and books—such as episodes of "Star Trek: Voyager" and "The X-Files," and the book "John Glenn: A Memoir." Search for Life features all the extraterrestrial news and events fit to print, and spaceKids has play areas and stories. ⓐⓐⓐⓐ

WINDOWS TO THE UNIVERSE
www.windows.umich.edu
This is possibly the coolest space site in, well, the universe. Meant to be a starting point for amateur astronomers, Windows to the Universe fits a world of space facts into simple, well-organized categories. From the homepage, click on Enter the Site to get to the index. Then click on a topic of interest to find images and information on the solar system, space missions, important personalities in space exploration and even space poetry. We especially like the section on space mythology. ⓐⓐⓐⓐ

ASTRONOMY IN YOUR FACE
www.sorgeweb.com/astronomy
Sky watchers may want to bookmark this page. It's a great source for information about upcoming celestial events and astronomy news. Explore the photographs of planets, nebulae, hurricanes and galaxies. The Astronomy Events Calendar charts a year's worth of happenings; events in the next week or two are highlighted on the homepage. Links to interesting astronomical software and screensavers can be found in the AIYF Downloads section. ⓐⓐⓐ

EARTHSPACE.NET
www.earthspace.net
Set up as a virtual tour of the universe, this site takes visitors to the nine planets and the sun, gives a guide to the constellations and offers a handful of interesting but somewhat unrelated hands-on activities: create fog in a bottle or make your own barometer. Each constellation diagram is accompanied by a brief description of the mythology behind the name, as well as descriptions of the individual stars that make up the group.

AN INQUIRER'S GUIDE TO THE UNIVERSE
www.fi.edu/planets
The imaginative activities and questions here are meant to spark discussions with children. The Guide first points visitors to an eclectic collection of space facts. Next, it leads readers through a hilarious and fascinating collection of space lore. Finally, the site shows users a collection of imaginary planets and asks for stories and thoughts on what life on another planet would be like. Submissions from others can be found in the Space Story Portfolio.

Tech Support

(originally reviewed October 1999)

AOL NETHELP
www.aol.com/nethelp
America Online's help section (AOL Keyword: Nethelp) offers everything from technical tidbits on Web publishing to instructions on searching the Net. Learn the art of downloading, zipping and unzipping files, decoding error messages, clearing caches and working with such old-school services as Gopher. Worried about what your children see? Check out the section on keeping kids safe. As with much of AOL, the interface is clean, and the content is readily accessible.

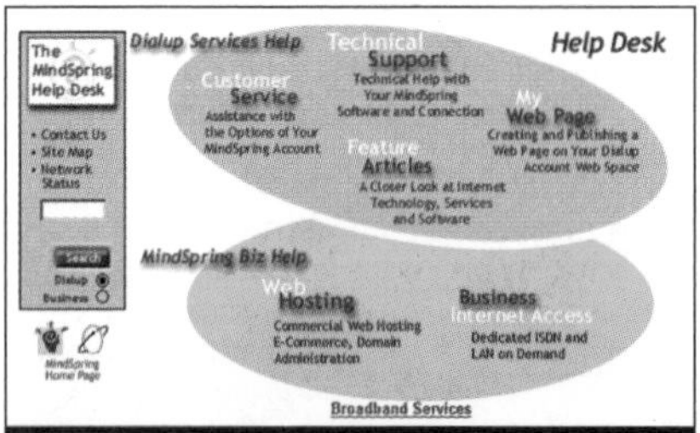

Learn about URLs, chatting and cookies at Mindspring's help site.

MICROSOFT PRODUCT SUPPORT
support.microsoft.com/directory
Microsoft offers a well-choreographed site with superb graphics and an elegant design. Both free and fee-based services are available via the Web; find the best support option by clicking on the product for which you need help. Internet Explorer help can be found at *www.microsoft.com/windows/ie/support/default.asp*. You'll find clear, step-by-step instructions for downloading, installing and trouble-shooting for IE. There's also a handy FAQ page and the Knowledge Base, a library of helpful articles.

THE MINDSPRING HELP DESK
help.mindspring.com
This 6-year-old, Atlanta-based Internet service provider has a content-rich site. You don't have to be a Mindspring customer to get something out of this site—the Feature Articles and My Web Page sections provide tools for general surfers. Learn about URLs, chatting, cookies and other Internet basics. More advanced users may want to study up on designing and maintaining their own sites.

APPLECARE SERVICE AND SUPPORT
www.apple.com/support
Multilingual support and technical exchange forums are available here, alongside step-by-step instructions for installing a range of Apple products. In the Support section, the Tech Info Library has useful articles ("Error Codes Explained," "Troubleshooting Startup Issues.") You can also find the latest Apple software updates and participate in hardware or software support discussions. Lost your Apple manual? Download them here. You'll need Adobe Acrobat Reader 3.0 or higher to read them.

NETSCAPE HELP
www.netscape.com/support
From configuration to trouble-shooting to connectivity, it's all here. Browse technical articles or read FAQs. Get advice from other Netscape users by visiting the NUGgies newsgroups. A File Library offers products such as downloadable help files and the newest Java Developers Kit. This comprehensive page also offers information on Netscape phone support. Look in the Hot News box to locate a page of links to Year 2000 resources.

shopping

Art Shopping

(originally reviewed November 1999)

CORBIS STORE
store.corbis.com
This site offers art prints, posters and screensavers at comparatively affordable prices. What makes this site special is its multifaceted way of delivering art: Customers can order a print to be shipped to them, download it as a digital image or send it off in an e-card. An easy ordering process, several framing options and recommendations from the staff add to this site's appeal. An impressive selection of Ansel Adams prints highlights this well-organized online gallery. ⓐⓐⓐⓐ

GLOBAL GALLERY
www.globalgallery.net
"Art shopping made easy" is the motto at this stylish, outstanding venue for purchasing prints online. For the number and quality of images displayed, this site's browsing speed is impressive. Check out the featured artist of the week, or peruse an intriguing collection of vintage advertisements. Aside from shopping, visitors can vote for the Millennium 100 Collection, a list of the most remarkable artistic works of the past 1,000 years, or read biographies of their favorite artists. ⓐⓐⓐⓐ

ALL ABOUT ART
www.allaboutart.com
This online print and poster shop combines top-quality service with an extensive catalog. The catalog is searchable by title, subject and artist, making the site's navigation as efficient as its design. Prints can be transferred to canvas or custom-framed for an added charge. Reassuring bonus: All About Art posts a policy of 100 percent refunds and free return shipping if you are dissatisfied with a product, including custom orders. ⓐⓐⓐ

BAREWALLS.COM
www.barewalls.com
Thousands of prints and posters at reasonable prices make this an ideal shopping source for apartment dwellers and college students. Prints include classic paintings by Claude Monet, Leonardo da Vinci and Vincent van Gogh, plus more modern works and photographs by the likes of Joan Miro and Robert Doisneau. Browse the collection by style, subject or artist, or use the search engine for keyword searches. Unsure what to buy? Take a peek at Current Favorites. ⓐⓐⓐ

FINE ART SITE
www.fineartsite.com
This Internet gallery is targeted at those serious about buying and selling original art (read: expensive). Prices range from hundreds of dollars to tens of thousands of dollars. Users can add to their art collection by bidding on works from a distinguished stable of artists. For a fee, you can have your art appraised and put up for sale; about half of the listings are from private sellers. On our last visit, the site featured works by Erte, David Hockney and Norman Rockwell, among others. Potential buyers can contact sellers with questions before making a purchase. ⓐⓐⓐ

ART-MART
www.art-mart.com
You'll find specs and images of prints, etchings, silk screens, oil paintings and posters at this gallery. The subject categories range from cityscapes to landscapes and everything in between. Browse the online store, or check out what's on the auction block. Art-mart claims to specialize in finding hard-to-get prints, so if a specific piece isn't listed, you can special order it. A simple layout makes for easy navigation, while the wide range of prices should appeal to a financially diverse assortment of collectors. ⓐⓐ

Coupons

(originally reviewed October 1999)

COOLSAVINGS.COM
www.coolsavings.com
With more than 2 million registered households, this is the definitive coupon Web site. It's easy: Spend a few minutes filling out information about yourself, then peruse the discount offers specially personalized for your account. Or you can search for deals by category. By using the site, you can save money and receive free promotional stuff, including trial issues of magazines and things from retailers such as Petsmart.com and barnesandnoble.com. Mac users need Netscape's browser to download coupons here. ⓐⓐⓐⓐ

COUPON SURFER
www.couponsurfer.com
This site is working hard to become your

favorite coupon distributor on the Net. It's free and easy to sign up, and the coupons are a decent value. The best part is that these e-coupons are only good for e-commerce, thus promoting shopping on the Web—and reducing traffic in actual malls. You can start shopping immediately—no waiting for coupons to come in the mail. ⓐⓐⓐⓐ

MYCOUPONS.COM
www.mycoupons.com
This is quite possibly the future of coupon-swapping among friends. Aside from links to retail coupons, there are also links to forums under Coupon/Rebate Swap. The forums allow consumers and merchants, including LensCrafters and Revlon, to share information or exchange deals. If you have something that you don't want, post a message to arrange a trade. Be sure to check out the freebies, too. ⓐⓐⓐⓐ

CENTSOFF.COM
www.centsoff.com
As the "first online coupon clipping and delivery service," this site boasts that its database contains more than 1 million coupons. The only problem is that signing up and selecting coupons takes a fair amount of time. There is also a convoluted billing process—you pay $5 for every 50 coupons you order, in addition to an annual membership fee—so read the fine print carefully. After that, the coupons come to you in the mail. ⓐⓐⓐ

EBATES.COM
www.ebates.com
Instead of offering coupons, ebates.com offers rebates. You can get up to 25 percent back on purchases at participating online stores. But let's face it, retailers aren't going to give all of their profits away—the average rebate is about 8 percent. A few stores require a minimum purchase, and some products aren't eligible for rebates. But the service is free, and the instructions are easy to follow. ⓐⓐⓐ

VAL-PAK COUPONS
www.valpak.com
Familiar with that fat envelope of coupons that periodically arrives in your mailbox? This site helps you make the coupons more useful. Join for free, and the site will generate coupons for your specific needs based on location—for everything from dining to automotive services. There is one glitch: You have to wait for the snail mail to deliver your coupons. ⓐⓐ

Electronics shopping is easy with the database at 800.com.

Electronics Shopping

(originally reviewed September 1999)

CYBERSHOP: CONSUMER ELECTRONICS
cybershop.com/categories/consumerelectronics9369.asp
If it plugs in or takes batteries, you'll probably find it here. This is a superstore at your beck and call, featuring thousands of electronic products, including microwaves, fans and vacuums, plus large kitchen appliances such as refrigerators and dishwashers. Rounding out the collection is an awesome selection of camcorders, cameras and portable stereos. Shipping charges, displayed on the order form, vary according to destination and shipper. ⓐⓐⓐⓐ

800.COM
www.800.com
Shopping is a snap here, with easy navigation and a searchable database designed to help you wade through a vast selection. Choose from home theater and audio components, boomboxes, MiniDisc players, telephones, camcorders and WebTV products. While you're here, cruise through the selection of movies and music to go with your new components. ⓐⓐⓐ

PCWONDERS.COM
www.pcwonders.com
These folks know about shopping. The site by BuyItNow.com and pcWonders.com carries brand-name electronics and products to fill the void of your audio, video, gaming, home security and communication needs. The items can be located by category—such as Computers, Software and "As Seen on TV"—or are searchable by manufacturer and are easy to find. Shipping prices vary but are listed at the bottom of a product's page, so you know what you're in for before you check out. ⓐⓐⓐ

GIANTSAVINGS.COM
www.giantsavings.com
Watch the lines between "want" and "need" blur as you peruse this fine selection of toys and tools. This is no-frills shopping for

everything from shavers, color printers and telescopes to telephones, cameras and home stereo components. Quick-loading graphics and low prices on many items will keep you coming back. If you have Sharper Image taste and a Wal-Mart budget, this shop is definitely worth a click or two. Shipping starts at $6.95. ⓐⓐⓐ

SERVICE MERCHANDISE
www.servicemerchandise.com
This solid national chain, best known for its broad line of jewelry, also offers a nice online selection of products in its electronics department. Audio equipment, office accessories, cameras and telephones anchor the site; a small section of electronic musical instruments adds a nice touch. A choice of shipping methods and a range of shipping rates appears on the order form. ⓐⓐ

Florists

(originally reviewed October 1999)

CALYX AND COROLLA
www.calyxandcorolla.com
For people who send only the best, this upscale florist sells exquisite bouquets from its elegant site. Shipping directly from the world's "best growers," the company guarantees that its flowers will last five to 10 days longer than most others—each rose is set on its own ice gel pillow. The arrangements are breathtaking and the selection is tops—from rare Casa Blanca lilies to orchids. You won't find any cheap carnations here. Fresh herb baskets, plants and preserved wreaths are also available. Shipping starts at $9.95. ⓐⓐⓐⓐ

1-800-FLOWERS.COM
www.1800flowers.com
In addition to a lovely selection of arrangements—some in creative vases and baskets—this site features a garden selection with perennials, vines, bulbs and seeds, as well as garden furniture and decorative accessories. Other gift options include gourmet baskets, wreaths and candles. A reminder service sends you an e-mail before important birthdays or anniversaries. Flower tips and do-it-yourself ideas round out this excellent site. Shipping for floral arrangements starts at $4.99. ⓐⓐⓐⓐ

FLORIST.COM
www.florist.com
Among a traditional assortment of bouquets and plants, there are some nice features here. There is a reminder service, as well as information about state flowers, the "language of flowers" and birthday flowers, which are akin to

Never forget another birthday with the 1-800-flowers.com reminder service.

birthstones. Florist.com also ships gourmet baskets and balloon arrangements. Shipping is $5.99. ⓐⓐⓐ

FTD
www.ftd.com
FTD is one of the best known florists, and its Web site doesn't disappoint. Its network of 75,000 retail florists delivers all over the world, and there are numerous categories from which to choose, including Winnie-the-Pooh and exotic flowers. Visitors can also send gourmet gifts or balloon bouquets. A standout is the Great Ideas page, which has tips, holiday traditions and flower lore. ⓐⓐⓐ

PROFLOWERS.COM
www.proflowers.com
This company says it buys fresh-cut flowers right from the grower, and then passes the savings on to the customer. The site is easy to surf, bright and colorful, with selection by flower type or occasion. There's also a complete list of arrangements from which to choose. Special programs include weekly deliveries for businesses, a flower guide, flower care and arranging tips, and a section in Spanish. Shipping starts at $7.95 and is via FedEx Overnight. ⓐⓐⓐ

Furniture Shopping

(originally reviewed October 1999)

FURNITURE.COM
www.furniture.com
Serious furniture shoppers should register here to take advantage of this site's free expert advice. Furniture.com offers a Room Planner (select a few items, first), online chat with consultants, a personal shopping service and free fabric swatches. The large furniture selection covers all the essentials and then some, and is

easily searched with the site's database. Just input your style, color and price range preferences, and you're on your way. ⓐⓐⓐⓐ

LIVING.COM
www.living.com
We had to tear ourselves away from this site before we whipped out the plastic and started buying things to redecorate our office. There's a lot of cool furniture here—retro velvet couches, law-office-style leather chairs, delicate love seats with carved wooden legs, oriental rugs, cafe tables and Shaker-style beds. Browse by item or room, and don't forget to check out decorator tips and advice in the site's online magazine. Shipping varies depending on the item. ⓐⓐⓐⓐ

ROOM & BOARD
www.roomandboard.com
This simple and attractive site has a small but elegant selection of contemporary furniture. Clean lines, unique details and neutral colors predominate, from curved-back chenille sofas to children's dressers with whimsical knobs. The inventory also includes accent tables, storage pieces, and dining room, bedroom and office furniture. The one downside is that there is no online ordering system—you have to use the company's toll-free number instead. Shipping charges are calculated when an order is placed. ⓐⓐⓐ

JCPENNEY FURNITURE STORE
www.jcpenneyfurniture.com
Expect solid, familiar styles and reasonable prices from this well-known retailer. The selection is basic: leather and fabric couches, mattresses, bedroom furniture, dining tables, computer furniture and a few unfinished pieces. Shipping is based on weight; a 100-pound item, for example, costs $28 to ship. ⓐⓐ

Jewelry Shopping

(originally reviewed December 1999)

GEMS AND JEWELS.COM
www.gemsandjewels.com
QVC—the cable TV show that sells jewelry and other products—delivers this site, which is professionally designed and fun to use. First, choose the type of item you want—silver, gold or gemstone. Then choose the piece—earrings, ring, necklace, bracelet or pin. From there you can narrow in on a specific item, such as emerald earrings or a San Marco bracelet. Or choose pieces from top designers and celebrities, such as Nolan Miller, Judith Jack and Joan Rivers. The selection is enormous, and there is a wide range of prices. Returns are accepted within 30 days; some items have a lifetime warranty. ⓐⓐⓐⓐ

MONDERA.COM
www.mondera.com
Start off at the Learning Center, its "diamond and jewelry information resource." Diamonds are featured heavily here, but the site also sells watches, bracelets, pins, earrings and necklaces. Style Passport tells you what's hot around the world—Buddha bead bracelets in New York and chokers in Milan. There's a 30-day return policy and free shipping. If you have questions, talk to a customer service representative via live chat or by phone. ⓐⓐⓐⓐ

DIAMOND INFORMATION CENTER
www.adiamondisforever.com
The best features about this site from ubiquitous diamond seller De Beers are the numerous tools to help you choose a diamond and the Design Your Own Engagement Ring function. Once you choose the ring particulars, e-mail them to your significant other as a not-so-subtle hint. From the four C's—cut, clarity, carat weight and color—to how much to spend and 12 proposal ideas, there are tips for everyone. You can't buy your ring here, but it's such an important purchase, you might not want to. ⓐⓐⓐ

FIRST JEWELRY
www.firstjewelry.com
Shopping for jewelry on this elegantly designed site could net you a rare African tanzanite ring or a diamond pendant. Categories are divided into styles (casual, traditional, exotic) or type (bracelets, necklaces, watches). There is advice in the form of mini-articles, so you can learn all about those pearls you want. Subscribe to the online newsletter or compile a Wish List. Shipping is free for a limited time. ⓐⓐⓐ

FORTUNOFF: JEWELRY
www.fortunoff.com/index.asp?dept_id=3000000
In business since 1922, Fortunoff has an easy-to-use Web site. The Jewelry section contains

shopping

hundreds of items in various categories, including Children, Estate & Antique, Men's, Platinum and Religious. Searches can be sorted by price or by type, such as kind of gemstone or carat. There's a 30-day return policy, and Fortunoff will match the prices of online competitors. Shipping for purchases that total more than $150 is free. Check the Advice Corner before you buy a diamond. ⓐⓐⓐ

GWEN'S JEWELRY AND GIFTS
www.gwensjewelry.com
It's not flashy, but the selection here is mind-boggling. Platinum, gold, silver and gemstones are available in every imaginable shape and form. Categories are clear and narrowly defined so you can immediately zero in on what you're seeking. There is also a large selection of non-jewelry gifts. Purchases can be tracked with the USPS tracking system. The site allows returns and exchanges, but be sure to read the fine print as there are exceptions. ⓐⓐ

MY JEWELRY
www.myjewelry.com
Affiliated with catalog giant Fingerhut, My Jewelry features a 30-day trial for its wares. The Design Your Own Ring section for engagement and class rings allows you to create and then purchase your piece online, or instead choose from among the 12,000 pieces the site offers. Master jeweler Steven Kaplan guides you through the site, sharing advice and tips. Other features include financing with a store credit card or ordering from the Fingerhut catalog. ⓐⓐⓐ

Ticketing

(originally reviewed November 1999)

TICKETMASTER ONLINE
www.ticketmaster.com
As the industry giant, Ticketmaster has tickets to more events than its competitors. So it's no surprise that its Web site is the best one out there. Search myriad musical, sporting, theatrical and family events by genre. A prominent search engine helps users find events by state. You can purchase accompanying CDs, T-shirts, videos or baseball caps online. The servers are sometimes unreliable, so buy your tickets during an off-peak time for best results. ⓐⓐⓐⓐ

AUDIENCES UNLIMITED, INC.
www.tvtickets.com
If you've ever wanted to attend a live taping of your favorite television show, then check out this Web site. It has free tickets to more than 30 sitcoms, including "Friends," "Just Shoot Me" and "That '70s Show." Of course, you have to be in Los Angeles to see a taping. Pick a show and an available date from the schedule and fill out the online form. Who knows? You might even get to meet the show's stars. ⓐⓐⓐ

TELE-CHARGE.COM
www.telecharge.com
Theater lovers can buy tickets for Broadway or off-Broadway shows, as well as performances from Boston to Los Angeles at this site. It also provides information about each show's plot, running time, awards, cast and crew. Plus, there are seating charts, theater information and recommendations about audience age. Tickets can be mailed to you or held at the box office. The only problem you'll have is choosing a show. ⓐⓐⓐ

TICKETS.COM
www.tickets.com
This unique site is working to combine all of the online ticket sales channels—from authorized vendors and box offices to auctions and brokers—in one place. Choose a concert, sports, theater, ballet, museum or other event, and you'll get a link to the vendors who have tickets. Frequently that vendor is Ticketmaster. Use the search engine to scout for events by city or venue. The selection is somewhat limited, but the convenience factor makes up for it. ⓐⓐⓐ

TICKETSNOW.COM
www.ticketsnow.com
From the Backstreet Boys to the San Francisco 49ers, this virtual broker sells those must-have tickets for sold-out events—but expect to pay top dollar for your seats. Yes, it's legal. The company is licensed in Illinois and is a Better Business Bureau member. The BBB says TicketsNow.com meets reliability standards, although this isn't a guarantee. Read the fine print before you purchase. ⓐⓐⓐ

TICKETWEB
www.ticketweb.com
This site focuses on small venues and clubs, as well as museums and art galleries. It sells the tickets online with less of a service charge than many competitors—$2 is the maximum fee. However, there are no tickets for most major venues. If you want to see the Guggenheim, the San Francisco Jazz Festival or the San Diego Zoo, then get online—not in line—at this ticket window. ⓐⓐⓐ

WHAT'S ON STAGE
www.whatsonstage.com

Planning a trip to the United Kingdom? Then check out this site that offers venue information, show schedules and ticket booking for everything from concerts to museums to tours. Tickets purchased online cannot be mailed. If you don't want to wait until the day of the event to pick them up, order over the phone. ⓐⓐⓐ

Print free tickets from www.tvtix.com.

FREE TV TICKETS
www.tvtix.com

If the words "I'd like to solve the puzzle'" have a special place in your heart, then get your tickets to the classic game show "Wheel of Fortune" at this site. Most tickets here are for just a couple of game shows, but there are others, such as "Dennis Miller Live" on HBO. Choose a show and date from the master list. Your tickets will be generated on your computer screen, ready to be printed out. The tickets are free, but you'll have to pay for your own way to Hollywood. ⓐⓐ

Virtual Malls

(originally reviewed November 1999)

FASHIONMALL.COM
www.fashionmall.com

It's great to have a virtual mall devoted entirely to fashion, but unless you're familiar with Manhattan, you could easily become lost here. Stores are grouped into six Lifestyles: Main Street, SoHo, Galleria, Madison, Luxe Life and The Edge. The SoHo stores, for example, feature more trendy items, while Madison—as in Avenue—has chic designer labels. You can also sort by Category—men's, women's, jewelry or bridal—or by Brand, such as Brooks Brothers or Skechers. Ask the Style Experts is a fun feature. ⓐⓐⓐⓐ

MALL.COM
www.mall.com

This has one of the neatest interfaces we've seen. It looks like a directory at a traditional shopping mall—you know, that building where the parking is a nightmare. Mall.com has many of the same stores as the shopping mall down the street, such as Nine West, Gap, Gymboree and Target. It offers a Personal Shopper service, which can give you advice on what to buy or even shop for you. The easy-to-use page makes it a cinch to shop here, too. ⓐⓐⓐⓐ

IMALL
www.imall.com

Created in 1994, iMall was one of the Internet's first e-commerce portals. Now with 14 convenient shopping departments, iMall still qualifies as one of the Net's most serviceable virtual malls. From socks to stereos, this site's boundless domain covers every imaginable shopping need. Easy-out bonus: The well-organized ordering procedure makes checkout practically effortless. ⓐⓐⓐ

MSN SHOPPING
shopping.msn.com

Like many virtual malls, this is more of a links station than a mall in the real-world sense. Choosing a merchant merely transports you to that company's homepage, instead of to a specialized interface. It is a convenient way to shop, however. MSN offers reputable retailers, including Red Envelope and Barnesandnoble.com. The best feature is the potentially addictive page of browsable, frequently updated Sales & Deals. ⓐⓐⓐ

WORLD WIDE WEBAZAAR
www.worldwidewebazaar.com

Although the name is a tad wordy, this virtual mall is a cut above most others. Each of the stores gives a friendly hello, with a description of the wares it sells and special deals currently available. This approach is much nicer than the plain laundry list of shopping links you get at other mall sites. However, there's a puzzling lack of clothing merchants to choose from, and the search engine could be more accurate. ⓐⓐⓐ

PLANET SHOPPING NETWORK
www.planetshopping.com

This is a big group of stores with a shopping interface that isn't perfect but is simple to use. PSN has a variety of retailers, though not many of them are major players in the traditional mall world. Its stronger categories include technology, business and sporting goods. A handy holiday shopping area offers gift ideas. We do have a couple of gripes: The lack of a search engine hurts this site a bit, and the sales list requires too much scrolling to find good stuff. ⓐⓐ

sports

Billiards

(originally reviewed January 2000)

WOMEN & BILLIARDS ONLINE MAGAZINE
www.wbom.com
OK, guys, this site promotes female players, but there are plenty of tips and resources for everyone. Check in for instructional features, women's tour updates, editorial commentary and stories by readers. Instructional columns describe simple drills to practice your skills. Articles by regular columnists include their bios and sometimes photos, which add a real-world touch to this virtual medium. Billiards fans who are also Internet users may enjoy the free Web space offered here.

AMATEUR BILLIARD NEWS
www.amateurbilliardnews.com
Although this site is based on a regional billiards magazine from Pittsburgh, it offers top-notch tips and information for players around the country. Enthusiasts can ask questions about maintaining a pool table, follow along with beginning and intermediate lessons from the Coach or read tips on choosing a cue. A Pool TV Guide, book review section and nicely organized links add depth to the site.

BILLIARD CONGRESS OF AMERICA
www.bca-pool.com
The information here is wide-ranging. Choose your topic from the rack of pool balls—Rules, History, Publications, Hall of Fame and Leagues are among the choices. Particularly useful are the tournament and association listings, which provide hotlinks to detailed information. Also worth visiting is the Links section, a well-organized page that connects players with news, chat, tips and leagues. This site is a good place to find resources, but you won't find instruction or tips.

BILLIARDS SEMINARS INT'L
www.bsintl.com
Site host Dick Jacobs draws on his own books for content. This means he is also promoting them, but he manages to do it without being too obtrusive. Stop in for strategies, instructions for re-tipping cues and a weekly Q&A. Do browse the Editorial Archive. It offers half a dozen articles by Jacobs on various topics, including aspects of a player's psyche, the toughest shot in billiards and approaching strangers to play.

CUE-TECH
www.poolschool.com
Although this pool school hawks its lessons online, its Web site is a good resource for some free tips and tricks. The tutorials cover practicing and the basics, including stance, grip and bridge. Get the free RealPlayer plug-in and watch instructional videos to learn how to shoot softly, use the "rake" and shoot close to the ball. Click on Tricks to watch videos of some fancy moves.

PLAYPOOL.COM
www.playpool.com
Looking for a nearby pool hall or a tournament in the United States? This is a good place to start your search. Just input the name of a city or a ZIP code in the Pool Hall Finder or the Tourney Finder. You'll get current lists of tournaments and places to play. The message board is moderately active, but the news coverage is slim, updating about once or twice a month. There are also tournament charts, score sheets and tournament planners that you can download from the site for free.

Boxing

(originally reviewed October 1999)

HBO: BOXING
www.hbo.com/boxing
A leader even among the top-tier boxing sites, this stellar site confirms that HBO is downright passionate about the "sweet science." Well-designed, a touch offbeat (see Joyce Carol Oates' literary tribute to boxing) and incredibly thorough, this site has weekly columns and fan forums. Mix in commentary from legends George Foreman, Larry Merchant and Roy Jones Jr., and HBO is a boxing resource that's guaranteed to knock you out.

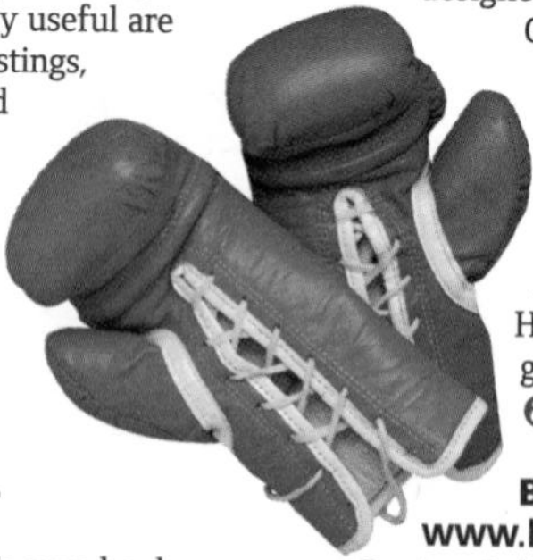

BOXING ONLINE
www.boxingonline.com
Boxing Online wants you to see it, not just read it. It does so by bringing the latest boxing news via a barrage of video clips from press conferences, fights and interviews. Live weekly events such as In This Corner and interviews with top fighters such as Oscar De La Hoya require Windows Media Player to view them. Rankings and analysis from the WBA, WBC and IBF are available, as are gritty features on boxing's hottest issues.

HOUSE OF BOXING
www.houseofboxing.com
With video workouts of top fighters such as Shane Mosley and ringside interviews with brawlers like Shannon Briggs, this site offers top fight scene coverage in the sport's typical in-your-face style. Articles laced with combative, controversial prose recall old-school boxing reporting. The site also includes subscription information for the HOB-published Latino Boxing Magazine, which the site claims is the Net's only bilingual boxing publication. ⓐⓐⓐ

BOXING ON THE WEB
www.ipcress.com/boxing
This straightforward site covers the basics of the boxing scene, from fight regulations to a breakdown of the 17 different weight classes. Listings of the current world champions by association and division shed light on the sometimes-confusing issue of who holds a title belt where. With profiles on hundreds of fighters, this site is ideal for novices seeking to upgrade their boxing knowledge. ⓐⓐ

Downhill Skiing

(originally reviewed November 1999)

GORP: DOWNHILL SKIING
www.gorp.com/gorp/activity/skiing/ski_down.htm
Downhill skiers shouldn't miss this site. Information on ski areas all over the world is divided by region. Each section varies depending on the type of skiing in that area: The New England section kicks off with recommendations for family ski trips and an insider's look at trail skiing, while Rocky Mountains features a guide to the top resorts and trails. Plus, there are forums, information about organized trips and links to online ski-gear retailers. ⓐⓐⓐⓐ

GOSKI
www.goski.com
Before you plan your next trip to the mountains, visit this enormous database of resort information. GoSki claims to have details about more than 2,000 resorts in 37 countries. For example, GoSki Italy has a list of ski resorts, commentary from skiers, a brief country profile and Local Links. Some listings also contain maps and currency converters. The site has a useful Weather section with current weather maps, a wind chill conversion table and an avalanche information center. Also look for gear reviews, travel planning help and message boards. ⓐⓐⓐⓐ

GORP GREAT OUTDOOR RECREATION PAGES
ATTRACTIONS ACTIVITIES LOCATIONS BOOKS/MEDIA TRAVEL GEAR ECLECTICA FEATURES
Rocky Mountain Remake
Colorado's Ski Resorts Get Better Than Ever
By Claire Walter
Next time you think skiing or snowboarding is expensive, consider that Colorado resorts invested more than $150 million — $102 million in new lifts, new terrain, improved snowmaking and other on-mountain facilities and $55.5 million in new base facilities, both for vacationers and locals. Add this to the $122.5 million sunk into Colorado slopes last year and $100 million the season before, and you begin to understand why everything from lift tickets to candy bars costs more in the mountains. Here are this year's major improvements.

Gorp: Downhill Skiing is an international guide to ski resorts.

SKINET.COM
www.skinet.com
Three of the sport's top magazines—Freeze, Skiing and Ski—have teamed up to produce this outstanding site packed with information. You will find current news, instructional articles, beautiful photos, extensive competition coverage and snow reports for mountains all over the globe. Handy features—including a gear finder, a reader survey of the top 60 resorts and helpful articles about boot technology and how to ski cheaply—give this site a definite edge. ⓐⓐⓐⓐ

EPICSKI
www.epicski.com
Ill-fitting ski boots can ruin a day on the slopes. However, the folks at EpicSki can help, bringing you the skinny on what's new in ski boots via a brand-by-brand report and a boot-fitting guide. The site recently launched new sections, including a Virtual Training Center. ⓐⓐⓐ

SKI.MOUNTAINZONE.COM
ski.mountainzone.com
This is a good site to visit for articles on extreme skiing, telemark racing and freestyle moves. There are also interviews with top skiers and reports from a variety of events, such as the Breckenridge Bump Buffet. Read Ski News to find out what is going on in downhill skiing, although the most recent articles are often out on the homepage. ⓐⓐ

SKIMAPS
www.skimaps.com
If you've ever wanted a trail map of Turkey's Uludaq or Israel's Mt. Hermon, this may be your

best bet. Search by country, or use the hypermap to browse a particular region. SkiMaps also has a resort and lodging search engine, lists of gear outfitters and articles about selecting boots, skiing for beginners and riding the chair lift. ◉◉

Extreme Sports

(originally reviewed November 1999)

GRAVITY GAMES
www.gravitygames.com
For nerves both shaky and steely, this action-oriented site aimed at type-A personalities is more than just informative. Sure, it has all the official stuff on the events and the athletes. But more than that, it's a visual bonanza. With photos and videos of everything related to skateboarding, freestyle motocross, street luge and wakeboarding, this site presents perilous stunts at all angles. ◉◉◉◉

SKATEBOARDING.COM
www.skateboarding.com
A crisp look and great content make this the best thing on wheels. Trick Tips feature instructions and photographs for cool-looking and painful-sounding stunts, among them the "backside noseblunt" and "fakie kickflip." Skateboard fans can also look for skate parks, catch up on skating news, read product reviews and chat with other skateboarders. ◉◉◉◉

ESPN: EXTREME SPORTS
espn.go.com/extreme
Created by one of the biggest names in sports broadcasting, this site highlights the X Games. The site's best feature is Xplained, a crash course in the history of skateboarding, aggressive in-line skating, bicycle stunt riding, sportclimbing, skysurfing, big-air snowboarding and other neck-threatening activities. ◉◉◉

EXTREMISTS
www.awezome.com
Many of the fast sports are here: snowboarding, motorbiking, bodyboarding, mountain biking, surfing and skiing. Drop in to learn about each sport and get tips on the necessary gear. You can also tune in for consumer reviews, view action photos or vote for the Extreme Top 50 Web sites. ◉◉◉

FROAD LUGE
www.roadluge.org
If skidding down pavement at 60 mph sounds like a thrill, this is the site for you. Described as "heaven a half-inch off the ground" and "skateboards on steroids," road luge is a growing

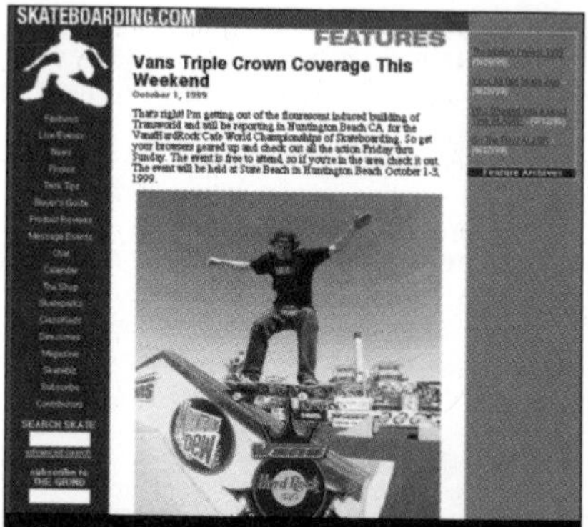
Find event coverage and tips at **www.skateboarding.com.**

X-sport. Check out the official rulebook, get the latest scores from competitions or put in your two cents in Road Spew. The site also profiles pro and amateur racers. ◉◉◉

Fishing

(originally reviewed September 1999)

FIELD & STREAM AND OUTDOOR LIFE: FISHING
www.fieldandstream.com/fishing
One of the best reasons for visiting this site is the Fish Finder, a database of game fish that provides information on habitat, distribution and physiology. The Fish Finder also offers an index of federal lands where you can fish for various species. For visitors who already know where they're going, this site supplies several dozen features on saltwater, freshwater and fly-fishing. Learn the six basic principles of landing a trophy bass or 10 ways to fool a smart trout. ◉◉◉◉

THE VIRTUAL FLYSHOP
www.flyshop.com
The Virtual Flyshop, Fly Fisherman magazine's online companion, features unparalleled analysis of regional fishing conditions. Visitors can research potential destinations such as California's McCloud River, British Columbia's Mighty Thompson River or the home of the "best saltwater fishing in the world," the saltwater flats of Belize. The site also regularly features information about conservation efforts, rod selection and fly tying. ◉◉◉◉

BEGINNER'S NETGUIDE TO FLYFISHING
www.myhost.com/flyfishing101
No idea what flyline tapers, leaders or improved clinch knots are? This site will teach

you basic information on fly-fishing equipment, assembly, knots and casting. Visitors are treated to large, crisp diagrams of essential knots, tables of suggested line weights that are cross-referenced to fish categories, and an animated demonstration of the ideal cast. ⓐⓐⓐ

FISHINGLINE.NET
www.fishingline.net
This large site devoted to freshwater fishing lets visitors pose questions to seasoned professionals or search for fishing hot spots by species of fish, type of water or state. Check in to find out which bait is best for bass or whether the fish are biting in Maine's beautiful Androscoggin River. Visitors can also join active chat room discussions with experienced anglers or delve into a sizable archive of features on everything from tournament tricks to night fishing. ⓐⓐⓐ

NOR'EAST SALTWATER ONLINE
www.noreast.com
Although this site focuses primarily on fishing conditions from New Jersey to Maine, there are excellent fly patterns and how-to information here for fishing anywhere. For those in the Northeast, read posted fishing reports, find boat charters or view image maps of sea temperatures updated several times daily from Rutgers University weather satellites. ⓐⓐⓐ

SALTWATER FISHING HOME PAGE
wmi.cais.com/saltfish
This mammoth fishing site is actually a collection of message boards that contain questions, answers and comments on saltwater fishing, fly-fishing and surf fishing. Anglers can browse a robust selection of tips and tactics, upcoming events and contests, fishing reports, and photos of the ones that didn't get away. For the latest articles and news updates, link to the Bass Fishing Home Page. ⓐⓐ

Hockey

(originally reviewed October 1999)

HOCKEY HALL OF FAME
www.hhof.com
How many games did Jean Ratelle play during his career? (1,281.) Or, better yet, who is Jean Ratelle? (Canadian center who played 21 NHL seasons.) Find plenty of facts like these at the Hockey Hall of Fame. The sleek, comprehensive site offers photos, statistics and bios of the top players, as well as a cool trivia game. Visit Records & Rankings for a look at milestones in hockey history. ⓐⓐⓐⓐ

NHL.COM
www.nhl.com
Browse the latest hockey news or join a live Q&A with a player at the NHL's official site—easily a top source of hockey information on the Web. During the season catch live audio broadcasts of every game and video of the latest game highlights. Sign up for the NHL.com newsletter while you're there, or boost your game knowledge at Hockey U. From stats and schedules to player diaries and league history, this is a must-see site for fans. ⓐⓐⓐⓐ

USA HOCKEY.COM
www.usahockey.com
The online home of USA Hockey—the sport's U.S. governing body—is a highly professional repository of hockey information. There are excellent coaching strategies, a parents' primer on youth hockey and facts on team training and women's, men's and junior championships. Starting a hockey league? Learn about game rules here and, more important, the kind of insurance you'll need. ⓐⓐⓐⓐ

THE INTERNET HOCKEY DATABASE
www.hockeydb.com
Card collectors in particular should pit stop here. This site is compiled by a rabid fan and offers checklists for all minor league and pro players who have ever had trading cards, as well as lists of complete card sets. A seemingly exhaustive list of logos is available for "every professional hockey team to ever suit up," as is an extensive archive of stats for each team and player. ⓐⓐⓐ

THE WOMEN'S HOCKEY WEB
www.whockey.com
This site is rich in content, but beware: The Canadian creator, Andria Hunter, gives her home team some preferential treatment. However, you'll find a universe of information on women's hockey—from stats and scores to player profiles and links. Need to know the final standings of the '96 European Pool B Championship in ... Slovakia? Look no further. ⓐⓐⓐ

Horse Racing

(originally reviewed October 1999)

THE BLOOD-HORSE INTERACTIVE
www.bloodhorse.com
Horse racing is a lot more than just watching horses circle a track. This site provides a wealth of

information for thoroughbred breeders, owners and enthusiasts. The Daily Edition offers recent news, live coverage of horse auctions, a stallion registry and forums on Dosage and Racing. There's also a link to Exclusively Equine.com, an online store where you can purchase racing photos and prints. Before you go, pull on your boots and take a Virtual Farm Tour. ⓐⓐⓐⓐ

CHURCHILL DOWNS
www.churchilldowns.com
One of the oldest racing tracks in the country and home of "the greatest two minutes in sports" —a k a the Kentucky Derby—also has one of the most comprehensive Web sites for racing fans. It includes an extensive gallery of Derby photos, as well as live racing from around the country. Learn race history and read the latest Barn Notes. There are even ideas for planning your own Derby party, complete with theme recipes and decorations. ⓐⓐⓐⓐ

OFFICIAL SITE OF THE BREEDERS' CUP CHAMPIONSHIP
www.breederscup.com
When the Breeders' Cup kicks off, there's no better place to keep up with the action than the official Web site. This easy-to-navigate site includes a history of the Breeders' Cup from its beginning in 1984, listings and information on breeders, jockeys, owners and trainers. You'll also find schedule and ticket information. ⓐⓐⓐⓐ

HORSEWIRE.COM
www.horsewire.com
Horse racing is all about picking winners, and this site is designed with that goal in mind. It contains reports from all the major tracks on horses, jockeys and trainers, and information on sure-bet winners and long shots. To access the free section of the site, users need to enter their e-mail addresses for periodic updates and newsletters. Unfortunately, a regular membership costs $24.95 per month. There's enough information in the free section to make it worth a visit. ⓐⓐⓐ

THE NEW YORK RACING ASSOCIATION
www.nyra.com
The NYRA operates some of the best-known racing venues, including Belmont Park, Aqueduct Race Track and Saratoga Race Course. This site helps racing enthusiasts keep up with race results and provides track-by-track standings for horses, trainers and jockeys. A handy glossary explains many horse terms. Downloadable PDF (portable document format) files for condition books on each of the weekend's races are available, and there is also access to NYRA publications such as The Horsemen's Guide. ⓐⓐⓐ

Kids Sports

(originally reviewed September 1999)

NHL: COOLEST KIDS
www.nhl.com/kids
Want to know which NHL player is the biggest prankster? Find out at this creative site's Team Central section, where interviews, profiles and fun facts expose every NHL team's funniest secrets. Yo, Coach! explains game rules and terms, while Game Time has fun, interactive games. Click on Cool Shots for video clips of blazing action on the ice. Street and e-mail addresses of all 30 teams make contacting your favorite NHL player a breeze. ⓐⓐⓐⓐ

SPORTS ILLUSTRATED FOR KIDS
www.sikids.com
With a layout as colorful as children themselves, Sports Illustrated for Kids is a great way to encourage youngsters to read while satiating their interest in sports. Kids can play games or read the Shorter Reporter for the latest sports news. The Sports Advice column lets kids offer helpful tips to common dilemmas submitted by readers; a recent topic covered what to do if no one on your team respects you. Regular features such as the Mystery Athlete and Laugh Locker help make this easy-to-use site a guaranteed hit. ⓐⓐⓐⓐ

SPORT! SCIENCE @ THE EXPLORATORIUM
www.exploratorium.edu/sports
Kids can give their brains a workout at this site from San Francisco's science museum, The Exploratorium. Take a scientific look at sports such as baseball, cycling, skateboarding, hockey, rock climbing and general physical fitness. It's all cool, from Shockwave games to fascinating facts about baseball bats and a breakdown of how much energy is created by a mid-ice collision in hockey. ⓐⓐⓐⓐ

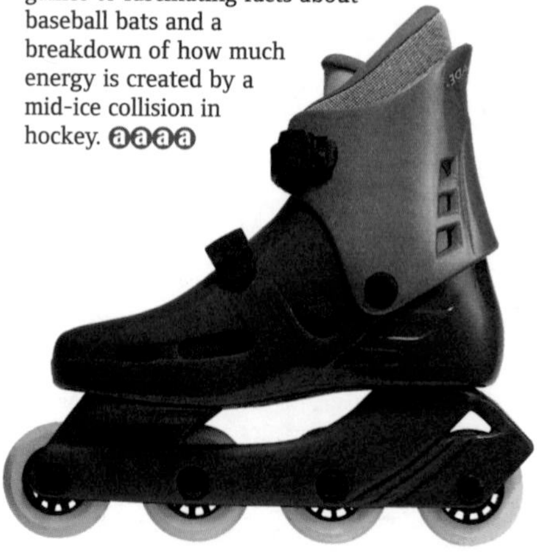

LITTLE LEAGUE ONLINE
www.littleleague.org

Not all of the world's 3 million Little League players will fulfill their fantasy of making it to the Little League World Series in Williamsport, Pa., but they can make it to this all-encompassing site. Fun features include the Little League Hall of Excellence tour and a star-filled database and photo album of players who have taken part in the summertime classic. Chances are, kids will enjoy this site almost as much as the real deal. ⓐⓐⓐ

Black Belt Kids is a useful site for both young students and their parents.

THE LOCKER ROOM: SPORTS FOR KIDS!
members.aol.com/msdaizy/sports/locker.html

Tips for practice, news and general rules on 12 different sports (a couple of sports were still under construction when we last checked) make The Locker Room one of the most diverse sports sites on the Net for kids. Large, bold type and catchy graphics will keep kids' attention. The site offers everything from warm-up exercises to advice on how to deal with a "dirty" player. ⓐⓐⓐ

PLAY FOOTBALL
www.playfootball.com

The NFL's official Web site for kids is loaded with interactive features. Articles and stat charts are written for a young audience—cartoon bubbles pop up with helpful tips and definitions. Kids can sprint to Games for interactive fun that includes Touchdown Trivia. Some games are Java-based or require Shockwave. There's information on NFL-sponsored events for kids such as the NFL Flag league. Like kids, this site has nonstop action. ⓐⓐⓐ

Martial Arts

(originally reviewed November 1999)

BLACK BELT KIDS
www.blackbeltmag.com/bbkids

If your child participates in martial arts or is thinking about it, this is the place for both of you to go. A wealth of features will keep kids inspired. There's information about different styles to help kids choose one to study, When I Was Your Age is stories from the masters, interviews and games. Don't miss The Empty Handed Master, a series of lessons about martial arts philosophy in story form. The text blocks can be long but are written so kids can comprehend them and adults won't get bored. ⓐⓐⓐⓐ

INTERNATIONAL TAEKWON-DO ASSOCIATION
www.itatkd.com

This Web site is for instructors, students and those with an interest in the discipline of tae kwon do. The philosophy of the art form, school etiquette, the meanings behind belt colors and terminology are explained, with updates clearly marked. Articles cover defense techniques and are supported by animated demonstrations of the techniques, which are useful visual aids but are a bit slow to load. Catalogs of books, videos and audio tapes are also available. ⓐⓐⓐⓐ

AIKIDO WORLD WEB JOURNAL
www.aikido-world.com

Almost everything you need to know about aikido is here, from events to tips to terminology. The downside: The type is small and the homepage is crowded. Of particular interest are the technical tips. Part of that section is under construction, but the basic exercises in place—complete with animations—are very good. Articles cover perspectives on aikido, from using the techniques in daily life to the concepts of honor and discipline. ⓐⓐⓐ

JEET KUNE DO WEB KWOON
home.interlynx.net/~lbrown/jkd.htm

This site gives a solid overview of the "formless" martial arts style created by Bruce Lee. Attacks, defenses, energies and principles are covered in depth, as is the evolution of the style. The site also gives instruction in the basic jeet kune do stance. For those who want more information, a list of suggested books and videos—most by Lee—is provided. ⓐⓐⓐ

THE UNITED STATES MARTIAL ARTS ASSOCIATION
www.mararts.org
The emphasis here is on resources for students, instructors, schools and organizations. There are timely updates on events and competitions throughout the United States, as well as an eclectic selection of articles on self-defense, confidence and technique. This is a good first step for the beginner or someone wanting broad information about various types of martial arts. ⓐⓐⓐ

GENERAL TAEKWONDO INFORMATION
www.barrel.net
Nothing fancy here, but the site covers the basics of tae kwon do history and techniques very effectively. A glossary of Korean terms (complete with phonetic pronunciation guides) is a nice touch, rounding out a selection that includes competition rules, belt requirements and diagrams of vital body points. For those interested in a variety of martial arts, the links section here is surprisingly large. ⓐⓐ

Mountaineering

(originally reviewed November 1999)

PEAKWARE WORLD MOUNTAIN ENCYCLOPEDIA
www.peakware.com
Using feedback from climbers around the world, this interactive site offers information on mountain peaks on all seven continents. Read the summit logs of other climbers for valuable firsthand advice and encouragement. The live mountain Webcams can be sluggish to load, but stunning images make them worth the wait. There are also relief maps of prominent peaks. This site is an ideal meeting place for mountaineering enthusiasts looking to share their high country adventures. ⓐⓐⓐⓐ

THE CANADIAN ROCKIES CLIMBING GUIDE
www.ualberta.ca/~gbarron
Get the lowdown on climbing the Canadian Rockies and Bugaboos. Whether you prefer sport, multipitch, ice or alpine climbing, there is plenty of valuable information here. First-time visitors should go to Overview to get a sense of Canada's major national parks and regulations. Also included is a summary of the dangers of mountaineering in these areas, including bear attacks, lightning strikes and frostbite. There are also numerous maps, links, geology notes, a bibliography, essential telephone numbers and weather information. ⓐⓐⓐ

THE COLD MOUNTAIN PAGE
www.cs.berkeley.edu/~qtluong/mountain/ice
This awesome ice-climbing and mountaineering site features many beautiful photographs from worldwide expeditions. Glimpse the surreal beauty of climbers inching their way up frozen waterfalls in the Alps, Canadian Rockies and British Columbia. Aside from offering a generous selection of regional climbing information, novices and experts can get advice or share stories in the rigorously edited Q&A. Don't miss the FAQ or the stories from Personal Trips. ⓐⓐⓐ

REI: LEARN & SHARE: CLIMBING
www.rei.com/reihtml/LEARN_SHARE/climb/qtapclimb.html
One of the Net's biggest and best outdoor stores, REI offers an extensive catalog of high-quality equipment. This section of the store, devoted to alpine mountain climbing, provides a brief introduction to basic equipment and safety. You can buy everything from dynamic ropes and rappel devices to harnesses, helmets and ice axes; and the prices are reasonable. Shoppers can also comb through general accessories, instructional manuals and route guides. ⓐⓐⓐ

MNTEVEREST.NET
www.mnteverest.net
This site contains all types of interesting facts about Mount Everest, from the earliest ascents to the most recent expeditions. The guide listings are useful for those who plan to visit the region, while a complete record of the mountain's history offers insightful but often chilling background—15 people died while attempting to climb the mountain in 1996. For those who can't make it to Nepal, books and videos are available to help paint the picture. ⓐⓐ

NBA Basketball

(originally reviewed October 1999)

FOX SPORTS: BASKETBALL
www.foxsports.com/nba
This site teams an impressive lineup of basketball analysts with a sleek design. Tune in here if you're looking for first-rate NBA coverage in that typically aggressive Fox style. All the basics—league news, scores and standings—are covered here, but it's the thorough division breakdowns and meticulously compiled team notebooks that set this site apart. Message forums for all 29 NBA teams round out this haven for pro-hoops fanatics. ⓐⓐⓐⓐ

NBA.COM
www.nba.com
Live chat and Q&A with superstars such as Tim Duncan and Reggie Miller headline this site's considerable interactive offerings. Ever expanding like the NBA itself, this site includes the scoop on the league's latest ventures and an archive of audio and video clips that is updated daily. For those whose taste in basketball runs to the nostalgic, the NBA History section includes features on top players, champion teams and great NBA moments. ⓐⓐⓐⓐ

THE SPORTING NEWS: NBA
www.sportingnews.com/nba
This site is classy and complete in every aspect, covering the NBA from baseline to baseline with a perfect blend of graphics, text and statistics. Comprehensive analysis from knowledgeable sources—including NBA-star-turned-commentator Bill Walton—is the true strength of this extensive site. With advanced basketball discussion outlets under Voice of the Fan and excellent player bios and rankings, this fan-friendly site more than fits the bill. ⓐⓐⓐⓐ

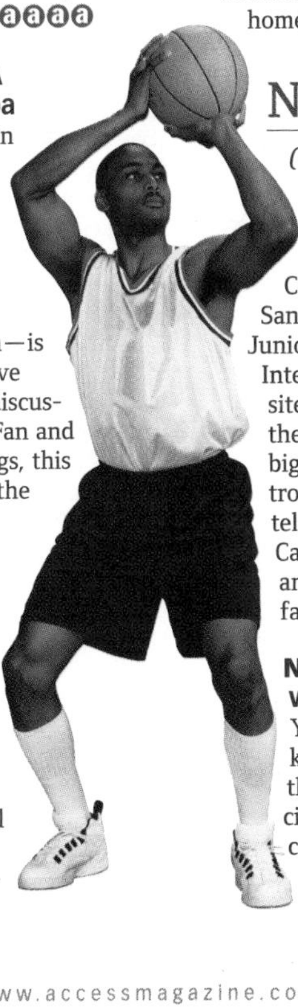

CBS SPORTSLINE: NBA
www.sportsline.com/u/basketball/nba
This well-designed site continues CBS SportsLine's standard of quality online sports coverage. Its pages offer vital facts on almost every NBA player, plus thorough breakdowns of all of the teams. Young fans can dribble their way through interactive games in the NBA Kids Zone. Click on NBA Store to check out team gear. Older hoops buffs will enjoy well-written columns and a year-by-year archive that contains articles about the NBA, plus stats and standings dating back to 1946. ⓐⓐⓐ

CNN/SI: NBA BASKETBALL
www.cnnsi.com/basketball
CNN and Sports Illustrated have teamed up to offer this straightforward but competent site chock full of NBA articles, scores and profiles. Fans can drop into Your Turn to sound off on hardwood happenings via chat, e-mail or message board. Math types will enjoy Statitudes, informative statistical analysis highlighting growing trends around the league. A listing of televised games on TBS and TNT makes this handy NBA guide complete. ⓐⓐⓐ

NBATALK.COM
www.nbatalk.com
One in a series of four outstanding sites from the Sportstalk Network, NBAtalk.com is a jackpot for fans seeking to dish out and take in some serious hoops analysis. Rumors, fueled daily, is overflowing with juicy NBA gossip sure to satisfy diehards of the hardwood. Slam-dunk feature: Links to local radio stations for every NBA team connect you to refreshingly biased hometown coverage of NBA games. ⓐⓐⓐ

NFL Football

(originally reviewed September 1999)

NFL ON FOX
www.foxsports.com/nfl
Combining a layout as smooth as a Deion Sanders suit with coverage as intense as a Junior Seau blitz, Fox Sports leads the Internet's crowded pack of pro football sites. Study the team profiles or check out the latest standings and stats. This site is big on news, and the columns tackle controversial issues head-on. Fox's schedule of televised games and reports from the Canadian Football League, NFL Europe and Arena Football round out this multifaceted site. ⓐⓐⓐⓐ

NFL.COM
www.nfl.com
Yard for yard, there's no better place to keep up with bruising gridiron action than the National Football League's official Web site. Before settling on your couch for the Sunday lineup, log on to this extensive site to score information on weekly matchups, injuries, trades

In your face: World Championship Wrestlers at www.wcw.com.

and more. Fans can enjoy hard-hitting profiles on all of the teams or step into the Coaches Club for the inside slant on every NFL franchise.

CBS SPORTSLINE: NFL
www.sportsline.com/nfl
Starting with its fans-first attitude and emphasis on interactive features, such as polls and chat, this comprehensive site is professional and easy to use. Plenty of fun activities await young NFL fans in the NFL Kids Zone, while older readers can delve into the Legends & Lore section to relive classic NFL moments. Daily articles, standings, scores and schedules combine to ensure you're always in touch with the action.

NFLTALK.COM
www.nfltalk.com
Because screaming at the television rarely gets the point across, NFLtalk.com is just the outlet fans need to release their Sunday afternoon angst. It's perfect for diehards who like to "politely" express their opinions. Send in a commentary or link to the message boards at NFLfans.com and tell that Giants fan what you think. This site also includes a nice mix of objective expert analysis and commentary on weekly matchups, trades, signings and other news.

PRO FOOTBALL HALL OF FAME
www.profootballhof.com
No matter the season, it's always a good time for a cyberstroll through the hallowed halls of the Pro Football Hall of Fame, in Canton, Ohio. Click on What's New to find out the latest news and upcoming events at the HOF. Team histories, bios on all HOF inductees and interactive games under Educational Programs top off this family-friendly site.

TOTAL SPORTS: NFL
www.totalsports.net/fbo/nfl
For breaking news and top NFL stories, few sites measure up to the timeliness and depth of coverage from Total Sports. Fueled by solid features and constant news and score updates, this site serves as a prime resource for NFL happenings.

Pro Wrestling

(originally reviewed December 1999)

1WRESTLING.COM
www.1wrestling.com
Starting with insights from longtime wrestling guru and 1wrestling.com founder Bob Ryder, this hard-core site is packed with scoops. Regularly updated, 1wrestling.com presents coverage that smart fans will appreciate. It has dozens of columns that cover both the business and entertainment ends of the wrestling industry. With results from the latest television ratings wars and a listing of live events nationwide, this site pins down the pro wrestling scene like few others.

SCOOPS WRESTLING
www.scoopswrestling.com
This impressive site offers daily news and columns on the madly popular extravaganza that is pro wrestling. Dedicated to coverage of colossal characters from major wrestling leagues such as the World Wrestling Federation and World Championship Wrestling, this site includes interactive forums, wrestler profiles, interviews and fantasy-wrestling games. Comprehensive and well-designed, this no-nonsense site offers in-depth coverage of an industry with a rapidly growing fan base.

WORLD WRESTLING FEDERATION
www.wwf.com
Packed with video clips, Webcasts and fan-favorite audio bites, this site is the ultimate resource for World Wrestling Federation devotees looking to stay on top of the league's non-stop action and ever-twisting plots. Fans can preview the latest showdown events, check out bios on their favorite wrestlers or find out when the WWF roadshow is coming to their town. From Vince McMahon's wily schemes to The Rock's electrifying smack downs, this site covers WWF action in high-flying form.

STONECOLD.COM
www.stonecold.com
For the latest news, photos, audio clips and merchandise for WWF superstar "Stone Cold"

Steve Austin, this site is ground zero. Check out Austin's Bio to chart his storybook ascent from loading dock laborer to arguably the best-known figure in professional wrestling. The SC Saloon offers downloadable images and interactive games; some require Shockwave or Flash. For the absolute lowdown on Stone Cold, this site is "the bottom line." ⓐⓐⓐ

WCW.COM
www.wcw.com
With previews of upcoming World Championship Wrestling matches and events, plus spotlights, bios and photographs of the league's hottest stars, WCW.com brings on the information harder than a Bill Goldberg clothesline. A full list of televised and live events enables fans to stay abreast of every grueling match. Fans can pick up authentic WCW gear in the online store. If you need to know who's slamming who in the fast and furious WCW world of turnbuckles and head butts, this is the site to see. ⓐⓐⓐ

Rock Climbing

(originally reviewed October 1999)

THE BOULDERING DOMAIN
www.bouldering.com
This sleek site specializes in bouldering news, including information on competitions, but it also offers climbing route information and a useful—if limited—list of off-site bouldering guides. Check out the conversion table—under Guides— for handy translations between the Vermin, Y.D.S., Fontainbleau and Peak rating systems. Don't miss the action-packed photos. ⓐⓐⓐ

CLIMBING MAGAZINE
www.climbing.com
Avid climbers should check in here for articles on a range of climbing issues, from environmental impact to historic climbs. Topics include musings on Mt. Everest and an interview with up-and-coming climber David Hume. Hot Flashes, a section of short news bits, highlights recent newsworthy ascents and climbers. There's also a listing of upcoming events. ⓐⓐⓐ

ROCKLIST.COM
www.rocklist.com
The real draw here are the links and recently upgraded Dataguide, a database of climbing destinations that are contributed by visitors. Many of the sections, such as the calendar, bulletin board and store, are promising but rather skimpy. The Women's Edge features technical advice specifically for female climbers; Learn the Ropes has basic technical information for all climbers. ⓐⓐⓐ

ROCKCLIMBING.COM
www.rockclimbing.com
This site deserves praise for its dedication. The bulletin boards are well-trafficked and can be helpful if you are trying to find some climbing buddies or get information about various routes and gear. The photo section is inspiring, and there is an impressive links section to gyms and clubs. ⓐⓐ

Snowboarding

(originally reviewed December 1999)

BOARD-IT.COM
www.board-it.com
This site has great information on gear, resorts and travel deals. News Updates cover the United States and Europe. If you're a new rider and want to learn the lingo, check out Trickionary for a glossary of hip terms you can use on the slopes or in the chat room. Be sure to check out the dope images in The Photo Gallery. ⓐⓐⓐⓐ

BOARD THE WORLD
www.boardtheworld.com
Maintained by people nicknamed Bear, Mouse and Juz, this refreshing little travel guide and online magazine is fun for all riders. At BTW you'll find reviews of resorts in 14 different countries that are written by and for snowboarders, a place to buy BTW shirts and sweaters, Bulletin Boards and a competition schedule. Using the hypermap under Weather, you can click on a country to find out what the conditions are at your favorite destination.

Note: The site has good information but can be slow to load. ⓐⓐⓐⓐ

ONBOARD: EUROPEAN SNOWBOARDING MAGAZINE
www.onboardmag.com
You will find a capable lineup of news, chat forums and letters here. The chat room seems reasonably well populated, but it's a European site, so expect to find other languages as well. Be patient, as the English is sometimes less than perfect. But this site has killer videos, photos of boarders gone mad and a great Links section that's rich and easy to use. This site's definitely worth a visit. ⓐⓐⓐⓐ

Catch some air with video clips at www.onboardmag.com.

SNOWBOARDER REVIEW.COM
www.snowboarderreview.com
This funky site has great graphics and offers riders pretty much anything they will need to prepare for the slopes. There's a forum for sharing snowboarding stories, or you can get technical advice from fellow riders in Tech Talk. Read the top industry news, or check out the product reviews for facts on all kinds of gear, including boots and accessories. ⓐⓐⓐⓐ

HISTORY OF SNOWBOARDING
www.sbhistory.de
Created by a high school student in Germany, this site delves into the history of snowboarding, from its invention in 1929—the year M. J. "Jack" Burchett threw together a piece of plywood, some clothesline and horse reins—to the 1998 Olympics in Nagano. The information doesn't run too deep, but it is enlightening. There's a section on Snowboarding Today and another that explains The Basics Of Snowboarding. The site is educational, although it could use the help of an interior decorator. ⓐⓐ

Walking

(originally reviewed October 1999)

THRIVE ONLINE: WALK IT OFF!
www.thriveonline.oxygen.com/fitness/walk/walkmain.html
Think you learned how to walk as a toddler? Fitness guru and trainer Karen Voight will tell you otherwise. With walking as the focal point, Voight inspires healthy living by offering information on stretching, yoga, low-fat food and a clear mind. Understanding her readers' time, space and budget constraints, she offers advice on half-hour walking workouts, affordable walking shoes, and no-gym-required exercises. A handy link in the Tools section will help you find good outdoor walks in your area. ⓐⓐⓐⓐ

THE WALKING CONNECTION
www.walkingconnection.com
Detailed and extensive, this company's site promotes adventurous walking tours, marathons and walking in general. You'll find a free e-mail newsletter, a bulletin board, health advice, walking gear and useful links. Inspirational articles encourage both fresh feet and well-worn soles, while archived newsletters trace the footsteps of previous voyages, complete with photos. Don't miss the technique information, exercises and FAQs in the Walking Tips section. ⓐⓐⓐⓐ

WALKING MAGAZINE
www.walkingmag.com
Straightforward and organized, this is the online version of Walking magazine. The in-depth sections are informative, easily navigable and mainly geared toward women. Special Web features include the Calorie Counter, which figures out how many calories you can burn during a walk. If you're a woman who can't "find time to shave your legs, much less exercise them," the Time Crunch Quiz will help you stick to a workout plan. Other sections offer useful tips and up-to-date listings of competitions, fun walks and fund-raisers nationwide. ⓐⓐⓐⓐ

AMERICAN VOLKSSPORT ASSOCIATION
www.ava.org
If you like the idea of organized, noncompetitive walks in pretty places, click on Find Walking Events on the AVA's homepage. The organization exists to get people off the couch and out into nature by promoting volksmarching—that means walking for fun with a club, family, pets or alone. A list of links to clubs and events in every U.S. state and parts of Canada makes it easy to join your local c hapter. Pre-planned walks range from easy to difficult. ⓐⓐⓐ

RACEWALK.COM
www.racewalk.com
Pumping elbows and swinging hips are just some of the many specifics covered in this enormous site. Proper racewalking technique is taught through photographs, diagrams and an interactive walking book. Also included is a brief history of the sport, the rules and regulations of the USA Track and Field Racewalk Committee, links to clubs and stretching exercises. ⓐⓐⓐ

Yoga

(originally reviewed October 1999)

YOGA ANAND ASHRAM
www.santosha.com
Dedicated to explaining yoga postures and their benefits, this site deserves a visit. The Yoga Postures section teaches basic positions through a series of easy-to-follow instructions and pictures. There is a difficulty rating for each posture, and each is listed by its English and Sanskrit names. A pull-down menu makes finding the right postures easy. Also visit Meditation and the Philosophy section to learn about the yoga sutras and the Bhagavad-Gita. ⓐⓐⓐⓐ

HUGGER-MUGGER YOGA PRODUCTS
www.huggermugger.com
Based in Salt Lake City, Utah, Hugger-Mugger Yoga Products offers an easy-to-handle ordering process and an extensive product line that includes mats, blocks, cushions, straps, clothing, physio balls and anything else a yoga buff might need. Visit the Gift Ideas section for cute tidbits such as tote bags and note cards. Books and tapes are also available. This site is strictly commercial, so don't look for enlightenment, just products. ⓐⓐⓐ

YOGACLASS.COM
www.yogaclass.com
Learn to focus your mind on the meditative principals of yoga here. Though the presentation is slightly confusing, the site teaches the essentials of yoga—breathing, chanting, stretching, working out and relaxing—using text instructions, audio lessons, video streams and pictures. Interesting feature: the Gurubot, a tool that customizes a yoga routine by playing lessons from its audio archive in a designated order. You will also find a chat room and an e-mail list. ⓐⓐⓐ

THE YOGA SITE
www.yogasite.com
Looking for a yoga class near you? The Yoga Site offers a state-by-state listing of classes, teachers and retreats—reviews included. It also describes and offers links to sites with different yoga styles, a primer on stress-relieving meditation and breathing exercises, as well as a great yoga FAQ page, videos and products. Too much time on the keyboard? Learn yoga exercises that can help to relieve the symptoms of carpal tunnel syndrome. The list of yoga schools is useful for aspiring instructors. ⓐⓐⓐ

INDIAEXPRESS NETWORK: INTRODUCTION TO YOGA
www.indiaexpress.com/mind/yoga
This site offers a clear introduction to basic yoga principles and postures. It focuses on hatha yoga, which is practiced for "purifying the body." Explanations of asanas (poses "for health and strength"), tips on where and when to do yoga, and what to wear are clear and helpful. Those interested in other aspects of Hindu lifestyle should check out the links to recipes, customs and faith. ⓐⓐ

YOGA PATHS
www.spiritweb.org/Spirit/Yoga/Overview.html
You'll find a dizzying array of information about the various yoga traditions here. The site includes FAQs, a glossary of Sanskrit terms, links to yoga institutions and essays on yoga philosophies. Besides an overview of the different yoga traditions, Yoga Paths has many links to great stuff: mailing lists, archives, chat rooms and—for video-capable surfers—SpiritWeb TV. Check out the events calendar, too. ⓐⓐ

YOYOGA WITH JOAN
www.yoyoga.com
This simple but thoughtful site reminds yoga enthusiasts of the vital link between body and mind. Check out the list of abstentions (called yamas) and observances (called niyamas) in the Philosophy section, or try the asana (pose) of the week. Yoga Tips and the Yo Joan question and answer sections address a variety of yoga issues and possibilities. ⓐⓐ

travel

Business Travel

(originally reviewed September 1999)

BIZTRAVEL.COM
www.biztravel.com

Other than packing bags, Biztravel.com does just about everything for the busy business traveler. The definitive Internet travel agent, this site offers easy one-stop shopping for flight reservations, hotel arrangements and rental-car bookings. Biztravel.com also helps track frequent-traveler points and miles. You have to register before you can take advantage of most functions, but members are eligible for exclusive travel deals and other benefits, including a paging service that alerts you to last-minute flight changes. This is the Concorde of business travel sites. ⓐⓐⓐⓐ

ITRAVELNOW
www.itravelnow.com

Part of the iShopOnline emporium, this site is ideal for the business traveler who wants to reserve flights, lodging and rental cars, then shop for books and music to take on the trip. Browse for a travel guide or magazine, available for purchase online. Additional features include a list of 40,000 hotels in 5,000 cities, regional weather reports, specific airport information and travel-related software recommendations. ⓐⓐⓐⓐ

TRAVELOCITY.COM: BUSINESS
business.travelocity.com

Previously part of Preview Travel, this all-encompassing site is designed to make the business traveler's journey as purposeful and simple as possible. Aside from the standard but still impressive online booking capability, this site offers advice on such issues as how to pack and what kind of luggage works best. Business Newswire provides daily updates of advertised airfares and changes within individual airline route service. Resources such as maps, driving directions and restaurant guides make this a good site to have bookmarked on your portable computer. Not only can you find a restaurant in a strange city, you can find out how to get to it. ⓐⓐⓐⓐ

TRIP.COM
www.trip.com

An endless supply of no-nonsense information, this site offers countless detailed options for the business traveler. In addition to the routine air, hotel and car-rental reservations offered by most travel sites, Trip.com features a bargain-fare finder that searches multiple airline sites, destination guides and a "flight tracker" that outlines a flight's actual path and travel time. Furthermore, this site is updated daily with travel-related news that is taken directly from the latest headlines. Travel managers might want to check out the corporate travel program. ⓐⓐⓐⓐ

FIT FOR BUSINESS
www.fitforbusiness.com

Geared toward people who live out of a suitcase, this site provides a good list of links to health and fitness resources. Jog over to sites like Musclenet or Swimmers Guide Online, which has a list of pools in your destination area. This site makes an earnest effort to provide the names and locations of hotels that offer superior fitness resources, whether they are golf courses or health clubs. The traveler can still make all the necessary arrangements via links to online reservation sites. ⓐⓐⓐ

GETTING THROUGH CUSTOMS
www.getcustoms.com/omnibus.html

Never use the "thumbs up" sign in Nigeria, and don't give gifts of handkerchiefs in China. You can find out why at this site, which features articles—many reprinted from airline flight magazines—on pertinent cultural issues that the business traveler may encounter. The primary focus is on how to avoid faux pas when traveling abroad. The helpful news pieces are accompanied by pointers to books that correspond to most of the topics. Before you go there, go here. ⓐⓐⓐ

LANDSEER ONLINE
www.landseer.com

This site classifies itself as a provider of links that help prepare visitors specifically for their next international business trip. Concise, to the point and free of showy graphics, Landseer OnLine covers everything from world facts to travel advisories. You can make reservations, check weather reports, find currency conversion rates and inquire about passport information. Those who travel within the United States shouldn't rule this site out; The Road House section provides a wealth of resources for domestic journeys. ⓐⓐⓐ

Family Travel

(originally reviewed November 1999)

FAMILY.COM: TRAVEL
family.go.com/Categories/Travel/?clk=NAV9_travel
Travel is just one of the many sections of this colorful family site from Go Network. Even if Disneyland—Disney is a Go partner—isn't high on your list of destinations, investigate options in the Family-Friendly City Guides. Then read suggestions from families who have already survived car trips in Road-Tested Vacations. Plus, you'll want to print out some of the car games here. The Travel Planner can save you some work. ⓐⓐⓐⓐ

PAMELA LANIER'S FAMILY TRAVEL
www.familytravelguides.com
The smart design here makes it easy to find a variety of free information about traveling with a family. Most of the articles and tips focus on travel in North America, but you can search for lodging around the world. Read Travel Tips, print out Road Food recipes or subscribe to a free biweekly travel e-newsletter. Of special interest: Travel Regions lets visitors research various destinations, such as New England states, the Great Lakes and Bluegrass Country. ⓐⓐⓐⓐ

AMERICAN PARK NETWORK: JUST FOR KIDS
www.americanparknetwork.com/activity/kids.html
Most national parks—including Acadia, Yosemite and the Grand Canyon—offer kids' activities and junior-ranger programs. From fishing to photography, wildlife viewing or snowshoeing, APN provides information and trip ideas for parks from Maine to Hawaii. Click on a park for a list of activities, or on a favorite activity for a list of parks. There's no better place for children to learn about the outdoors. ⓐⓐⓐ

FAMILY TRAVEL FORUM
www.familytravelforum.com
Though there's a variable membership fee for full access to this site, nonmembers can browse a wide assortment of family-focused articles on destinations such as Boston or Bermuda. Each article includes links to additional Web resources, accommodation information and brief descriptions of fun activities for children. There are plenty of seasonally appropriate suggestions and general advice on traveling with kids. With "have kids, still travel" as a motto, this site is sure to please. ⓐⓐⓐ

Plan a trip with familytravelguides.com.

FODORS.COM: SMART TRAVEL TIPS: CHILDREN
www.fodors.com/traveltips/children
"Get your kids actively involved in planning your trip from the very beginning" is the first piece of advice at this site. The well-known travel-guide series has put together a brief but helpful page of family-specific travel advice. Parents can prepare for the worst by learning how to avoid kids' common gripes about airplanes, car travel and hotels. There are also links to other Web resources, such as to tips for kids flying alone. ⓐⓐ

KIDS AVENUE
www.aaa.com/misc/mainpg.htm
As any parent knows, kids can be brutally honest. This unique site from the AAA offers vacation recommendations only from kids about Things to Do and Stuff to See. Scan through the Places to Go before planning your next family trip—if a destination gets a thumbs-up here, you can bet that your kids will like it, too. Your young travelers can submit blurbs about their favorite adventures under Your Best Vacation. This site is a bit skimpy, but continued advice from visitors should improve its value. ⓐⓐ

TIPS FOR TRAVELING WITH CHILDREN
www.geocities.com/Heartland/Park/5407/Travelwithchild.html
At this site you'll find plenty of smart, practical advice from parents who've been there. The tips here are indispensible: which seats to request on a plane; pack your child's bag on top in the trunk so it's easy to retrieve things from it; and make a countdown calendar to build excitement for an upcoming family trip. Be sure to spend some time checking out the car and restaurant games, sightseeing rules, and advice on buying souvenirs. ⓐⓐ

Island Getaways

(originally reviewed January 2000)

CAYMAN ISLANDS
www.caymanislands.ky
From world-class water sports to picturesque natural surroundings, there's plenty to see and do in the Cayman Islands. The resources here include visitor services, transportation, dining, maps and island activities, so you can find just about all the information you'll need to plan your trip. Easily navigable, this site covers all three islands—Grand Cayman, Little Cayman and Cayman Brac—in a style as clear as the turquoise water that surrounds them. If a tropical trip sounds like the perfect romantic getaway, send that special someone a hint: an e-postcard of the Caymans. ⓐⓐⓐⓐ

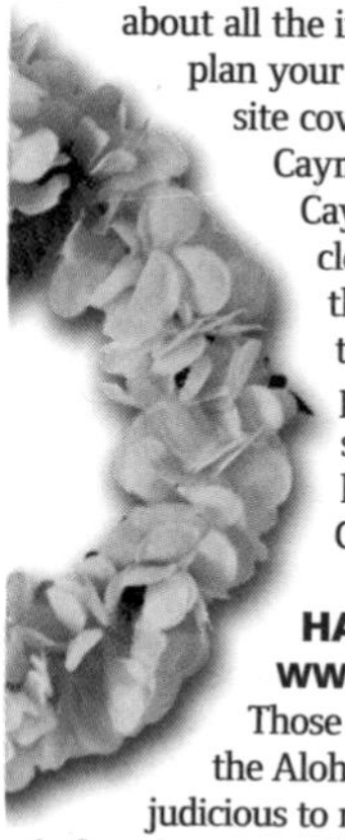

HAWAI'I
www.gohawaii.com
Those wise enough to plan a trip to the Aloha State would be equally judicious to make a stop at this site before departure. Island Highlights offers a comprehensive layout of Hawaii's six main isles, while sections addressing accommodations, weather and transportation are handy for planning. Designed with tropical colors and photos, this site also includes honeymoon suggestions and an incredible database of Hawaiian events. ⓐⓐⓐⓐ

ARUBA: ORIGINAL OFFICIAL TRAVEL GUIDE
www.interknowledge.com/aruba
From the nightlife to the wildlife, this site simply but effectively provides the travel lowdown on the island of Aruba. An introduction to Aruba's history and culture adds some perspective to your Caribbean destination, while informative travel tips cover everything from shopping and currency to passports and taxes. Any questions left unanswered by the site can be sent to the Aruba Ministry of Tourism via e-mail, under Aruba Questions and Answers. ⓐⓐⓐ

USVI-ON-LINE
www.usvi-on-line.com
This comprehensive travel guide to the U.S. Virgin Islands is one in a series of three excellent sites highlighting tropical destinations. Users can search for pertinent information—including weather forecasts, car rentals and airline carriers—by island or by topic. From historic St. Croix to rustic St. John to bustling St. Thomas, each island has its own lists for dining, resorts, maps, travel tips and things to do. ⓐⓐⓐ

VIRTUAL JAMAICA
www.virtualjamaica.com
Not sure whether to start your Jamaican getaway with the progressive bustle of the capital city of Kingston or the backcountry beauty of the Blue Mountains? Then check out this site to learn about both city and country in a style as dynamic as Jamaica itself. Currency exchange rates and city profiles make great resources for travel preparation. Scores of alluring photos offer a glimpse of all that awaits visitors to this vibrant Caribbean island. If Jamaica's not in the budget this year, then you might want to put on some reggae music and savor the exotic photos that are on display here. ⓐⓐⓐ

BERMUDA.COM
www.bermuda.com
This site and the expert information on Bermuda's weather, accommodations, transportation and sightseeing are sure to inspire a mid-winter getaway. Here's a terrific planning aid: Drop by the discussion forum for feedback from travelers who have been to Bermuda, or read up on local news in the Bermuda Sun newspaper to find out before you arrive what's happening on the tiny island with pink sand beaches. ⓐⓐ

Virtual Tours

(originally reviewed September 1999)

ALCATRAZ ISLAND TOURS & SLIDE SHOWS
www.nps.gov/alcatraz/tours
The island affectionately known as "The Rock" by its incarcerated residents served as a high-

security prison for 34 years. The National Park Service offers a fascinating, nine-part virtual tour of the island, complete with slide shows, an around-the-island boat tour and 360-degree QuickTime VR panoramas. Each tour stop features enough information to please both the casual tourist and the hard-core enthusiast. ⓐⓐⓐⓐ

CARNEGIE HALL: VIRTUAL VISIT
www.carnegiehall.org/visit
New York's 100-year-old concert venue, located at 57th Street and Seventh Avenue, is awe-inspiring, even if enjoyed virtually. In addition to an impressive timeline that stretches back to the 1880s and a virtual walk-through complete with audio accompaniment, this stylish site offers a 360-degree, fully navigable view of the Main Hall. Don't forget to stop by the gift shop on your way out. ⓐⓐⓐⓐ

A TOUR OF DURHAM CATHEDRAL & CASTLE
www.dur.ac.uk/~dla0www/c_tour/tour1.html
There's nothing like poking around a creepy old castle to get the adrenalin flowing. Durham Castle and Durham Cathedral are both featured on this site. Wander around both of the 900-year-old edifices, and read up on the history—this place is crawling with it, from William the Conqueror's order of construction to the burial of various saints on the grounds. Hint: Click on the photos to enlarge them. This site is informative, provoking and cheaper than a flight to England. ⓐⓐⓐⓐ

CENTRAL PARK
www.centralpark.org
The legendary 843-acre sanctuary of museums, trees, bike paths and statues deep in the heart of Manhattan can be a bit daunting in person, not to mention too far away for some people to visit. Before checking out the real thing, take this inspired Web tour, which allows you to actually "wander" by choosing to head north, south, east, or west from your current position. Of course, you can head directly to the Met, Bowling Green, Puppet House or other park favorites, if you're so inclined. One downside: no map to see where on the grounds you are. ⓐⓐⓐ

JELLY BELLY FACTORY TOUR
www.jellybelly.com/tour.html
This is a tasty little Web tour. Follow the creation of Jelly Bellies from a vat of slurry (gooey sugar stuff) to the polishing process—each step humorously described and accompanied by color photos of Jelly Belly's California and Illinois kitchens.

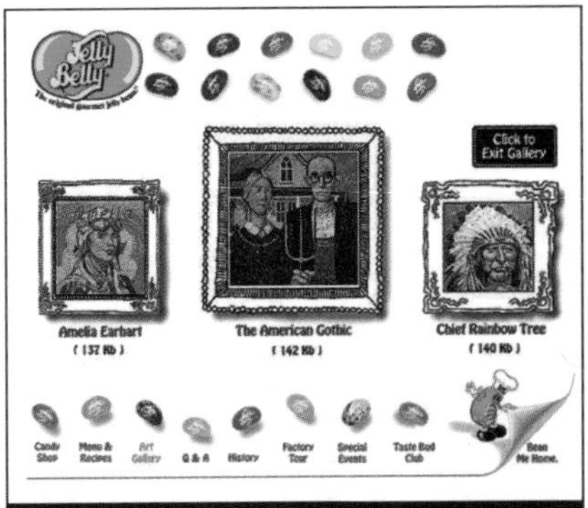

Take the Jelly Belly Factory Tour and see art of a new medium: jelly beans.

Click on History for an entertaining synopsis of the candy's background—did you know it was the first jelly bean in outer space? The tour doesn't take long, but then, neither does chowing down a bag of Jelly Bellies. Just like on a real tour, you can stock up at the candy shop. ⓐⓐⓐ

World Travel

(originally reviewed January 2000)

THE AFRICA GUIDE
www.africaguide.com
No matter which African country you're considering as a destination, this professionally crafted, content-rich site is likely to quench your thirst. It covers 51 countries. News, the Clickable Image Map, instructive articles and medical information will help you plan your trip. Enjoy captivating shots of wildlife, people and scenery in the Photo Library. The Overlanding section contains links to companies that offer guided tours. If you're concerned about safety, read the State Department travel advisories in the Visitor Information section of each country. ⓐⓐⓐⓐ

VIRTUAL ANTARCTICA
www.terraquest.com/antarctica
Point and click along with adventurers who sailed from Argentina across Drake's Passage to Antarctica, all so that you could experience the whole thing on the Web. The site blends a great layout and fabulous imagery with lots of information on Antarctica's history and ecology. Start with The View from the Bridge, which is really just a fancy site map. There's a paucity of Antarctica information elsewhere online, so check in here before starting your search. ⓐⓐⓐⓐ

ACCOMMODATING ASIA ...
www.accomasia.com
Since China alone covers millions of square miles and contains about one-fifth of humanity, you'd better do your homework before heading into the throngs of Asia. This fun site offers plenty of resources to help you prepare for a visit to Hong Kong and Macau, Japan, Indonesia, Thailand and Malaysia. Learn about languages, customs, money, safety and even computing on the road. ⓐⓐⓐ

AUSTRALIAN TOURISM NET
www.atn.com.au
Heading down under, are you? Then stop by Australian Tourism Net. The hypermap allows you to easily access information for lodging, transportation, tours, fishing schools, sailing schools, boat charters and other things you might like to do there. If aboriginal art and culture interest you, plan a tour of them here, too. This site is designed to make sure you have a good trip, mates. ⓐⓐⓐ

THE EUROPEAN TOURIST INFORMATION CENTER
www.iol.ie/~discover/europe.htm
Whether you're planning on nibbling cheese and sipping Bordeaux on the Champs-Elysées or attending the bullfights in Barcelona, you'll want to visit this strangely arranged but immensely useful site. There are many valuable links here, and most of the content is arranged by country. Additional resources include climate information, statistics, rail schedules, subway guides and health facts. Downside: There are a few dead links scattered about. ⓐⓐⓐ

LATINWORLD
www.latinworld.com
Click on the Countries section of this trilingual site to narrow your search. Locate cybercafes so you can plug yourself in while you're away. If leisure is more your scene, there is information about music, culture and sports. The site is well designed with good photos and an easy-to-use format, despite an unfortunate number of dead links. ⓐⓐ

TRAVEL.ORG: NORTH AMERICA
www.travel.org/na.html
If you're pining for the vast expanses of Canada, the culture and cuisine of Mexico City or the good-old U.S. of A., Travel.org offers maps and information for destinations all over North America. The content is thorough in some places and slim in others; the Mexico section has the least to offer. The layout is a bit pedestrian, but it's nothing a nice smattering of graphics couldn't fix. All in all, this is a rich vein to tap before you head out. ⓐⓐ